Screenplays and Concepts by Channing Chea

CIGNUS STUDIO

AfroFantasy
Omnibus: Episodes 7-12

Copyright © 2024 by Channing Chea

CIGNUS STUDIO

Published by **CIGNUS STUDIO**
Columbus, OH

ISBN: 979-8-218-49125-3

Printed in the United States.

Cover and interior illustrations by Siraj Anwer.

First Edition: August, 2024

Acknowledgements

Storytelling continues to be a window into other lives. The real and fictional stories we see in media allow us to view perspectives we may not have had the opportunity to experience otherwise.

I pray that this story brings all who read it a new perspective that we can apply to our own lives.

–Channing

Table of Contents

AFROFANTASY

SCREENPLAY BY CHANNING CHEA

<u>AFROFANTASY</u>

107 – "The Expedition"

Written by

Channing Chea

AFROFANTASY

"THE EXPEDITION"

<u>TEASER</u>

FADE IN:

EXT. URBAN CAIRO APARTMENT - NIGHT

Two TEENS briskly walk through an impoverished neighborhood
in Cairo. Their faces are cowled by the shadow of their
HOODIES. They arrive at an inconspicuous apartment and KNOCK.

The door cracks open and DOOR MAN pokes his head out.

                    DOOR MAN
          Who is there?

                    TEEN 1
          It's us!

                    DOOR MAN
          Kind of hard to see with those
          hoods on you.

                    TEEN 1
          That's the idea!

                    TEEN 2
          Can you just let us in?

                    DOOR MAN
          There has to be trust here,
          brother.

The Teens sigh, drop there hoods, and we see their faces for
the first time. YOUSSEF and MIDO, 16 and 15, thin-framed
Egyptian natives feeling in over their heads, satisfy the
Door Man. He lets them in.

INT. URBAN CAIRO APARTMENT - NIGHT

Youssef and Mido are ushered into a living room and pointed
to the couch. WET SPOTS dot the unfinished floor.

                    DOOR MAN
               (calls out)
          Ali, they are here!

ALI, early 20s with a beard that ages his face, steps into
the living room. He has youthful energy but a shifty aura.

9

                    ALI
          Youssef! Mido! Welcome back! Good
          to see you two again.

He daps up the teens and pulls up a chair in front of them.

                    ALI
          I didn't expect to see you so soon…

Mido looks at Youssef, lets him do the talking.

                    YOUSSEF
          We're here to take the offer.

                    ALI
          I see. That's good news!

Ali steps over to a closet, pulls a BACKPACK from the back of
it, and returns to his seat. Metal CLINKS inside the bag.

                    ALI
          Firstly, how much debt is owed?

                    YOUSSEF
          1,500 guineh.

                    ALI
          What about you, Mido?

                    MIDO
               (hesitates)
          2,000.

                    ALI
          Sounds like times have been tough,
          but you both are making a very good
          decision for your families.

Ali pulls two BARS of solid GOLD from the bag, gives one to
each boy. The bars are smooth, amateurishly molded, but hefty
all the same. The teens examine the bars. So this is what
wealth feels like.

                    ALI
          Make sure you get that to your
          families. When you're done…
               (opens his arms)
          …your new family will be waiting
          for you.

Faint FOOTFALLS can be heard on the roof. They get Ali's
attention. He signals to Door Man who goes to investigate.

                    YOUSSEF
          How did you get all this?

                    ALI
          Amazing what wealth the people can
          create for themselves when the
          government doesn't steal it.

                    MIDO
          I still think it's lies.
               (Youssef elbows Mido)
          Just sayin'. I don't think it's
          safe.

                    ALI
          Why wouldn't it be?

                    MIDO
          I heard that the Waalisha doesn't
          have enough people yet and the
          government is still targeting you.
               (Ali listens, astute)
          What happens when they come after
          us? We can't outgun the military.

                    ALI
          As for your first concern, brother,
          we're growing bigger every day. And
          you two are adding to the family.
          As for your second…

Ali waves his hand along the floor, and the puddles respond.
They follow his fingers, coalesce and float around his hand.
He demonstrates this skill as if it's nothing special, but
the Teens are flabbergasted.

                    ALI
          Guns aren't the only ways wars are
          won.

There's another THUD on the roof—then a CRASH! Door Man drops
through a HOLE his own body creates in the ceiling, smashing
into the floor, back-first. DUST fills the room.

Youssef and Mido bolt, gold bars in hand. Ali stands on
guard, prepares the bit of water he has for an attack.

The shadow of a man appears though the dust. As it clears,
the man's face can be seen. It's BUZIBA.

                    ALI
          Are you with the government?!
               (Buziba says nothing)
          Fine!

11

Ali waves his arm and GUSHES the water at Buziba, but he swats away the feeble attempt and goes for his own strike.

He rushes in, grabs Ali's face, and throws him through the apartment wall.

EXT. URBAN CAIRO APARTMENT - CONTINUOUS

Youssef and Mido are barely out of the neighborhood when Ali BLASTS through the wall. He tumbles, tries to get up. Buziba steps through the hole in the wall.

Ali throws a weak punch, but before it lands, a COAL PILLAR erupts from below, knocks him up and onto the roof. The pillar recedes before Buziba leaps up there himself.

EXT. URBAN CAIRO APARTMENT - ON THE ROOF - CONTINUOUS

Ali is weak and beaten. His body halfway dangles over the hole Door Man fell through. Buziba stands beside him.

                    BUZIBA
          How many others have you shown that
          ability to? Do not lie.

                    ALI
          Not enough.

                    BUZIBA
          Where did you learn it?

                    ALI
          It was a gift from the Leader.

                    BUZIBA
          Your leader has damned you. Just as
          you have damned those boys.

Buziba grabs Ali by the throat, hangs him over the hole.

                    BUZIBA
          Final chance.

Ali hacks blood. He stares into the night with determination. He accepts his fate, rehearses words that may not be his own.

                    ALI
          We have an opportunity to build
          something new and different. A
          community, not an institution. A
          village, not a bureaucracy. I won't
          risk it all pleading for my life.

                        BUZIBA
              Very well.

Buziba reaches for Ali's mouth, but—

                        ALI
              Why would a Rwandan stop us?
                   (Buziba freezes)
              Surprised? You wear it all over.
              That hair, the clothes… you are
              Tutsi.

                        BUZIBA
              Why mention irrelevant—

                        ALI
              You of all people should know how
              they fail us! All the silence and
              corruption while the rest of us
              suffer. Why would you defend them?
              Let the Waalisha—

Ali's mouth is covered by Buziba's hand. His body convulses
as hot coal slides down his throat. Buziba drops him through
the ceiling hole before he finishes dying.

Buziba turns, stares into the distance, sees the teens
running away. Faint dread is visible on his face. He prepares
to give chase when—

                        MARULA (V.O.)
              Buziba, stay close by.

Buziba adjusts his GOLDEN EARPIECE.

                        BUZIBA
              I still have trash to clean up.

INT. NORTHERN TEMPLE CHAMBER - NIGHT

A vast and empty hall is decorated with familiar Atlantean
RUNES. Light from the apex of a SHRINE illuminates the
chamber. Behind the shrine stands MARULA, 30s, a warrior
dressed like Acacia, but her sword is much smaller.

                        MARULA
              We have a bigger problem to deal
              with. Besides, that thief is near…

                                        FADE OUT.

                    END OF TEASER

ACT ONE

FADE IN:

EXT. D.R. CONGO - NORTHERN HILLS - DAY

Patched grass on the rolling hills of the Northern Congo
resemble a quilt of multiple greens that blanket the
landscape. In the distance, a lush canopy of a rainforest is
visible. That's where DARREN and ASA are headed.

They hike at a brisk pace through the hills. Darren is
focused on the trail, agitated by something unsaid. Asa
squints into her hand at an OBJECT that resembles a sundial
but behaves like a compass.

                    ASA
          You really think it's here?

                    DARREN
          "A remote jungle in the Congo
          that's highly inaccessible to non-
          Fluxers." I really wish she was a
          little more specific, but this
          country is also a solid midpoint
          between the temples we've seen.

                    ASA
          The Wayfinder Khadija gave us does
          seem to point this way, so we have
          to be on the right track. You
          getting any tingle from your Umoya?

                    DARREN
          No… are you?

                    ASA
          You're the one who's touched the
          Wind Shard… and with a Soul Flux. I
          thought you were the one with the
          answers here.

                    DARREN
          Well, I don't… have any answers.

                    ASA
          You have to know something useful.
          How else did you get your Soul
          Flux? I'm still waiting for you to
          offer to teach me, by the way.

                    DARREN
          I can't.

                    ASA
          Why not?

                    DARREN
                (grunts)
          Cuz I don't know how I got it.

                    ASA
          Didn't everyone say you get it by
          knowing who you are? I thought
          you'd be happier about that.

Darren stops abruptly. Asa does too.

                    DARREN
          I don't know, okay? I still don't
          know *anything* about who I am, and I
          have no way of figuring it out. And
          I sure as hell don't know why my
          Soul Flux came.

                    ASA
          Then let's talk about it, Darren!
          We can figure it out together. You
          don't have to keep things from me.

                    DARREN
          What's to talk about, huh? I've
          crossed Africa trying to find my
          heritage so I can not die with the
          same regret Gumma did!
                (shakes off fear)
          I don't want that. If I can't find
          it for myself, I wish I could at
          least find it for her sake. But I
          can't! All I can do is keep chasing
          this fantasy kingdom and hope
          that—just maybe—it will get me
          closer to the answer I need. So,
          there… we talked about it.

Darren ends the talk by walking again, but he is stopped by—

                    ASA
          I'm sorry.

                    DARREN
          What?

15

                    ASA
          I feel like that's what everybody
          wants to hear me say. I am. I'm
          sorry I can't tell what's on your
          mind, or that I don't know what
          you're going through. I'm trying to
          understand. I'm trying to help! But
          everyone keeps treating me like the
          bad guy and I'm just trying to
          figure out what you want me to do.
          So please just tell me.

                    DARREN
          What do you *want* to do?

                    ASA
          I just want to help you…

They stare at each other, hoping an answer would come from
the other, but they are both left wanting.

But then, rapid-fire GUNSHOTS boom through the air, steals
their attention. They both look toward the hills.

                    ASA
          Is that a machine gun?
               (hears screams)
          Someone's in trouble! Do you think
          it's—

                    DARREN
          The Waalisha!

They both sprint toward the sounds.

EXT. NORTH CONGO VILLAGE - DAY

The couple arrives at a VILLAGE, but the screams have
stopped. There is only WAILING and MOANING. We see why…

Warm BODIES litter the ground. People of all sizes and ages
lie in pools of their own blood. The blood stains the dark
and fertile dirt and the knees of those who kneel beside
them, showering them with fresh tears.

More VILLAGERS emerge from hiding spots, adding to the
mourners. Half of them search for loved ones, scan the bodies
for familiar faces. Others administer first aid with
efficiency that only comes from routine.

The Americans are mortified, silent. It's too much for Asa.
She slides back, subconsciously seeks an exit, but she
stumbles on something. She turns see it: a severed foot.

It's then that they both see who it belongs to. A woman tied to a hut hangs motionless over her pruned ankles. The bleeding has long since stopped.

>   ASA
>   Oh my god… oh my god…

>   DARREN
>   What the hell… just happened?

A MIDDLE-AGED MAN approaches them, greets them with a gun.

>   MIDDLE-AGED MAN
>   Who are you?! Hands up!

Darren complies, but Asa does not. She fixates on the woman.

>   MIDDLE-AGED MAN
>   Are you ADF?! ARE YOU ADF?!

>   DARREN
>   No! I don't know what that is!

>   MIDDLE-AGED MAN
>   Why are you here?

>   DARREN
>   We were traveling through and
>   rushed over when we heard the guns!
>   We aren't here to hurt anyone.

Middle-Aged Man studies Darren, then Asa. They are both too distraught to be a threat. He lowers his gun.

>   MIDDLE-AGED MAN
>   If you stay, you will help.

He walks away, leaves the couple. Darren puts a hand on Asa's shoulder, snaps her from her trance.

>   DARREN
>   Come on, let's see what we can do.

INT. NORTH CONGO VILLAGE - MEDICAL TENT - DAY

Bodies are lined up on the ground and along the wall of a tent. Many are covered with blankets until insufficiency requires large LEAVES to be used.

MILITIA TRUCKS pull into the village, but no villagers react to them. MILITIA unload their trucks with supplies and distribute them. The villagers accept them but say nothing.

Asa covers a young child with a leaf. She notices the blood on her hand and goes to find a sink. Darren is already by it.

Middle-Aged Man finds them both, hands them towels.

                    DARREN
          Who did all this—the Waalisha?

                    MIDDLE-AGED MAN
          No-no, this was the ADF. Waalisha
          offered us protection, but we did
          not trust them.
               (shakes head)
          We should have taken their offer.
          They would have been more help than
          the ever-tardy militia.

                    DARREN
          Who's the ADF?

                    ASA
          Allied Democratic Forces.

                    DARREN
          How do you—

                    ASA
          Before we came, I googled "worse
          things that can happen to you in
          Africa". The ADF was number one on
          the list.

                    MIDDLE-AGED MAN
          They come and go at random. You
          should leave before they return.

He dries his hands and moves on, not needing a response.

Darren looks at Asa, who has trouble removing the blood stains from her hand.

                    DARREN
          What do you know about these ADF?

                    ASA
          Ruthless. Monsters. Worse than the
          Waalisha. You probably figured
          that.

                    DARREN
          Anything we can do?

                    ASA
          If we both had Soul Fluxes—maybe.
          But this Militia is here to stop
          them. Well… they should've been.

                    DARREN
          Maybe we should leave this to them.
             (sighs)
          I see why Arjana is so
          inaccessible. Let's go.

Darren leads Asa out of the tent. She hesitates, gives the
village a final glance, but she follows. The two depart the
village, careful to avoid bloody puddles.

EXT. BESIEGED RWANDAN TOWN - DAY, FLASHBACK

A TUTSI FAMILY sprints through puddles of blood. There are
only three of them—a MOTHER, a FATHER, and a TUTSI BOY.

The Boy is nearly yanked off the ground by the Mother, who in
turn is led by the Father through a field of WARRING BODIES.

They weave through fellow Tutsis, some running like they are,
others fighting off their pursuers for as long as they can…
but resistance proves futile.

They are pursued by a numerous HUTU MOB who are armed with
MACHETES and demonstrably good at using them. They savagely
mow down any Tutsi men who resist. And they *do* resist, but
the enemy's numbers are too great. They fall.

But the Family keeps running.

They weave through fighters, hurdle corpses, knock away Hutu
who get too close, but they manage to survive their escape.
Until they arrive at a CLIFF…

The cliff overhangs a LAKE 80 feet below—just far enough to
be lethal. The Father scans the scene, spots a HOVERCRAFT
drifting nearby.

                    TUTSI FATHER
          Climb down!

                    TUTSI MOTHER
          It is too steep!

A machete HACKS into someone's chest, precedes a SCREAM. This
catches the Father's attention. The mob closes in on children
and wives whose husbands are cut down in a final stand.

Tutsi Father and Mother exchange a glance. They know this is it. The Father kneels and embraces his son.

                    TUTSI FATHER
          Be brave, son—strong! I love you…

The Boy hugs back out of habit, but he doesn't realize this is goodbye. Fear clouds his perception.

The Father and Mother embrace. Tears stream down both faces. They whisper something encouraging, mournful into each other's ears.

                    TUTSI FATHER
          Now go!

Mother is not ready, but she falls back when a HUTU MAN runs over to her and leads with the downswing of a machete. The blade almost reaches her face but—

Father intercepts, blocks with his arm! The blade digs through his ulna but it holds, becoming a shield for his family. Hutu Man struggles to remove the blade, but Father pulls him in and reaches for his attacker. Father claws at Hutu Man's eyes, buys his family just a little more time.

                    TUTSI MOTHER
              (takes Boy's hand)
          We will jump!

The Boy is terrified as they inch toward the ledge. The hovercraft glides closer…

Hutu Man escapes Father's clutches and swings the blade at his neck. He sprints for Mother and the Boy before Father even hits the ground.

Mother doesn't wait—she picks up the Boy and leaps off the cliff. They plummet into the lake, narrowly missing the rocks below. It's not until the two resurface does Mother finally release her grip on the Boy.

The Boy gasps for air, but Mother is quiet as the hovercraft floats over. The craft only has three passengers, all of whom are Caucasian but only the DRIVER is wearing U.S. ARMY FATIGUES. GLENDA, late 20s, reaches for the Boy and brings him aboard.

                    GLENDA
          You're okay—you're safe now. Are
          you hurt?

The Boy shakes his head but looks for his mom. JOHN, early 30s, the other passenger, pulls her limp body onboard.

                         JOHN
             Ma'am, can you hear—Oh, Jesus…

BLOOD leaks from a blade-shaped wound on her back. The blood
leaves a trail in the dirty water.

The Boy sees his lifeless Mother, enters shock. He
hyperventilates as the passengers converse.

                         GLENDA
             We need to take him to a hospital!

                         JOHN
             The hospital isn't any safer for
             him than this place.

                         GLENDA
             At least he'll be closer to the
             authorities.

                         JOHN
             The authorities are the problem,
             Glenda! He can't go there.

The hovercraft pulls away from the cliff as rocks fall from
the sky. The Boy becomes erratic and a panic attack ensues.

Glenda goes to the Boy, pulls him into a motherly embrace.
The Boy begins to WAIL and sinks into the woman's bosom.

                         GLENDA
             It's okay, you can let it all out
             now… It's over.
                  (beat)
             My name's Glenda. What's yours?

The Boy finally pulls his head away and musters enough
strength to speak.

END FLASHBACK.

EXT. URBAN CAIRO PARK - DAY

Buziba gazes into a pond with mournful eyes as a voice
CRACKLES into his earpiece.

                         MARULA (V.O.)
             Buziba, it is time.

Buziba is pulled from this thoughts and his scowl returns.

INT. NORTHERN TEMPLE CHAMBER - DAY

Marula still stands beside the glowing SHARD, but she is
joined by SAGE, 30s, who is also adorned with Arjanan ARMOR,
but it sits atop western-looking clothes.

                    MARULA
          Sage has arrived, which makes you
          the last person to show up…

                    BUZIBA (V.O.)
          I can't let any Waalisha slip
          through the cracks. There must be
          more stationed here.

                    MARULA
          Drop it, already. You know this
          takes priority. Besides…

INT. CAIRO HOTEL ROOM - DAY

PHARAOH gazes out the hotel window, where the OBELISKS of the
Giza Plateau can be seen. In his hand is the MASK OF ARJANA,
already illuminated with the location of the Northern Temple.

                    MARULA (V.O.)
          If we do our jobs right, we'll be
          able to get the Wind Shard back.

He goes to a SAFE in the room and opens it. The GLOWING Wind
Shard sits inside. He pulls it out and replaces it with the
Mask. He shuts the safe, but he pockets the Shard. It's the
only thing he takes with him as he walks out the door.

EXT. NORTHERN CONGO FOREST - DAY

Darren and Asa keep walking through the forest, the weight of
what they witnessed is heavy on their minds.

The trees open up to reveal a VILLAGE with a stream that runs
through it. HUTS and CABINS are sprinkled throughout.

                    ASA
          It's another village…

                    DARREN
          We're pretty far out here. Maybe
          the ADF hasn't—

                    ASA
          We need to warn them… Come on.

Asa rushes into the village. Darren trails behind, but he pauses as he hears something. He turns to follow the sound of an incoming CARAVAN of vehicles.

EXT. FOREST CONGO VILLAGE - CONTINUOUS

Asa approaches a LOCAL WOMAN with a basket of vegetables on her head. She is intercepted as she walks toward a hut.

                    ASA
          Excuse me, is your security nearby?

Local Woman is alarmed—keeps walking.

                    ASA
          I just need to warn them. You all
          should get to safety. The ADF is
          close!

This rouses more alarm, and nearby villagers walk away. The ones that do not chide her from a distance.

                    ASA
          I don't want to scare you, but you
          need to get ready—

                    DARREN
          Someone's coming!
               (runs to Asa)
          I just heard cars coming. It's
          either the militia or the ADF.

                    ASA
               (to the villagers)
          Please, you have to hide!

A man walks toward them, he is old, but not geriatric. This is ALBERT, 60s, a man who has seen too much, and is done seeing them.

                    ALBERT
          We told you no last time! Nothing
          has changed since then!

                    DARREN
          What are you talking about?

                    ALBERT
          We do not need any help from the
          Waalisha. We do not want your gold
          nor your protection!

23

> ASA
> We aren't the Waalisha!

> VILLAGE BOY
> THEY ARE COMING!

A TRIBAL HORN is blown by a Village Boy. It is haunting enough that the Villagers know this is not a drill. They scramble for shelter while Albert draws a HANDGUN.

> ALBERT
> Did you two lead them here? Fools!

He finds cover beside a vehicle and prepares for the invasion. Asa doesn't move. She is frozen with guilt.

> ASA
> *Did* we… lead them? Oh God…

> DARREN
> Of course we didn't. How could—

> ASA
> We have to help them.

> DARREN
> I want to… I thought you said
> there's nothing we can do?

> ASA
> If this is our fault, we have to…

A pained desperation bleeds from her eyes. Darren acknowledges it.

> DARREN
> Okay, what should we do?

> ASA
> Whatever we can.

A hodgepodge of TRUCKS rolls into the village. Darren picks up Albert and carries him into the nearest hut. Albert barely has time to contest before all three are in the hut.

A SQUAD LEADER is the first to hop off the leading truck. He looks around, amused by the villagers' attempt to hide. He shouts something in French, and ADF GOON 1 walks to the hut, knocks on the door.

The other couple dozen of ADF GOONS take their place in front of the other homes, GUNS aimed and ready to fire.

> SQUAD LEADER
> Albert, we have come for our second
> helping. Do you have the food?

There is no response. Squad Leader nods to ADF GOON 1, who proceeds to break down the door.

> SQUAD LEADER
> It is better to pay your taxes than
> make us play the collector, but if
> you insist.

ADF Goon 1 enters the hut. A quiet beat passes. Then, Goon 1 is ejected from the hut, gets slammed into the truck he arrived on. He's out cold.

Squad Leader shakes his alarm enough to yell—

> SQUAD LEADER
> FIRE!

The Goons unleash upon the village, spraying the homes with bullets. DEBRIS flies through the air.

They fire relentlessly until something catches their eye. They look up to see a COLUMN of WATER rise from the stream. The Goons scream, switch their aim to the water, but it does not stop it from falling on them.

The wave crashes on a half dozen Goons, washes away a few others. The water rises to form a 6-foot wave, and it attacks the invaders like a sentient spirit.

Squad Leader pulls the pin of a GRENADE, prepares to toss it, but a STONE COLUMN from the ground knocks it from his hand and toward a truck. The grenade rolls beneath it and explodes, taking the trucks and nearby Goons with it.

Squad Leader sees the column recede into the ground and notices where it came from. Darren and Asa are at the Hut's door. Whatever sorcery is at work, it is clearly their doing.

> SQUAD LEADER
> Those two! EVERYONE FIRE AT THEM!

Darren raises a STEEL SHIELD before the hut as all remaining ADF Goons turn their fire onto the Americans. The bullets hitting the shield are a thunderous hailstorm. It holds for mere moments before bullets begin to pierce it.

More grenades land at the shield's base. They detonate, blowing what is left of the barrier away, knocking the Americans down.

Squad Leader approaches and aims his gun at them. He curses something in French, but before he pulls the trigger—

A FLASH passes through Squad Leader's weapon arm, leaves a gust in its wake. The gun falls to the ground. He looks down, notices the gun. It takes him a beat to realize his hand is still grasping it.

He screams as he realizes his arm has been severed. One more windy flash blows in, severs his head just as quickly. Squad Leader's body collapses unceremoniously.

Darren and Asa share the Goons' confusion and alarm, but a voice wrangles their attention.

A familiar thick-necked and muscular man wielding a SHOTEL emerges from the trees. This man is MUNI. Fighters MALICK and SAMBA, both late teens, are beside him.

                    MUNI
          There is no need for alarm. This
          village just became much bigger.

Asa and Darren are incredulous.

                    ASA
          Is that…

                    DARREN
          …The Waalisha?

Muni notices the Americans for the first time. His eyes meet Darren's. Hatred bleeds from them, but it disappears when—

ADF Goons open fire on the Waalisha.

Malick stomps the ground, raises a DIRT WALL that the others fall behind. It crumbles quickly, but Samba hops from behind the wall and BLOWS FIRE at the ADF. The gunshots stop, and the Waalisha move in to attack. A brawl ensues.

                    DARREN
          Should we be picking a side?

                    ASA
          The one that ends the fight faster!

The ADF's stray bullets ricochet off cars, impact huts, adds to the mayhem.

                    DARREN
          Lesser of two evils, it is!

The Waalisha launch their attacks, each with his own Flux, but they are not efficient. Some attacks miss, and they are left as vulnerable targets. Malick creates another wall and the three dive behind. The bullets close in.

Then water rises from the puddles, forms thick TENDRILS that grab at the ADF's guns. The tendrils lift them, attempting to wrestle away the firearms. This leaves them open.

Darren rushes in. TIME SLOWS as he looks at Muni, and his eyes flit as he instantly analyzes the shotel.

Darren stomps a DIRT PILLAR out of the ground, grabs it. As he swings, it transmutes into STEEL. And as it nears the ADF Goon's chest, it assumes the shape of Muni's shotel.

Darren's sword lodges itself in the Goon's chest, kills him.

Muni smiles mischievously. He walks to the fallen Goon and loots a grenade from the body.

                    MUNI
          The village grows! Set the pit!

The Waalisha Fighters understand. Malick clutches at the ground, strains himself to create a large hole. Samba uses fire to incentivize the ADF Goons to release their guns and fall into the pit. All of them do.

Darren notices the plan and raises multiple STEEL BEAMS around the hole's perimeter, ensuring no one escapes.

Asa releases her influence on the water, lets it fall. Darren relaxes, thinks the fight is over.

But Muni is not done. He walks to the edge of the pit, brandishes the grenade.

                    MUNI
          And now, the tyranny ends…
               (tosses grenade into pit;
                grips sword)
          VANGUARD SHEAR!

He swings the blade, throwing from it a RADIANT wind shear that slices the grenade from a distance.

A chain of explosions follows as one grenade detonates the others on the ADF's persons. DIRT and SHRAPNEL are thrown through the air as thunderous booms drown the ADF's screams.

Asa and Darren dive for the floor until the explosions finally cease. They check each other, then themselves, to make sure all limbs are accounted for.

As dust and red mists settle, Muni fades into view. He stands over the pit, but he turns to see the Americans. He tries to hide antipathy behind a forced but placid smile.

                    MUNI
          Americans, it has been a while.

                                        FADE OUT.

                    END OF ACT ONE

ACT TWO

EXT. FOREST CONGO VILLAGE - DAY

Albert leads teams of Villagers into damage control mode.
Injured are accounted for and tended to, the damage to homes
is assessed, and fallen ADF Goons are stripped of weapons and
thrown into the still-smoking pit.

Asa extinguishes a rogue fire, quenches it with water.

The Waalisha help. Malick assists in tending to the injured
while Samba inhales away any fires he may have caused. Muni
cleans up debris, but he is distracted by a phone call.

And Darren watches them all intently. He steps closer to Asa.

                    ASA
          Anything suspicious?

                    DARREN
          Not yet…

Albert notices the couple, approaches them. His face is much
softer than before.

                    ALBERT
          You two have done enough for now.
          Please, go rest.
               (the couple hesitates)
          I insist, go eat. If anything comes
          up we will send for you.

INT. FOREST CONGO VILLAGE - CABIN - DAY

They enter a large cabin and find an open table to sit. A
Villager serves them each a FULL PLATE, but the couple has
trouble eating.

                    ASA
          That trick you pulled with the
          sword was pretty neat. You're quite
          the craftsman, huh?

Darren cracks a smile, but it fades as they are joined by the
Waalisha. They sit across from the couple.

                    MUNI
          Do you mind if we join you?

                    ASA
          Yes, we would.

                    MUNI
          Well, my hands are tied. Albert
          insisted we come eat!

                    DARREN
          What the hell are you doing here?

                    MALICK
          We have come to offer protection
          against the ADF. We did not think
          they would come so soon.

                    SAMBA
          We are also here to extend an
          invitation to the locals!

                    ASA
          An invitation to what?

                    MUNI
          To join our community.

                    DARREN
          Of course—you're recruiting people.

                    MUNI
          We have come, peacefully, to invite
          this village into something bigger.

                    DARREN
          You come peacefully, but the first
          thing that happens when you arrive
          is a literal blood bath.

                    MALICK
          It is a last resort, but we will
          fight if we have to!

                    ASA
          It wasn't a last resort at
          Kilimanjaro!

Malick and Samba realize they are missing context.

                    MUNI
          I have been… instructed… to leave
          Kilimanjaro in the past.

                    ASA
          Smart move. It must suck to have a
          loss like that on your record.

Muni's eyes sharpen, anger bleeding through fragile poise.

                    MUNI
          I *lost* more than you know on that
          day…

Malick and Samba find the context. They've heard of these
Americans…

Albert enters the cabin, finds the group.

                    ALBERT
          It was 'Muni', correct? May I speak
          with you privately?

                    MUNI
          There doesn't need to be secrets
          between us! Go ahead!

                    ALBERT
               (uncomfortable)
          We will accept your deal, if it
          still stands.

                    MUNI
          If it did not, we would not be
          here. Samba, would you please?

Samba gets up, takes off his BACKPACK, unloads it onto the
table. Two sharp GOLDEN STAKES drop onto the table. Muni
slides them over to an awestruck Albert. He grabs them,
verifies their authenticity. He is convinced.

                    ALBERT
          Just like that?

                    MUNI
          There is also your end of the deal.
          How many men will you offer?

                    ALBERT
          We can only offer eleven. We need
          the younger boys for work.

                    MUNI
          That is fair.
               (extends hand; Albert
                shakes)
          Welcome to the community.

                    ASA
          Whoa—wait! You can't join them! If
          this is about the ADF, they're gone
          now. What are you doing?

                    ALBERT
          Sometimes it is wisest to join the
          larger tribe. Until today, I
          thought that was us.

                    MUNI
               (to Albert)
          Please gather the recruits for me.

Albert nods and exits the cabin, taking the gold with him.

                    DARREN
          You're buying recruits? Where are
          you even getting that gold?

                    MUNI
          We have always been resourceful.
               (takes a bite; beat)
          That sword you created looks just
          like mine. Is that the next
          evolution of your power?

                    DARREN
          I'm not te—You know what? I'll
          answer that question if you answer
          mine in return.

                    MUNI
          Diplomacy is nothing if not
          negotiation. Sure.

                    DARREN
          Yes, it's the next level. It's
          called a Soul Flux, and it's the
          combination of all my other Fluxes.
          Mine lets me create and mold steel.

                    MUNI
          Soul Flux?

                    SAMBA
          That sounds like Miss Amani's…

                    DARREN
          My turn. How do all of you have a
          power? You used to be the only one.

Muni grins like a child who knows a special secret.

                    MUNI
          For a second, I was beginning to
          think you know everything about
          this power.

Albert returns to the door and waves Muni over. He, Malick, and Samba rise from the table.

                    MUNI
          As a peace offering, let me show
          you exactly how it's done.

The three Waalisha exit the cabin. The couple follows.

EXT. FOREST CONGO VILLAGE - CABIN - CONTINUOUS

Darren and Asa exit and see 11 RECRUITS, all from teen to young adults. They huddle around Albert, while Muni approaches them. Malick and Samba watch with anticipation.

                    ALBERT
          You are all doing a brave thing…

                    MUNI
          Yes, you are! There's no better
          cause than committing yourself to
          protecting your tribe. Only now,
          your tribe is getting bigger!

Muni pauses, side-eyes Darren, ensures he's watching. Then his demeanor switches to something more serious.

                    MUNI
          You boys have witnessed more
          violence than any man should ever
          see, but it is not your fault. It
          is not your village's fault. It is
          only the fault of the Congo. The
          government officials who were
          placed in office to protect you sit
          in those very offices and do
          nothing! They turn a blind eye to
          the bloodshed their own negligence
          has unleashed upon this nation.

Muni earns a small audience among the curious villagers.

                    MUNI
          And it is not just the Congo. There
          are more dictators in Africa than
          any other continent! Why is that?
          Because our leaders, our
          governments, have failed us. There
          is not, nor has ever been, a
          structure of authority that has not
          devolved into tyranny.
                    (MORE)

33

                    MUNI (CONT'D)
        The only structure that truly
        allows people to flourish is the
        one *led* by the people.
                (villagers perk up)
        Young men, by joining the Waalisha
        Khufu, you join a tribe led and
        stewarded by people who are
        accountable to each other; who will
        protect each other. There is no
        tribe larger than all tribes
        united.
                (Muni extends hand)
        You have all agreed to lend your
        strength to the Waalisha. Now, let
        us bestow you with the strength to
        protect your new tribe!

The Recruits all step forward, captivated and ready to
receive whatever is being offered. Muni takes a deep breath,
before shouting and releasing a powerful WIND from his hand.

All the recruits are swept up in it, thrown a dozen feet
back, slammed against the cabin walls.

Asa moves forward, ready to attack, but she's cut off by
Malick. He holds a finger up—a sign to wait…

RECRUIT 1 peels away from the wall, struggles to get up. He's
angry and wants to attack, but he halts when he notices WATER
from a puddle beneath him DANCING in response to his anger.

RECRUITS 2 and 3 react similarly, prepare to strike, but are
distracted by the FIRE and WIND that responds to their
emotions. The other Recruits experience the same.

                    MUNI
        The family grows.

Muni is proud of his creations. The Villagers are amazed and
excited at the possibilities now unlocked for them.

Darren and Asa are horrified.

                    ASA
        He unlocked their Fluxes… himself?!

                    DARREN
        But… he needs a catalyst for that.
        I didn't see one…

                    ASA
        How many of *them* can use Umoya now?

Darren's eyes sink into puddles below. He dreads the answer.

EXT. MILITARY COMPOUND - GATE - EVENING

Pharaoh arrives at a MILITARY COMPOUND. To the left, the GIZA
PLATEAU is visible in the distance, vanishing into a heat
mirage. But what Pharaoh wants is before him.

He walks to a SECURITY POST at the compound entrance and
speaks to SOLDIER A, a native Egyptian.

>   PHARAOH
>   (hands over his PASSPORT)
>   My name is Osas Pharaoh, activist
>   local to South Africa and aid to
>   President Moustapha of Senegal. I
>   was granted access to visit the
>   Unfinished Pyramid.

>   SOLDIER A
>   Visit the what?

>   PHARAOH
>   …Zawhet El Aryan. Is it not here?

>   SOLDIER A
>   Oh, yes… one moment.
>   (checks computer)
>   I see you're a public figure, but I
>   cannot grant you access. You are
>   not on the approved guest list.

>   PHARAOH
>   I see. I must have my days
>   confused.

Soldier A hands Pharaoh his passport. Pharaoh reaches past
it, grabs the Soldier and sends ELECTRICITY through his body.

The tased Soldier faints. Pharaoh steps over the gate and
casually resumes his search.

EXT. MILITARY COMPOUND - ZAWYET EL ARYAN - CONTINUOUS

Pharaoh walks an incognito path to his destination, avoids
suspicion. It doesn't take him long to find what he is
looking for. But he is not happy with what he sees…

He arrives at a SAND FIELD that looks like it has collapsed
into itself. Trash, gravel, and weeds sprout from the ditch.
It's a conspicuous dump in an otherwise sterile compound.

He steps into the field. The Shard in his pocket glows,
confirms his location. He is not pleased, but neither are the
SOLDIERS who discover him.

                    SOLDIER B
          How did you get in here?

                    PHARAOH
          Do you know what this place is?

                    SOLDIER C
               (into radio)
          Security, please confirm visitor
          count.
               (to Pharaoh)
          Can you show us some ID?

                    PHARAOH
          A structure as old as the pyramids…
          a monument to the history you
          Mwarabu ardently appropriate. So
          why have you trashed it?!

A distressed transmission comes from the RADIO. SOLDIER A has
been found. Soldiers B and C respond by training their guns
on Pharaoh.

Pharaoh seethes, tries to calm himself. Black electricity
arcs from his body, but he chooses another route.

The Soldiers approach, but a FIRE manifests behind them,
engulfs them both. Pharaoh watches as they are consumed by
his flame. He doesn't move on until they stop moving.

More SOLDIERS arrive on the scene, but Pharaoh is gone.

EXT. FOREST CONGO VILLAGE - EVENING

As Twilight sets in, the Village emotionally recovers from
the ADF assault. The youngest and eldest males work on
patching and repairing the wrecked cabins, while the women
tend to the injured and prepare meals.

But the Waalisha are evangelizing their new Recruits. The
Recruits converse with Samba and Malick, testing and playing
with their newfound powers. Muni engages with them.

And Darren doesn't let them out of his sight. He watches
them, on guard for foul play, but nothing comes if it. They
are young men goofing around.

Darren tries to relax, takes a seat, gazes at the blossoming
STARS. He's relaxed enough to not hear LOLIE, 8, walk up to
him. Her hair is tied in a high bun that shapes her head like
a curious Hershey Kiss. She tugs Darren's jacket.

                    LOLIE
          Are you with them?

                    DARREN
          No, I'm not.

                    LOLIE
          But you are helping us?

                    DARREN
          Yes, I am helping—

                    LOLIE
          Can you do magic, too?

                    DARREN
            (hesitates)
          I, uhm, yeah I can.

                    LOLIE
            (her face lights up)
          Do you move stars?!

                    DARREN
          Um… no. Why do you think—

                    LOLIE
            (points at sky)
          Then why is that one moving?

Darren looks up, alarmed. A star is indeed moving.

                    DARREN
          Oh, that's not me. It's just a
          satellite.

                    LOLIE
          What's a satellite?

Darren finally drops his guard, realizes this is just a
curious child.

                    DARREN
          It's a big computer that circles
          the planet and helps everyone's
          phones work.

Lolie processes, keeps looking up.

                    LOLIE
          How does it get up there?

                        DARREN
          Countries with a lot of money put
          them on rockets and launch them
          into the sky.

                        LOLIE
          Eish! Who drives the rocket?

                        DARREN
               (chuckles)
          You don't drive rockets.

                        LOLIE
          But it sounds fun! I want to
          anyway… What do rockets look like?

Darren laughs, grabs a bit of dirt. He squeezes, molds it
into a metal toy. After a few seconds he presents the girl
with a tiny TOY ROCKET.

                        DARREN
          This is what rockets look like.

Stars are in Lolie's eyes as she takes the tiny toy. She
holds it up, imagines it flying through the sky.

                        DARREN
          You know, maybe you'll drive your
          own rocket one day.

                        ASA (O.S.)
          Psst.

Darren turns, sees Asa beckon him over from around a cabin.

                        DARREN
               (to Lolie)
          I gotta go, but I'll be back, okay?

Lolie is flying her imaginary rocket, engrossed in her dream.
Darren smiles and goes to meet Asa.

She leads him into the trees, away from the village. Muni
notices, but he is distracted by CAR HEADLIGHTS that enter
the village—another small caravan.

EXT. FOREST CONGO VILLAGE - DEEP BRUSH - CONTINUOUS

They stand near the stream but also within the cover of
foliage. A short waterfall pours into an even lower stream
that leads into the forest.

The moving water is just loud enough to mask their words.

                    ASA
          So, what should we do?

                    DARREN
          I don't know.

                    ASA
               (beat)
          I don't wanna leave them.

                    DARREN
          I know… but we might have to.

                    ASA
          Come on, hun, with that psychopath
          here? They'd never be able to
          defend themselves…

                    DARREN
          Yeah, but for the time being, at
          least, I think they'll be fine. I
          don't know what they're doing, but
          if they wanted to take over they
          would have by now. I doubt we could
          stop them. Besides, if they can use
          Umoya now, it's all the more reason
          we need to find Arjana as soon as
          possible.

                    ASA
          We still have no idea where it is,
          Darren. I understand it's
          important, but we—
               (beat)
          I can't leave another village
          behind…

Darren sighs. They both stare out into the forest, the trees
and rolling hills are a vast haystack hiding a needle.

A RUSTLE in the bushes steals their attention. They raise
their guard until Lolie steps through.

                    LOLIE
          Mr. Muni wanted to talk to you.

The couple exchange a worrying look.

                    DARREN
          Okay, fine.

                    LOLIE
          What were you doing out here?

                    DARREN
          We were watching the sunset. It's a
          nice view from here.

                    LOLIE
               (squints)
          I can't see anything but the
          mountain.

                    ASA
          What mountain?

Lolie giggles, assumes it's a joke. She points to the forest.

                    LOLIE
          You are silly. That one!

Darren and Asa follow the girl's finger, but they only see
the vast forest that stretches beyond the horizon.

                    LOLIE
          Come on!

She tugs Darren's arm and leads him toward the village, but
Muni meets them before they arrive.

                    MUNI
          Thank you, Lolie. This is far
          enough.

She nods and skips away.

                    ASA
          What do you want?

                    MUNI
          Someone else has decided how our
          relationship will progress. I am
          taking you to her.

                    ASA
          You're not *taking* us anywhere.

                    MUNI
          I would love for you to choose the
          hard way, but that is not what's
          needed right now.
               (menace seethes through)
          Come with me.

The bushes behind Muni rustle as people approach.

                    DARREN
          No.

Muni struggles to hide his glee. He reaches for his sword.

>   MUNI
>   The hard way is more fun anyway…

Darren stomps a metal POLE out of the ground. Its end grabs
Muni's arm, anchors him in place.

>   DARREN
>   (to Asa)
>   Come on!

The Americans bolt. Muni struggles to break free, but a
GOLDEN SPEAR erupts from the earth, BREAKS the pole
immobilizing Muni. He rips the rest of the metal away as more
SPEARS launch from the dirt, shoot toward the Americans.

Darren and Asa run to the waterfall again. They gauge the
fall. It's far, but not deadly.

>   ASA
>   I'll use my Flux to catch us!

>   DARREN
>   Good idea.

They prepare to jump, but multiple lances rain from the sky.
One rips through Darren's shoulder, the other grazes Asa's
leg. They are both knocked over.

Darren tries to recover, but one more thin GOLDEN SPIKE
erupts from the ground, grazes his torso and pins him by his
jacket. He and Asa are both down…

A person steps from behind the foliage, but it's not Muni.
It's AMANI. She stares at the couple with rage boiling behind
a face that attempts to remain poised.

The tip of another gold spear rises from below both
Americans. The point presses against their chests.

>   AMANI
>   Do not move.

>   DARREN
>   Another Soul Flux…? Who are—AGH!

The point penetrates Darren's chest, draws blood.

>   AMANI
>   Do not speak, either.

Muni, Malick, and Recruit 1 arrive. Muni points to Darren.

41

                    MUNI
          These are the two. That's the one.

                    AMANI
          So you are the one who killed by
          baby brother…
                    (lance presses deeper)

                    MUNI
          Not yet, remember? Amani!

Amani pulls back and the lance retracts. She covers her face,
seemingly embarrassed by her action.

                    AMANI
          Sorry… revenge is not the goal.
                    (to Muni)
          Didn't you say there was a third?

                    MUNI
          I haven't seen a third since we
          arrived. It is only these two.

                    AMANI
          Very well. Bring them.

                    MUNI
                    (grins)
          We won't need them both.

                    AMANI
          Then an eye for an eye.

Muni unsheathes his sword, starts for Asa. Darren watches the
Waalisha close in. His mind races for an idea. He finds one.

He points to the forest behind him.

                    DARREN
          The third… is just over there
          camping out on the mountain. If you
          want her too, I can take you.

The Waalisha gaze at the forest for a beat.

                    MUNI
          What are you talking about? There
          is no mountain.

                    RECRUIT 1
          I could have sworn there was one
          before…

Darren chuckles, having heard what he needed. A beat passes.

                    DARREN
          Asa, I wish we could finish this
          journey together, but it doesn't
          look like that's gonna happen now.
          So find the mountain…

                    ASA
          Darren, what are—

A STEEL PLATE forms beneath Asa, lifting to reveal a LONG
METAL NOODLE that coils into a loaded SPRING.

                    DARREN
          And get me a souvenir!

The spring uncompresses, launches Asa off the cliff. She
screams for Darren as she plummets into the river below.

                    MUNI
          Sneaky American!

Muni pounds Darren with the hilt of his sword. It only takes
a few hits before he is knocked out. Malick and Recruit 1
pick him up and takes him with them.

EXT. CONGO FOREST - DOWNSTREAM - CONTINUOUS

Asa emerges from the stream, nurses her wounded leg.

                    ASA
          Why did you do that!? You can't
          fight them alone! How will I even
          find…

She realizes something. She looks at the Congo Forest as the
sun sets. All that can be seen is an empty skyline… She
consults the Wayfinder. It points into the skyline.

                    ASA
          Fine, I'll find it myself! You
          better be alive when I bring you
          this souvenir!

                                        FADE OUT.

                    END OF ACT TWO

ACT THREE

FADE IN:

EXT. GIZA NECROPOLIS - SPHINX - NIGHT

Pharaoh walks the necropolis, anxiously searches for
something. He doesn't find it. He approaches the SPHINX,
closed to tourists, but also unguarded.

He hops the barrier and walks to the monument. He admires it
from a few feet away, then moves in to touch it.

As he appreciates it, the Shard in his pocket glows
conspicuously. He withdraws his hand and the glow subsides.
He smiles; he has found what he wanted.

Pharaoh hops onto the Sphinx's back, begins to examine it.
The Shard glows again, peaking at a depression on the
monument. Pharaoh brushes sand away to reveal THREE
CONCENTRIC CIRCLES carved into the stone—a familiar lock.

A SPHINX GUARD takes notice of Pharaoh, exposes him with a
FLASHLIGHT.

                    SPHINX GUARD
          Hey you, get down from there!

Pharaoh hardly looks over, but he squeezes the SHARD.
Suddenly, a mini WINDSTORM spawns, kicks up dust and blows
back the guard.

The wind subsides. Sphinx Guard gets up again and looks for
Pharaoh, but he is gone.

INT. CHAMBER BENEATH THE SPHINX - HALL OF RECORDS - NIGHT

Pharaoh creates a small FLAME to hold, illuminating a
claustrophobic chamber that is filled with aged and rotting
PAPYRUS SCROLLS.

Airborne dust creates a light trail from the flame to its
focus. A hallway entrance is visible. Pharaoh advances.

INT. CHAMBER BENEATH THE SPHINX - CORRIDOR - CONTINUOUS

The corridor extends endlessly. Pharaoh proceeds until…

A LIGHT appears at the end of the tunnel, reveals itself as a
door to another chamber. Pharaoh braces as he enters…

INT. NORTHERN TEMPLE CHAMBER - CONTINUOUS

The Northern Temple is vast, with Atlantean RUNES and art decorating the walls. But the entire room features the shrine in the center that harbors the room's only light source.

The enshrined Shard's light intensifies, reacting to the one in Pharaoh's pocket as he gets closer. He admires it before reaching for it.

But he hops back, barely avoiding Marula as she ejects from the floor itself. Her blade misses its attempt at his neck.

Before he can counter, Sage appears before him, detonates an invisible BOMB from his palm. The explosion tumbles Pharaoh.

He recovers, grimacing, and retreats to the door. He is feet away before a COAL WALL rises and blocks the exit. Buziba lands a punch on the unsuspecting target, knocking him over.

Buziba, Marula, and Sage close in. Pharaoh barely has the time to summon BLACK ELECTRICITY all around him to repel the attackers. It works, giving him time to gain distance. He gathers himself as the three warriors convene.

                    SAGE
          Lightning? I can see how Acacia
          lost. She would have no defense
          against a Soul Flux that rare.

                    MARULA
          That is no excuse! This fool almost
          lost his head three times over. He
          is clearly not a fighter.

                    PHARAOH
          You wasted your element of
          surprise. I guarantee you won't get
          a chance like that again.

                    BUZIBA
          You are the thief who stole the
          Mask from Johannesburg. Your sins
          have finally caught up to you.

Pharaoh subtly eyes the enshrined Shard, its light tinted more red than the white of his own. His foot inches toward the Shard, but another invisible bomb detonates by his foot.

                    SAGE
          Stay still.

Marula walks over to the shrine, blocks Pharaoh's path to it.

                    MARULA
          I only sense one Shard on him, so I
          suppose Khadija fulfilled her duty.

                    BUZIBA
          That is still one more than he
          should have.

                    MARULA
          Then we will relieve him of it.

Buziba claws the floor, which causes the earth by Pharaoh to
move. COAL CLASPS go for his feet, but he jumps, evades them.
This earns an explosion to his face that blasts him back onto
the ground. Pharaoh gets back up to see STEAM fade from
Sage's palm.

                    SAGE
          I will not ask you again.

Buziba takes careful steps toward Pharaoh.

                    PHARAOH
          Are you all from Arjana? That's the
          name of the Remnant Kingdom, no?

                    BUZIBA
          You are not entitled to an answer.
          Hand me the Wind Shard, or I will
          take it by force.

                    PHARAOH
          Then am I allowed to move?

                    SAGE
          Slowly.

Pharaoh removes the Shard from his pocket, raises it. As
Buziba approaches, the light reveals his features.

                    PHARAOH
          A Tutsi?

Marula's hands emerge from the ground, drags Pharaoh into the
floor by his ankles, leaves his top half exposed.

Buziba goes for the Shard, but Pharaoh launches another wave
of electricity to repel Buziba. Marula let's go, resurfaces
by the shrine.

Sage fires another bomb. This one Pharaoh sees coming. An
EBONY BOLT intercepts the bomb early, sparing him. With one
more BOLT, Pharaoh breaks through the ground, frees himself.

                    SAGE
This will be challenging.

                    MARULA
The correct word is *fun*.

                    PHARAOH
A Tutsi warrior fights for Arjana?

                    MARULA
It's a clever disguise to fool
outsiders like you from finding the
agents that hide among you. It
appears you cannot see through
every trap.

                    PHARAOH
The clothes and hair can be faked,
but the torment that burns through
those eyes cannot be.
     (to Buziba)
You were present during the
genocide, weren't you?

                    BUZIBA
You mention a past life—a past
existence. Service to Arjana is my
only life now.

                    PHARAOH
Ah, but trauma of that extent can
never truly be left in the past. To
think… an entire group of people
murdered for the shape of their
nose. Why serve a people that left
you to die?

A nerve is struck. Buziba charges forward, but Pharaoh
employs the Wind Shard to blow him back toward his comrades.
Buziba raises a COAL WALL that the three shelter behind.

Pharaoh shouts, musters all his strength to push the wall
over. All wind in the chamber gathers, funnels into a typhoon
that drills into Buziba's wall, but the barrier still stands.
Pharaoh scowls. *How is the Shard not enough?*

Another EXPLOSION hits his back, halts the typhoon, nearly
knocks him out. Pharaoh turns to see Marula and Sage behind
him somehow.

Now Marula approaches. She swims through the ground like a
shark, her hands grab Pharaoh like teeth. Sage charges what
appears to be a BALL of STEAM.

Pharaoh panics, this time employing WIND to repel his attackers. They don't fall back as far as they should.

>   SAGE
>   He hasn't figured it out yet.
>   Marula!

Marula opens a hole in the floor beneath Sage, who instantly charges dozens of STEAM BOMBS. He holds them in the air.

But Buziba isn't done. A COAL SPIKE goes for Pharaoh's feet, forces him to jump to evade. But jumping is a mistake…

While airborne, Pharaoh sees dozens of holes open in the walls and floor. They surround him. Now, Sage feeds all the bombs into the hole beneath him.

>   SAGE
>   **STEAMBURST!**

The steam bombs fire from the holes. They all hit Pharaoh at once, bombard him with explosions until the last burst knocks him to the ground. The Wind Shard drops from his limp grasp.

Sage moves toward Pharaoh's motionless body. He seems unconscious.

>   MARULA
>   You see? Fun. Where else would we
>   have had the chance to try that?

>   SAGE
>   We are fortunate he did not realize
>   the Wind Shard would not work well
>   in an environment with limited air
>   supply. Otherwise, he may have
>   resorted to his lightning. *That*
>   would not have been fun.

Sage nonchalantly scans Pharaoh's bloodied body, determines he's not a threat. Sage reaches for the Wind Shard when—

Pharaoh grabs his arm, funnels BLACK LIGHTNING through his body—INTO his body. Sage screams as he is electrocuted within seconds. His burned corpse collapses.

>   MARULA
>   Sage!

Pharaoh recovers the Shard and attempts to gather himself. He's in rough shape.

Sage's body sinks into the floor. He resurfaces beside Marula. She examines his body but is only mildly upset.

                    BUZIBA
          You are in no condition to fight.
          Even with the Shard, you do not
          have enough air to use it to its
          potential. Surrender—

                    PHARAOH
          That is your fault!

Buziba is confused. Pharaoh points to one corner of the
chamber that houses a large but damaged door, barricaded with
GARBAGE and SAND from the outside.

                    PHARAOH
          I know what that is. That door
          would've led to Zawyet El Aryan!
          This chamber is sealed off… because
          you let the Egyptians destroy that
          ancient monument!

                    MARULA
          This temple is easier to conceal if
          the main entrance is destroyed. And
          it limits Aero and Hydrofluxers
          from operating down here. Why would
          that concern us?

                    PHARAOH
          Because this place is Africa's
          heritage! It belongs to our people,
          but you've allowed Mwarabu to
          destroy it!

                    MARULA
          Arjana's past is not Africa's
          heritage.

Pharaoh struggles to get to his feet. He mugs Buziba.

                    PHARAOH
          And you accept this?

                    BUZIBA
          What wouldn't I accept?

                    PHARAOH
          Arjana has stood aside and allowed
          its treasures to be trampled on,
          but it has also allowed its
          brothers to be ravaged by
          threats—inside and out. I recognize
          that agony in your eye. An
          injustice was done to you and your
          people.
                         (MORE)

PHARAOH (CONT'D)
So tell me… When the Tutsi were
being massacred by the million,
where was Arjana?

Buziba's eyes soften for the first time… A beat passes.

MARULA
Arjana was surviving.

PHARAOH
You are fine serving a kingdom that
turns a blind eye to the suffering
of millions?

Buziba's eyes quake as they are consumed by a memory…

MEMORY FLASH: The Caucasian couple leads the Young Tutsi
through a city littered with the bodies of unfortunate
Tutsis. The only thing protecting his identity is a HOODIE.
Each corpse burns an image into the boy's memory.

MARULA
(scoffs)
Their suffering is their own
problem. Arjana learned its lesson
and has spent all these millennia
living in peace. The violent
conflicts of the outsiders are a
result of their own feebleminded
leadership, and the victims of that
violence are truly the most feeble.

Buziba's eyes pierce Marula.

BUZIBA
Watch your mouth, Marula.

MARULA
No need to be offended, Buziba. If
it is true that you were once an
outsider—which is a topic we will
revisit—then you clearly proved to
be one of the stronger ones. Why
else would Arjana take you in?

BUZIBA
A topic we will revisit, indeed.

Buziba walks to the enshrined Shard and grabs it. With a loud
grunt he slams the ground.

The entire floor of the chamber turns deep black. Then a red
tint intensifies as he squeezes his Shard, and the black
floor shifts into MOLTEN LAVA.

Pharaoh has no floor to run to. He employs his own Shard to summon just enough wind to lift him above the molten floor. He hovers unsteadily.

Marula takes refuge by Buziba, where the only patch of safe footing remains.

>   BUZIBA
>   Right now, we have work to do.

EXT. DEEP CONGO JUNGLE - NIGHT

Asa trudges along, beats down branches and foliage.

She pulls out her phone, zooms in on the picture of the Mask of Arjana.

>   ASA
>   Come on, it's gotta be here…

She consults her COMPASS. It goes haywire, claims everywhere is North, and her phone signal is dead. She is almost lost.

Then she checks the Wayfinder. Its arrow remains confidently pointed forward. Even the STARS corroborated its findings. She finds the North Star and smiles.

>   ASA
>   This thing really works. I've gotta
>   be close!

She proceeds into the forest, having decided a direction.

But a BUSH she passes comes alive, anthropomorphizes as a layer of LIGHT fades like a hologram. ARJANAN SCOUT reveals himself to us, wearing similar armor to Marula and Sage.

Arjanan Scout looks around, bewildered to how this outsider saw through the ruse. He looks at the sky, sees the stars. He waves his arm and the stars seemingly shift and randomize—another hologram.

He assumes his disguise again as he follows Asa.

>   FADE OUT.

                    END OF ACT THREE

ACT FOUR

FADE IN:

EXT. KIGALI, RWANDA - U.S. EMBASSY - NIGHT, FLASHBACK

Hundreds of AMERICAN CITIZENS wait anxiously in the courtyard
of the U.S. Embassy. Their faces are wrought with the stress
that comes from being separated from a bloody battlefield by
no more than a fence. The violence does not invade their
sanctuary, but the sounds of war do.

U.S. SOLDIERS attempt to ease the Citizens by securing the
entrances, but the burden is heavy on them. They also secure
a HELIPAD, ensuring it is clear for incoming aircrafts.

John exchanges words with a few Soldiers. They seem
apologetic, but stern. John is incredulous and dismayed.

Glenda sits against the Embassy wall, her arm wrapped around
the young Tutsi Boy. The Boy tries to shake images out of his
head that keep rehearsing.

                    GLENDA
            It's all right. We're already
            halfway home.

The BOOM of a nearby explosion rattles the Boy. Glenda's
embrace only slightly eases him.

Finally, the Embassy gate opens and multiple BUSSES are
ushered through. They line up around the courtyard. From
above, a CHINOOK descends onto the helipad. The waiting
Citizens celebrate as if Jesus himself has returned.

                    GLENDA
            We'll be out of here soon!

As the Citizens file into lines for boarding, John shoves
through to get to Glenda and the Boy.

                    JOHN
                (to Tutsi Boy)
            Stay close behind us! Still have
            that hoodie?
                (Tutsi Boy nods)

                    GLENDA
            What's going on?

                    JOHN
            We're taking the chopper. Come on!

The entire population of the embassy crams into the busses efficiently, PASSPORTS scanned as each person boards. John, Glenda, and the Boy join a line that board the Chinook. The Boy is hidden, sandwiched between the adults, hood-up, but he is still noticed.

                    U.S. SOLDIER 1
          Wait, where's this kid's passport?

John feigns searching for documents.

                    U.S. SOLDIER 2
          I told you you could not bring him!

                    GLENDA
          Why can't we bring him?!

                    U.S. SOLDIER 1
          U.S. citizens only. I'm sorry.

Other officials and passengers file through, not interested in their discussion.

                    GLENDA
          Where is he supposed to go?

                    U.S. SOLDIER 1
          I don't know, but he can't come
          with us.

                    U.S. SOLDIER 2
          Ma'am, please get on or move aside!

They are shoved aside by others that climb aboard.

                    GLENDA
          John, you have to convince them! We
          can't just—

More GUNSHOTS and EXPLOSIONS fill the air. John's face shows the resignation of a man out of time.

                    JOHN
          Glenda, we might have to…

                    GLENDA
          Leave him?! We can't!

The Chinook propeller begins accelerating. Now is the time. John shows his and Glenda's passport to the soldiers.

                    JOHN
              (to Tutsi Boy; remorseful)
          Sorry, tike. Be strong…

John climbs aboard. Glenda hugs the Tutsi boy but has trouble meeting his gaze. He is confused. She is ashamed.

The loaded busses move out, exiting from where they came. Nothing remains but the helicopter.

>   GLENDA
>   I'm so sorry…

She is yanked away by the a Soldier as the Chinook takes off. The Tutsi Boy below reaches out, looks increasingly helpless as he becomes another body in a warzone. The cries of the Boy are drowned in the CRACKS of gunshots.

END FLASHBACK.

INT. NORTHERN TEMPLE CHAMBER - NIGHT

Black lightning CRACKLES as Pharaoh hurls it at—

>   MARULA
>   BUZIBA!

Buziba snaps out of the memory, raises a COAL WALL just in time to block the Ebony Bolt.

>   MARULA (CONT'D)
>   Get your wits about you!

>   BUZIBA
>   Why don't you assist?

>   MARULA
>   I cannot use my Flux because of all
>   this lava! Clear me a path.

Buziba waves over the floor, reverts enough of the molten floor to clear a path to the wall. Marula grins and sinks into the ground.

Pharaoh rides the wind, zooms through the chamber as he avoids the lava floor.

But the lava GEYSERS at Buziba's command, barely misses Pharaoh. There's little time to counterattack.

>   PHARAOH
>   You are protecting that Stone on
>   behalf of a nation that turned a
>   blind eye to mass murder!

                         BUZIBA
          It were the outside nations that
          left my people in the destruction.
          Arjana picked up what was left.

More lava geysers. Pharaoh dodges and throws an Ebony Bolt.

                        PHARAOH
          Only after spectating from afar.

The Bolt hits, destroys a COAL BARRIER. The broken barrier
collapses, splashes lava toward Buziba. He knocks it away.

                    PHARAOH (CONT'D)
          In your hands is a power that could
          have prevented the genocide, and
          Arjana did nothing with it. It was
          hidden in this chamber!

                      MARULA (O.S.)
          That is how it will remain!

Marula's voice hides in walls. She's nowhere and everywhere.

                      MARULA (O.S.)
          Arjana's resources are not to be
          wasted on primitive minds; the weak
          of heart. This power has been
          abused before…

Buziba raises a COAL PLATFORM. He bounds off of it, air-
tackles Pharaoh, slams him toward the chamber wall.

Marula emerges from wall, grabs Pharaoh and slips her SWORD
under his throat.

                    MARULA (CONT'D)
          …but never again.

Before the blade slices, Pharaoh pushes it away with a GUST.
Marula drops the sword into the lava. She retreats back into
the wall before Pharaoh throws another bolt at her.

                        PHARAOH
          You call saving millions of lives
          an abuse?

                      MARULA (O.S.)
          How could Arjana save you from
          yourselves? One conflict always
          begets another with you all,
          whether you are invaded from other
          continents or just invading each
          other. It is pointless.

55

Buziba's stone face starts to crack.

> BUZIBA
> Shut up, Marula.

And Pharaoh notices.

> PHARAOH
> Is that all we are—victims of
> ourselves?

> MARULA (O.S.)
> Truly! Your leaders' iniquity
> spreads like wildfire, and your
> populace is just as guilty. They
> are all too feeble to resist and
> too stupid to know when they
> should. They are pathetic.

> BUZIBA
> Shut UP!

Buziba's anger causes the ground to erupt. PILLARS of lava
shoot up indiscriminately. Pharaoh can hardly avoid, and
neither can Marula as the molten rock splashes the wall.

The red waves calm again and Marula resurfaces beside Buziba.

> MARULA
> What is with you? Calm yourself!

Buziba's voice has trouble masking his internal turmoil.

> BUZIBA
> They were not feeble. My parents
> gave everything to save me.

> MARULA
> Poor, Buziba. I meant no disrespect
> to them. I am sure they fought
> valiantly! But objectively, they
> were not strong enough to save you
> in the end. The Kingdom did that.

Pain seizes Buziba's chest. He recalls his parents' strength.

> PHARAOH
> So what should we do? If your
> Kingdom refuses to share its wisdom
> with the rest of this sinful world,
> what is left for us?

> MARULA
> For all I care, you outsiders can
> extinguish each other like the
> barbarians you pretend not to be.
> Arjana will continue to pave its
> own future.

> PHARAOH
> And you will just leave the rest of
> the world in the dark?

> MARULA
> (scoffs)
> I do not care where we leave you,
> but you cannot come with us!

Buziba cracks. He bounds for Marula, grabs her face like his
Tutsi Father grabbed the Hutu Man. Marula is confused, but
the only explanation she gets is Buziba's mournful scream.

He squeezes her face, and lava from all over RUSHES her,
swallows her alive. He lets go as she is drowned, burned,
sizzled by the molten rock. The lava soon recedes and reveals
nothing but Marula's metal armor. She is gone.

As Buziba calms, the lava hardens. Pharaoh descends, touches
the ground. It's a walkable floor again. He walks to Buziba.

> PHARAOH
> She was only partly correct. The
> world did fail you, but so did
> Arjana.

> BUZIBA
> As I have heard… as I have seen.

> PHARAOH
> The Rwandan genocide hardened you
> as the apartheid hardened me. We
> both hold fragments of the key that
> can break the cycle of iniquity
> that has plagued our peoples.
> (holds up wind shard)
> I can unlock a new era of peace,
> but I need the full key.

Buziba hesitates, considers, but declines. He pockets the
Fire Shard. Pharaoh smiles, does the same.

> PHARAOH (CONT'D)
> I suppose you need time to
> consider. What will you do with it?

> BUZIBA
> Arjana has had enough time with
> this Shard. Perhaps this power
> should not be stewarded by a
> nation, but by a community…

> PHARAOH
> Well, if the people is who you will
> give it to, I have no reason to
> take it from you.

Pharaoh finds the entrance he came through, fires an Ebony
Bolt at the Coal blockade, blows it open.

> PHARAOH
> I look forward to seeing the world
> you work toward.

Pharaoh starts for the door.

> BUZIBA
> And what world will you build?

> PHARAOH
> (grins)
> You will see it soon enough.

Pharaoh exits the chamber.

I/E. CENTRAL AFRICAN REPUBLIC - CARAVAN TRUCK - NIGHT

Darren's eyes crack open. He attempts to move only to realize
he is bound by GOLD CUFFS. Around him, several Waalisha have
their guns trained on him. Across from him sits Muni.

> MUNI
> Finally awake? That trick you
> pulled to save the Muzungu was
> clever. We might have use for you
> after all.

> DARREN
> Where are we going?

> MUNI
> Home. Tell me, do you think the
> Muzungu will come rescue you?

> DARREN
> I sure hope not.

> MUNI
> Where else would she go?

EXT. DEEP CONGO JUNGLE - MYSTERIOUS LANDMARK - NIGHT

The Wayfinder points to a TREE as tall as a small building. It is one of dozens that line the perimeter of an ESCARPMENT that's covered in vines and foliage.

                    DARREN (V.O.)
          Hopefully, somewhere safe.

Nothing on the tree itself stands out except for the CONCENTRIC CIRCLES of Atlantis carved into its trunk.

Asa manages an exhausted smile.

She places her hand inside the circles and they LIGHT UP. The tree shakes, and the hanging vines vanish as if it were just an illusion. But the escarpment remains…

Before her, the terrain splits and a passage appears. On the other side, a light glows inside the passageway. Asa's smile turns into a laugh of relief.

                    ASA
          Hold on, Darren. I'll be back soon.

She takes a step forward when—

A GLEAMING ARROW fires from the passage, pierces her chest.

Asa can't move or breathe. All she can do is fall backward. The arrow dissipates as she hits the ground, but her breath doesn't return. The Wayfinder drops from her hand.

Asa's vision fails her, and all we can see is the silhouette of an ARJANAN WARRIOR approach her as she slips out of consciousness.

                              FADE TO BLACK.

                    END OF SHOW

C1GNUS STUD1O

108

AFROFANTASY

SCREENPLAY BY CHANNING LHEA

AFROFANTASY

108 - "The Remnant Kingdom"

Written by

Channing Chea

AFROFANTASY

"THE REMNANT KINGDOM"

<u>TEASER</u>

FADE IN:

EXT. WAALISHA CARAVAN - DARFUR, SUDAN - DAY

The Waalisha caravan, SIX TRUCKS deep, treks down a desert
road. It passes an abandoned village on the way to a MOUNTAIN
RANGE that barely fills the barren desert skyline.

I/E. WAALISHA TRUCK - DARFUR, SUDAN - CONTINUOUS

SUNLIGHT bleeds through the covered windows of one Waalisha
Trucks. MUNI uncovers a window, allows the light to flood the
truck's interior as he peers outside.

DARREN squints as the light blinds him. He is calm, despite
several WAALISHA FIGHTERS training their guns on him.

                    DARREN
          Where are we now?

                    MUNI
          The last stronghold in Sudan that
          has not been taken by the State:
          Jebel Marra.

INT. ARJANA - QUEEN'S THRONE ROOM - DAY

ASA's eyes peel open. She realizes she is immobilized, bound
and suspended from a CROSS-SHAPED TREE sprouting from a
QUARTZ floor. A VOICE pulls her from pending anxiety.

                    QUEEN ASASE
          Another explorer stumbles through…

Asa finds the speaker. QUEEN ASASE, a woman aged beyond time
and adorned with precious metals, sits on a THRONE carved
from GEMSTONES. She holds the UMOYA WAYFINDER in her hand.

Accompanying the Queen are three regal Arjanans who are also
adorned in ARMOR of varying splendor and practicality:
ANANSI, 40s male, whose armor appears ceremonial; TANO, 50s
male, whose armor is the most functional; and BIA, 30s
female, whose armor is a compromise between extremes.

Tano is closest to Asa, standing between her and the Queen.

63

Bia and Anansi stand on either side of Asase. They all study
the American suspended from the tree. Their faces display
varying levels of concern, but none are welcoming.

Except for Queen Asase herself. She wears a pleasant smile,
but it feels like a mask that hides a burden underneath.

> QUEEN ASASE
> You have discovered a great thing,
> indeed. Unfortunately, no one will
> hear how your journey ended.

                                        FADE OUT.

                          END OF TEASER

<u>ACT ONE</u>

FADE IN:

INT. ARJANA - QUEEN'S THRONE ROOM - DAY

Asa yanks, tests the VINES that bind her to the tree. They do
not budge. Her eyes meet the Queen's.

> ASA
> Is this Arjana? I need—

Asa HACKS blood. It falls to the floor by Tano's feet.

> ANANSI
> Tano, where did you hit her?

> TANO
> My dart pierced her lung. I am
> certain I did not miss.

> BIA
> (teases)
> Are you?

> TANO
> Yes. I am.

> ANANSI
> If that is true, then the only way
> she could survive such a strike is
> if she were awakened to Umoya.

> BIA
> Or perhaps Tano has gone soft.

> TANO
> Do you truly think so little of me?

> ANANSI
> In any case, she is almost healed,
> so perhaps she *has* awakened it.
> What would Her Divinity like to do?

The Queen fiddles with the Wayfinder, studies the American.

> QUEEN ASASE
> It is just the four of us, Anansi.
> There's no need for formality.
> Tano, are you sure she was carrying
> this?

                    TANO
          Yes, she dropped it once I pierced
          her. She was consulting it.

                    ASA
               (fights coughs)
          It was a gift from Khadija, the
          West Guardian… She gave it to us—

Tano points to Asa. From the ether he summons the **GLEAM DART**,
a laser arrow that forms from his hand. The Dart shoots over
to Asa's face, menaces her from below her nose.

                    TANO
          It is dangerous to lie when on
          trial.

                    QUEEN ASASE
          Please refrain from executing the
          intruder until she has had an
          opportunity to testify. We should
          give her a chance to catch her
          breath. Until then, let us confirm
          Anansi's theory. Bia, please fetch
          our witness.

                    BIA
          Yes, mother.

Bia walks past Asa to a blank wall. She places her hand on it
and it slides open, reveals a passage with someone waiting on
the other side. This is UDANGA, 30s male, the ARJANAN SCOUT
from the Congo Jungle.

He follows Bia into the room and bows in front of the Queen.

                    UDANGA
          Your Divinity.

                    QUEEN ASASE
          Hello, Udanga. I am told you came
          across this intruder last night.

Udanga turns around, notices the tree and the woman on it.

                    UDANGA
          Yes, that is her! I saw her using a
          Wayfinder to navigate the forest. I
          knew something was suspicious when
          she wasn't deterred by my **PHANTASM**.
          She saw right through the mountain
          and came right for Arjana!
               (MORE)

                    UDANGA (CONT'D)
          I even tried to throw her off
          course by scattering the stars, but
          nothing worked.

                    ANANSI
          Are you certain your Soul Flux was
          active?

                    UDANGA
          Of course, sir. Everyone I saw in
          the area changed course at the
          sight of the mountain. All but her…

                    ANANSI
          That corroborates Tano's report and
          confirms our hypothesis.

                    QUEEN ASASE
              (nods)
          Thank you, Udanga, that is all.

                    UDANGA
          Yes, Your Divinity.

Udanga bows once more then leaves through the door he entered
from. The wall seals as he exits. Asa gathers her breath.

                    ASA
          Excuse me. I get that I'm on trial,
          but can you tell me why I'm in
          trouble?

                    QUEEN ASASE
          She who stumbles into a den of
          lions is an unfortunate soul. She
          who purposely seeks out that den
          may succeed in her goal, but is
          equally unfortunate.
              (her smile shrinks)
          I will grant you the next few
          moments to deliver your defense.
          Please be concise.

                    ASA
          My husband and I were given that
          Wayfinder by Khadija, the Guardian
          of the West Temple. She asked us to
          warn you about the man who is
          attacking the temples and trying to
          steal the Shards!

                    BIA
          Why did Khadija not inform us
          herself?

                    ASA
          The temple was attacked when we
          were there—by the same man looking
          for the Shards. Her son died in the
          attack… so she had to stay behind.

                    ANANSI
          If you and your husband were both
          told to come, where is he?

                    TANO
          Is he still wandering in the
          jungle?

                    ASA
          No, he—he's been captured by a
          terrorist group that ambushed us on
          the way here… which is the other
          reason I'm here…
               (beat)
          Would you please help me rescue
          him?

                    BIA
               (laughs)
          You could not save yourselves with
          your awakened Umoya?

                    ASA
          The Waalisha can use Umoya, too!
          But I don't know—

                    BIA
          Others can use it?!

                    ASA
          That's what I'm trying to tell you!
          There are a bunch of people out
          there who can use this power now,
          and if we don't stop them, one of
          them might unite the Ophiuchus
          Stone!

All in the room fall silent—shocked.

                    BIA
          This is outrageous! How do you even
          know about all of this? The Curse
          should have ended you by now…

                    ASA
          If you mean the coal guy, he sure
          tried to.

The Queen silently observes Asa, processes her words. Then she waves her hand, and the tree Asa hangs from releases her, recedes into the floor. Tano's Gleam Dart follows its target.

                    BIA
          Mother, what—

                    QUEEN ASASE
          Of the few who have stumbled upon
          the Kingdom, none have ever known
          who we are. But this woman appears
          to have been informed by someone.

                    BIA
          She could be following a rumor…
          Just another greedy treasure
          hunter.

                    QUEEN ASASE
          Anansi, do you believe this
          outsider could have learned about
          the Ophiuchus Stone from any source
          that is not one of our own?

Anansi is surprised by the query. He ponders the question.

                    ANANSI
          That is unlikely. It is also
          unlikely that this woman gleaned
          information from a Guardian against
          their will, which means…

                    QUEEN ASASE
          The information was volunteered.
          This lends credence to her claims.
          Tano, would you please…

Tano is uneasy, but he steps back and dissipates the Dart. As it vanishes, Asa figures she is allowed raise her head. Her eyes meet the Queen's again.

                    QUEEN ASASE
          We will hear what you have to say,
          but this time, please start from
          the beginning.

EXT. PORT SUDAN - WAREHOUSES - DAY

CRANES and stacked SHIPPING CONTAINERS line the low skyline of Port Sudan, and massive vessels drift into the docks. It's a steel jungle of stacked, multicolor blocks.

BUZIBA stands on the roof of a warehouse. He searches for something, consults his own WAYFINDER. The dial spins until it finds its way…

It points toward the port. Buziba proceeds.

EXT. PORT SUDAN - THE DOCKS - DAY

He arrives at a stack of containers that oversees a soon-to-be-occupied dock. A much smaller ship floats in, one too small to be anything but a pirate's vessel.

Buziba checks the Wayfinder again. The needle flits between two points. One is a SMUGGLER, 40s male, pretending to mind his business. And two is the massive CRATE behind him. Smuggler waits for the ship to dock, but that won't happen.

Smuggler leans against the crate when COAL CLASPS grab his ankles. He panics, tries to pull free as the coal burns him.

Buziba drops from the containers and approaches the dock. The PIRATE CREW sees him and likewise panics, immediately turning the ship around.

But Buziba swats at the ground, causes a bubbling rumble beneath the water's surface. Suddenly, the ship runs aground and begins to capsize. The Pirate Crew abandons ship.

Buziba turns back to the Smuggler.

                    BUZIBA
          And now, for you.

Smuggler punches the air, sends a surprise BURST of wind at Buziba. Buziba blocks by raising a COAL WALL.

Smuggler follows with a flurry of punches, each with an offensive burst, but Buziba swerves, dodges the air itself until he is close enough to punch Smuggler's chest.

Smuggler clutches his nearly-caved chest, then more COAL CLASPS emerge from the ground and seize his hands.

Buziba briefly inspects the crate before punching through the wood. GOLD CYLINDERS pour from the side as he tears it open.

                    SMUGGLER
          You can take it all! Please just
          let me go.

                    BUZIBA
          You would give away all this hard-
          mined gold?

Buziba holds the Wayfinder to the gold. The needle excites.

> BUZIBA
> Or perhaps it was not mined…

> SMUGGLER
> I can get more. Just take it!

Buziba invades Smuggler's personal space—eyeballs him.

> BUZIBA
> Take me to the source.

EXT. JEBEL MARRA - WAALISHA CAMP - DAY

The Waalisha Caravan arrives at an impoverished but POPULATED settlement on the MOUNTAIN. They unload everything from RECRUITS and FOOD CRATES to their lone captive: Darren.

SAMBA takes his empty BACKPACK and walks away into the camp. MALICK wrangles the attention of the Recruits.

> MALICK
> All of you who are new, follow me!

He heads off, leading the young Recruits into the settlement. Darren almost follows, but Muni stops him.

> MUNI
> Not you. You come with us.

AMANI steps out of her truck. She starts for the camp, and Darren, encouraged by the point of Muni's SWORD, follows her.

They pass dozens of HUTS, TENTS, and other makeshift shelters that lined the camp outskirts. As they continue, CABINS appear. HUNDREDS of WOMEN and CHILDREN flood the area, many escorted or assisted by GUNMEN. None seem to mind the guns.

The three pass Samba by one of the shelters, reloading his backpack with homemade GOLD BULLIONS pulled from a cache that's organized into piles. Darren gawks at the bullions.

They finally arrive at a relatively large cabin and enter.

INT. JEBEL MARRA - HQ COMMAND - CONTINUOUS

Muni, Amani, and Darren walk through a familiar setup of COMPUTERS and OPERATIVES manning them. They wave, welcome the heroes and newcomer, but they return to work when they enter…

INT. JEBEL MARRA - HQ COMMAND - AMANI'S LAB - CONTINUOUS

TESLA COILS, WEAPONS, and SCIENCE CRAFTS of all kinds are
strewn about the area. The den resembles an amateur science
lab more than the hub of an extremist.

Muni closes the door behind them and ushers Darren to a seat.
Amani pulls up a seat beside Darren.

>   AMANI
>   Please make yourself comfortable. I
>   just want to talk to you.

Darren eyes Muni's sword; fidgets in the gold cuffs.

>   DARREN
>   Kinda hard to do that considering…

Amani gives Muni a nod. He hesitates but sheathes his sword.

Amani then leans forward, touches Darren's cuffs. They revert
back into stone and crumble to the floor.

>   DARREN
>   That's a start. Can't say I have
>   much of anything to say to you
>   though.

>   MUNI
>   I feel the same, American.

>   AMANI
>   *But*… our feelings are not what
>   informs our decisions. My name is
>   Amani Suleyman. What is your name?
>   (Darren scowls)
>   Look, I understand we have been on
>   opposite ends of an unfortunate
>   struggle, but I am asking that we
>   put that quarrel behind us now.

>   DARREN
>   Behind us?! It was just last night
>   that you tried to kill my wife
>   before taking me prisoner, but
>   that's all water under the bridge?

>   MUNI
>   It was not even two weeks ago that
>   you and your Muzungu wife killed
>   multiple of our comrades.

                    DARREN
          You attack us on Kilimanjaro and
          you're the victims?

                    MUNI
          You attacked our brother and me as
          we fled! We lost that battle. Have
          you no honor?

                    AMANI
          It does not matter—

                    DARREN
          Blowing you murderers away was
          payback for what you had just done
          to us! How did you both survive
          that, anyway?

                    MUNI
          We "both" did not, which is why
          your wife's head is tempting—

                    AMANI
          ENOUGH!
               (to Darren)
          We have lost more by your hands
          than you could ever understand. So
          accept this olive branch and be
          grateful we do not demand
          recompense.
               (to Muni; pleads)
          Muni, we are so close. Make his
          death count.

Muni seethes through his teeth. He goes to sit. He remains in
the room but occupies a different space in his mind.

                    AMANI
          We have a responsibility to all
          those people outside, and we need
          the skills and knowledge you have
          about these abilities.

                    DARREN
          I don't care how many people there
          are. A village full of terrorists
          are still terrorists. Why would I
          help you?

                    AMANI
          Those people are not fighters by
          choice. They are displaced citizens
          of a nation that has betrayed them.
               (MORE)

73

                    AMANI (CONT'D)
All of us are. Not
extremists—rebels.

                    DARREN
Again, *you're* the victims, huh?

                    MUNI
You Americans… so above violence
when you are just too privileged to
have ever needed it yourself. Let's
feed him to the Janjaweed and see
how long until he's knocked off his
high horse.

                    AMANI
It is not his fault, Muni. Just the
product of another broken
institution.

                    DARREN
You know what? I'd love to hear
what excuse you have for trying to
topple a kingdom and bringing kids
into a war. Go ahead, I'm all ears.

Muni remains resigned to his corner, but Amani is relieved by
Darren's posture. She leans back, retreats into her memories.

                    AMANI
I cannot give you a lesson in
politics or even history, but at
the very least, I can tell you our
story.

                                        FADE OUT.

                    <u>END OF ACT ONE</u>

ACT TWO

EXT. DARFUR VILLAGE - FIFTEEN YEARS AGO - DAY, FLASHBACK

TEEN AMANI pulls water from a WELL. She pours it into a small
BARREL-filled to its brim—so TEEN MUNI can pick it up. He
balances it on his head as Teen Amani fills a smaller barrel
for herself to carry. They prepare to depart.

But CHILD JOSEPH tugs his sister's arm, demands something to
carry. She gives him a bucket to fill. They set off.

> AMANI (V.O.)
> We grew up in Darfur. Our family
> was fortunate to stay away from
> much of the tyranny of our
> government. But one day that
> fortune ran out.

They walk through huts and homes in a town filled with
VILLAGERS. The town is peaceful, until…

GUNSHOTS crack through the air, incite a panic. The Villagers
disperse, enter their huts… but the Suleyman trio have
nowhere to hide. They drop their water.

In the distance, they can see them—the JANJAWEED, a ragtag
but lethal militia. They arrive in trucks, not bothering to
get out as they spray the village with swarms of bullets.

Teen Muni looks at the fleeing Villagers. He freezes, fear
taking over, but he's yanked out of paralysis by his sister.

> TEEN AMANI
> Come on!

Teen Amani grabs both of her bothers and sprints for cover.

The trio dips behind the cover of a stone stairwell. As
bullets fly, debris crumbles and obscures them from view.
Child Joseph cries and trembles, and his brother pulls him
near. The three huddle, but Teen Amani peeks outside.

Bodies drop, young and old. The Janjaweed run over those who
they don't bother to shoot.

An ELDERLY VILLAGER tries to run, but her bones don't allow a
sprint. A truck chases her down, one RIDER unsheathes a
MACHETE. Once close enough, he takes his swing…

Teen Amani flinches from the sight, but then she's horrified. She leaves her hiding spot and runs deeper into the village.

                    TEEN MUNI
          Amani, stop!

But she's already gone. The girl sprints, undeterred by flying bullets and screams until she reaches her destination.

INT. DARFUR VILLAGE - SULEYMAN HOME - CONTINUOUS

She barges into a hut and looks around.

                    TEEN AMANI
          Baba! Mama!

FATHER SULEYMAN and MOTHER SULEYMAN are there, ever so slightly relieved.

                    MOTHER SULEYMAN
          Amani, get inside!

                    FATHER SULEYMAN
          Where are your brothers?!

An EXPLOSION startles them. Through the open door, they see GASEOUS PROJECTILES tumble outside, choking nearby Villagers. Some fizzle out. Others explode like grenades.

Above, one projectile crashes through the roof. It lands in the center of the hut. Father Suleyman reacts, shoving his daughter behind a flipped table. He grabs his wife. Teen Amani only manages a scream before…

The grenade explodes, fills the room with a heavy red mist.

The brothers arrive in the hut, just in time to see the horrors left for them. It's not until Teen Amani screams from the sight that her brothers notice her.

Teen Muni embraces his sister and brother, guards them from the sight as best he can. They huddle again in a corner until the sounds of CACKLES and gunshots finally fade.

EXT. DARFUR VILLAGE - LATER

A haunting silence signals safety. That's when Villagers emerge from their shelters, their presence indicated by wails and cries.

Teen Muni steps outside. The desert sun beats down on what has become a battlefield. He barely has his faculties.

He looks inside to see his sister holding Child Joseph tight. His eyes are wide, cold, confused. She wipes the trail of fallen tears from her face and steps outside the hut. Her eyes now show something new: rage, indignation.

The three exit the hut, observe what has become of their home. Despairing Villagers surround them. They all share the same horror, yet the siblings felt alone.

Then an ADULT DARFURIAN enters the frame. He notices the siblings. They are shaken, so he reaches into his SATCHEL and pulls bottled water. He shares the water with the siblings. They accept graciously, surprised by his generosity.

The siblings head out into the village and assist others.

EXT. JEBEL MARRA - REBEL SETTLEMENT - NINE YEARS AGO - DAY

YOUNG AMANI pulls water from a well again. This time she carries it alone up a long mountain path.

> AMANI (V.O.)
> Years later, we had built a new
> life for ourselves. We were part of
> a new community… a new home.

She arrives in a large settlement. Nothing like the modern Waalisha camp, but livable enough for hundreds of people.

She delivers her water to a SCARRED MAN. He hands her some bread, nods his thanks and takes the water onward, where thirsty CHILDREN wait.

Within eyeshot, TEEN JOSEPH receives instruction from a fellow SETTLER on how to work on cars.

> AMANI (V.O.)
> The previous president had been
> deposed. There were still random
> attacks from insurgent Janjaweed,
> but we had hope that the killing
> was over.

Amani smiles at her growing brother, walks to someone nearby.

It's YOUNG MUNI. He downstrokes an AXE, chops wood on a STUMP. He piles the wood against a natural wall on the mountain. Young Amani hands him a piece of the bread.

He accepts and eats it, and they enjoy the moment. Then what seems like a bird's shadow passes under the sun, flickering the light below. Young Amani gazes up, looks for the bird.

                    AMANI (V.O.)
           We were wrong…

The bird glistens in light, drops something that WHISTLES as
it descends, explodes as it hits the ground.

The settlement is under attack! Bullets join the sounds of
falling bombs as some Settlers are picked off.

HORNS blare to signal the attack. Settlers all over run for
cover. But the Suleyman siblings do not. They pick up arms
and run for the frontlines.

The siblings return fire at the Janjaweed, but the assault is
ephemeral. The militia retreats, having done their damage.

The Settlers regroup. They tend to their injured, fire at
airplanes that depart the airspace. The siblings exchange
confused and troubled looks.

Young Amani's face shows a familiar rage.

INT. JEBEL MARRA – REBEL SETTLEMENT – MEDICAL TENT – EVENING

The siblings do their best to assist in the medical
initiative. Young Muni carries the injured to beds, Young
Amani directs him to open locations, and Teen Joseph Jerry-
rigs inadequate equipment into operation. Other Settlers
treat the injured.

Then another Settler enters the tent, spreads news that some
gather to hear. The news brings them dread.

                    AMANI (V.O.)
           We learned the new leaders in power
           continued the ethnic cleanse. The
           Janjaweed became the R.S.F. The
           uniforms were different, but
           nothing else changed.

EXT. JEBEL MARRA – REBEL SETTLEMENT – MEDICAL TENT – EVENING

Young Amani steps out of the tent, followed by her brothers.

The poise becoming of her slips into a near madness while her
body remains still, but she is pulled from it when Young Muni
places a hand on her shoulder.

>   AMANI (V.O.)
>   After I learned the news, I thought
>   the solution was simple: Expel from
>   Sudan the Arab leaders that tried
>   so hard to exterminate us.

They all embrace again, but as Young Amani pulls away, the
madness becomes a frightening focus. The brothers know what
this means.

EXT. KHARTOUM, SUDAN - URBAN ALLEY - EIGHT YEARS AGO - NIGHT

A MAN in a SHEMAGH sneaks through an alley. He looks around
before knocking on a door. It opens and he enters.

INT. KHARTOUM, SUDAN - SECRET BASE - CONTINUOUS

The man removes his shemagh when inside. It's Young Muni. He
joins a table with dozens of REBELS circled around it. They
explore a BLUEPRINT of a large government building.

>   AMANI (V.O.)
>   To end the conflict, it was worth
>   the try.

Young Amani points to the main office inside. She speaks into
a WALKIE on her shoulder.

Responses come from several other WALKIES placed around the
blueprint, each placement representative of the speakers'
locations.

All responses indicate the rebels are in place. They move
toward the exit, armed, waiting for their signal. Young Amani
reveals a DEVICE with a RED BUTTON on it. She presses it.

EXT. KHARTOUM, SUDAN - CAPITAL - NIGHT

From above, we see several corners of the Capital building
burst into flame. Billowing red plumes rise into the air.

INT. KHARTOUM, SUDAN - CAPITAL - PRESIDENT'S OFFICE - NIGHT

The explosions RATTLE the office, where an unsuspecting
GENERAL NAZEER, 50s, a clean man who wears his decorations on
his sleeve, sits drinking with PRESIDENT IBRAHIM, 60s, a man
who wears his meals just above his belt.

The two rise in alarm. General Nazeer shouts something in
Arabic to nearby RSF SOLDIERS. They run off.

Nazeer pulls a HANDGUN from his belt, right beside his ornate
SHOTEL. He is surprised, but he is not unprepared.

EXT. KHARTOUM, SUDAN - CAPITAL - NIGHT

A SEDAN skids to the curb of the capital. The driver is Teen
Joseph. He keeps the car running as armed Rebels pour out.
Leading the charge is Teen Amani, Teen Muni right behind her.

Coughing RSF Soldiers emerge from the smoking hole in the
building. They aim at the Rebels, but they choke too hard to
shoot. The Rebels pick them off and enter the building.

INT. KHARTOUM, SUDAN - CAPITAL - CORRIDOR - CONTINUOUS

The Rebels look around. They spilt up. Comrade Rebels head
south and engage more of the RSF, but the Suleyman siblings
head north. The fire burns in their eyes.

DOWN THE CORRIDOR

They arrive at a large and ornate wooden door. This is the
President's office. The siblings give each other a reassuring
glance before Teen Amani reaches for the doorknob.

I/E. KHARTOUM, SUDAN - CAPITAL - CONTINUOUS

Teen Joseph keeps watch in the car. He peers into the
distance and sees a suited man crossing the road away from
the capital, escorted by a dozen RSF Soldiers. It's President
Ibrahim. Teen Joseph grabs his WALKIE.

                    TEEN JOSEPH
              Amani, the president escaped! He is
              outside the building now!

INT. KHARTOUM, SUDAN - CAPITAL - CORRIDOR - CONTINUOUS

The siblings hear their brother's message. Their reassurance
is gone. There is only confusion until…

POW! BULLETS fire from the opposite side of the door. One
grazes Young Muni, and he and his sister jump to the floor.
Young Muni grabs a grenade from his belt and kicks open the
door, tosses it inside the office. He rolls over, covers his
sister.

The grenade explodes and the bullets momentarily stop. The
siblings rise again and enter the office.

INT. KHARTOUM, SUDAN - CAPITAL - PRESIDENT'S OFFICE - CONTINUOUS

The siblings enter, search for the shooter through the smoke. The General's coughing gives him away. He leans against the wall. His face obscured by smoke.

                    AMANI (V.O.)
          The invasion was successful, but
          the coup d'état failed. If nothing
          else, I hoped I could kill the Arab
          general who was responsible for
          massacring my family. But then I
          saw his face…

The smoke clears. General Nazeer's eyes meet Young Amani's, and her blood runs cold.

                    AMANI
          He looked like me… like my
          brothers, my comrades… any other
          Sudanese man.

She drops her gun… unable to process what she sees. Nazeer acts while she is frozen. He lifts his gun, shoots Young Muni's gun out of his hand.

But he runs out of ammo. He goes for Young Amani's gun, picks it up, but Young Muni grabs it too, tries to wrestle it away.

                    YOUNG MUNI
          Amani, do something!

She snaps out of it, looks around. The first thing she sees is a golden FLAGPOLE with a spiked point. She pulls it down, strips it of its flag in the process.

Nazeer gains leverage. Muni is almost in front of its barrel.

But Young Amani SHOUTS, throws the flagpole like a javelin. Its point digs into Nazeer's leg. The gun's barrel drops.

Young Muni takes the moment to reach for Nazeer's shotel. With one motion he pulls it from its sheath, and in another he swings down, severing the gun hand. Nazeer screams, falls.

The siblings gather themselves. Their walkie picks up again.

                    TEEN JOSEPH (V.O.)
          Everyone retreat! More RSF are
          incoming—get out of there!

Shotel in hand, Young Muni grabs his sister, leads her out of the office. She follows, but sneaks a final look at Nazeer…

I/E. KHARTOUM, SUDAN - CAPITAL - NIGHT

The siblings are the last ones to hop in the sedan before
Teen Joseph speeds away. The countenance of the Rebels is
celebratory. They have made their point. But Young Amani is
still processing, confused.

> AMANI (V.O.)
> We escaped with our lives, but I
> felt defeated. How could a Sudanese
> man justify shedding the blood of
> his own people? How could he
> massacre thousands; uproot the
> lives of hundreds of thousands?

END FLASHBACK.

INT. JEBEL MARRA - HQ COMMAND - AMANI'S LAB - DAY

Darren listens intently to the story. Muni and Amani battle
internal pain as they recall the events.

> AMANI
> What could be more evil than the
> prejudices of ethnic supremacy? How
> much money could make a man abuse
> his office to that extent?
> (beat)
> But of course, that was it… It was
> not the money or the prejudice. It
> was something much simpler: the
> office itself. One need not look
> any further than Africa herself to
> see the affect of Power on those
> who wield it. There are more
> dictators here than any other
> continent. So much poverty and
> disease that we have become the
> poster for it. How could our
> leaders—in a land so rich with
> resources—not have the wealth to
> help their people?

Amani's voice raises as she becomes more convicted.

> AMANI
> They do, but they have been
> corrupted by something stronger
> than wealth; deeper than race…
> Power.
> (MORE)

                    AMANI (CONT'D)
That is why we formed the Waalisha
Khufu: to create a force to fight
against the evils of corrupt
leadership. The inevitable evil of
government.

                    DARREN
That almost sounds noble. But you
know… if you were to get rid of all
the bad governments, that would
make you the only bad leader left.

                    AMANI
That may be so, but I never wanted
to be a leader. All I want to do is
contribute to a community that is
free from the pitfalls of
authority. I'll fight the notion
that I should be followed until I
die! If I bring us up this
mountain, I won't do it from the
front, but I will push every one of
my comrades from behind until we
made it to the top together. In
this case, it looks like I might
need to push an American with us.

                    DARREN
Darren… is my name.

Amani smiles wholeheartedly.

                    AMANI
Well, now we are getting somewhere.

INT. ARJANA - QUEEN'S THRONE ROOM - DAY

All in the throne room hear Asa's story with varied
skepticism, worry, and surprise. The Queen still processes.

                    ASA
Darren allowed me to escape, and I
came straight here using the
Wayfinder. And now, this…

                    BIA
How could a couple outsiders be so
unlucky to run into multiple
guardians? How lucky you are to
escape every time.

                    ASA
          It told you, it wasn't escaping.
          Acacia encouraged us to find the
          next shard, so we did.

                    TANO
          How can we trust that you did not
          ambush Acacia and interrogate her?

Asa frowns but uncovers her wrist, reveals the RING BURN.

                    ASA
          Here, she gave me this burn when
          she taught us about Unity Fluxes.

                    TANO
          If she was attempting to sync with
          you, how did you burn?

                    ASA
          Because, I—

                    ANANSI
          It is unlikely to work on the first
          attempt. Certainly, if Acacia
          intended to maim her, she would
          have done so. But the fact Acacia
          revealed such a technique at all
          implies some level of trust.

                    TANO
          It implies whenever she meets
          Temple Guardians, they end up dead.
          Is that wrong?

                    BIA
          Tano, what are you on about?

                    TANO
          Hear this assessment and tell me if
          I am wrong, Anansi. First, these
          outsiders go to Lesotho and a
          terrorist organization attempts to
          overthrow the monarchy. Then they
          visit the South Temple and meet
          Acacia, who shortly after is
          confirmed dead. Finally, she says
          they visit Khadija, but she cannot
          inform Arjana of this new threat
          because her son, yet another
          guardian, is murdered.

                    ANANSI
          Not inaccurate thus far…

                    TANO
          Then, as she journeys here, she
          comes across multiple war-struck
          villages.

                    ASA
          What's your point?

                    TANO
          It seems wherever this outsider
          goes, destruction follows.

Asa becomes unsettled. The words hit deeper than they should.

                    ASA
          You can't blame that stuff on me. I
          wasn't even there when most of it
          happened!

                    ANANSI
               (ponders)
          You are both only half correct.
          This outsider has indeed only been
          present for half of these
          misfortunes, but a rotten apple
          need not be present long to spoil
          its barrel. Alternatively, this is
          an unprecedented time. She is
          likely responding to being included
          in these events against her will.

Tano growls with dissatisfaction. He turns to Bia.

                    BIA
          Anansi has a point. I doubt she
          even wants to be in Africa right
          now.

                    ASA
               (softly)
          Why… do you think that?

                    TANO
          Whether she does or not, that does
          not change that she is exceptional
          at finding danger.

Tano summons another Gleam Dart, menaces Asa's face again.

                    TANO
          I won't allow her to bring it here.

                    QUEEN ASASE
          That is enough, Tano.

                    TANO
          Your Divinity, I have determined
          that this outsider poses a threat
          to the Kingdom. As is my duty, I
          wish to deliver the sentence.

                    QUEEN ASASE
          I acknowledge your conjecture.
          However, I do not permit execution.

                    TANO
          But she has trespassed on forbidden
          lands many times over! This alone
          earns her death.

                    QUEEN ASASE
          This would be the ordinary course
          of action, yes, but I sense no
          malicious intent from her.

Anansi and Bia send a quizzical look toward the Queen.

                    BIA
          So, do you want us to let her go?

                    TANO
          I cannot do that.

The Gleam Dart proceeds toward Asa's neck. She scoots back
just to avoid it.

                    TANO
          If we let another outsider go after
          learning about the Kingdom, she
          will only return and bring
          devastation. I will not let that
          happen.

The Dart accelerates, almost pierces Asa's body before it
drops, dissipates as it slams into the ground. The Dart is
crushed by an invisible force. As Asa looks up, she sees the
same phenomenon crush Tano. Bia and Anansi are not fazed, but
the Queen's hand is outstretched.

                    QUEEN ASASE
          Direct insubordination against the
          Queen is also a capital offense.
          Should this be overlooked?

Tano tries to push himself up. Then the downforce increases,
presses a growing crater into the cracking floor.

                    QUEEN ASASE
          Shall the sentence be execution? Or
          will it be—

                    TANO
          Mercy!

                    QUEEN ASASE
           Mercy, indeed.

The Queen lowers her hand and the downforce lets up. Tano's
body and the floor rebound from the pressure.

Tano spins and bows his head toward the Queen.

                    TANO
          I apologize, Your Divinity. I—

                    QUEEN ASASE
           Hush. Your zeal is too much for me.
           Return to your post.

Tano nods, rises, walks away. A hint of animosity bleeds
through his expression as he exits through the hidden door.

                    QUEEN ASASE
           As I was saying… Mercy will be the
           route I take.

                    ASA
           Oh my god, thank you so much,
           ma'am!

Asa gets up, begins to move around casually, but ROOTS from
the floor sprout and catch her ankles…

                    QUEEN ASASE
           I never said you would not be
           sentenced. Now, give us a moment as
           we deliberate.

The roots grow into a tree again. It lifts Asa, tosses her
into a corner of the room. Then the quartz floor rises, seals
her into a crystalline capsule.

                    BIA
           What is on your mind?

The Queen reclines on her throne, gazes at the ceiling.

                    QUEEN ASASE
           So many fires to put out, and too
           much water to quench it with…

                    BIA
What do you mean by that?

                    QUEEN ASASE
We have four major threats to our
welfare; the first being this
"Waalisha". A radical group with
access to Umoya will only bring
violence.

                    BIA
That is not really a problem, is
it? A small platoon of Arjanan
soldiers can wipe them out easily.

                    QUEEN ASASE
You are right. It would be simple.
     (gestures to Anansi)
But if we do that…

                    ANANSI
The platoon size required to
eliminate that many Fluxers,
unskilled as they may be, would
raise too much alarm and draw
attention to our existence…

                    QUEEN ASASE
Sharp as ever. Smoke may signal a
fire, but ashes drowned in water
are just as revealing.

                    BIA
But that is why we have Buziba!

                    QUEEN ASASE
Correct again. He should be
snuffing fires before they begin,
but he has been ineffective as of
late and unresponsive since going
to the Northern Temple. He is my
second concern, but that leads me
to the third…
     (she scowls)
The Fire Shard has been stolen.

Bia is in shock.

                    ANANSI
That makes two total taken.

                    BIA
How?! Where were Sage and Marula?
Where was Buziba?!

                    QUEEN ASASE
          That is irrelevant. We need to
          prioritize keeping the remaining
          two Shards safe and catching the
          thief.

                    BIA
          That is extremely relevant! If
          those two and Buziba aren't around,
          we need to deploy many more
          guardians—dozens of them!

                    ANANSI
          You already know why we cannot do
          that. Deploying too many Arjanans
          risks exposing the Kingdom.

                    BIA
          Then send me and the Spectral
          Guard! We can't just do nothing!

                    QUEEN ASASE
          You and the Spectral Guard will be
          dealing with our fourth and final
          problem.

                    BIA
          There's another?

                    QUEEN ASASE
          This American. She is an outsider
          that has trespassed on forbidden
          land and is awakened to Umoya.
          However, if Khadija entrusted her
          to deliver this message, it would
          be wrong to kill or imprison her.

                    ANANSI
          So what do you plan to do with her?

Queen Asase grins again, pleased by her own cleverness.

                    QUEEN ASASE
          Haven't figured it out yet, eh?
               (Anansi shrugs; puzzled)
          We are going to make our fourth
          problem solve the first three for
          us.

IN THE CRYSTALLINE CAPSULE

Asa BANGS on the thick wall.

                    ASA
          I think I should be a part of this
          convo too! I don't wanna wait in
          here—it's hot! Please…

She finally tires and slides down the wall. She is quiet for
a moment, and then… her phone CHIRPS.

Puzzled, she pulls out her PHONE. It's not plugged into
anything, but it's charging…

                    ASA
          How…

Her attention goes to the opposite wall. The wall's
TRANSLUCENCE hints to an outdoor area on the other side. Asa
gets up, attempts to peer through the barrier. Multiple large
triangular buildings cast shadows…

Then the capsule opens behind her. She turns to see Bia,
scowling like an annoyed babysitter. She sighs.

                    BIA
          Come with me.

                              FADE OUT.

                    END OF ACT TWO

ACT THREE

FADE IN:

INT. JEBEL MARRA - HQ COMMAND - AMANI'S LAB - DAY

Amani pours herself, Muni, and Darren water to drink. Darren
eyes it suspiciously but partakes when the others down it.

                    DARREN
          I still don't understand what you
          need me for.

                    AMANI
          Yes, it isn't fair to ask a
          foreigner to join our cause. That
          would be asking a lot of you.

                    DARREN
          So why did you kidnap me?

                    MUNI
          Because you know things about our
          new talents that the rest of us do
          not.

                    DARREN
          I'd prefer to keep it that way.

                    AMANI
          I understand that you do not
          approve of us, but this is a matter
          of self-defense.

                    DARREN
          You're not armed enough as it is?
          You seem to be getting on just fine
          without my help.

                    MUNI
          Against an oppressive government? A
          regime's resources are virtually
          infinite compared to ours. These
          abilities give us something they
          won't expect, but that is not
          enough.

                    AMANI
          We managed to spread the ability
          among our people, but only Muni and
          I have managed to achieve a higher
          level. We cannot figure out why.

                    DARREN
          And by spread, you mean assaulting
          them with it until you get results.

                    MUNI
          Trial by fire.
               (to Amani)
          Also, he once called this higher
          level a Soul Flux. He can use it as
          well, but the Muzungu did not.

                    AMANI
          I see.

Amani pours them all another drink, but Darren refuses this
time. She takes a sip.

                    DARREN
          I'll be more careful not to let you
          glean any more information from me.

                    AMANI
          Hear us, Darren, when we say that
          the Waalisha have had many enemies
          for years before we began taking
          the offensive. These enemies have
          grown in number in the past year.

                    DARREN
          That's your fault.

                    MUNI
          Was it our fault that our nation
          purged us from our own homes?!

                    DARREN
          Was Lesotho that nation?!

                    AMANI
          Yes, we made enemies too, but
          either way, innocent people reside
          here in Jebel Marra and rely on us
          to keep them safe. We can do that
          with these "fluxes", but we need
          your guidance to do it properly.

A KNOCK on the door interrupts them. Muni opens it to see
Malick on the other side. He holds someone's hand; a young
girl who stands behind him.

                    MALICK
               (to Muni)
          Sorry to bother you, but she really
          wanted to say hello.

LOLIE steps from behind Malick, smiles and gives a shy wave.

>   LOLIE
>   Hi, Mr. Muni!

>   MUNI
>   Hello, little one!

Darren sees the girl and is shocked.

>   DARREN
>   Lolie?!

>   LOLIE
>   Hi, Mr… I forgot your name.

>   DARREN
>   What are you—
>   (to Muni)
>   What's she doing here?

>   MUNI
>   Little Lolie lost her parents in a
>   past ADF attack, before the one we
>   stopped. The village had trouble
>   providing for her, so we took her
>   in.

>   DARREN
>   You brought her to this place that
>   you're telling me is a warzone?

Darren goes to the door, kneels down to talk to Lolie.

>   DARREN
>   Did they hurt you?

>   LOLIE
>   (shakes head)
>   I wanted to come.

>   MUNI
>   You see? It was her choice.

>   DARREN
>   She's a kid! She's too young to
>   make that choice on her own!

>   MUNI
>   She would not need to make that
>   choice if we did not live in a
>   world that forced it on her!

                    AMANI
          I understand your frustration,
          Darren, but Lolie is not the only
          young one here. That is why we need
          to protect them.

                    DARREN
          Screw off!

Darren takes Lolie's hand from Malick and walks away with
her. Malick looks at Muni for direction.

                    MUNI
          Make sure they don't leave the
          mountain.

Malick nods and follows them. Muni closes the door.

                    AMANI
          Do you think bringing her here was
          wisest?

                    MUNI
          Time will tell. Speaking of which,
          how long do we have?

Amani goes to the window, peers out of it. She stares at the
open desert in the distance.

                    AMANI
          I don't know. I just hope the
          American comes around soon.

EXT. JEBEL MARRA - HQ COMMAND - DAY

Darren leads Lolie outside. He walks away from the cabin,
toward a path down the mountain, but Malick cuts him off.

                    MALICK
          Muni told me not to let you leave.

                    DARREN
          Fine, then you take her somewhere
          else!

Malick places a hand on Lolie, who is increasingly unsettled.

                    MALICK
          Why worry her like that? She is
          perfectly safe here.

                    DARREN
          Mixed messages all around! Is
          everyone here safe or do you need
          my help to fight off your enemies?

                    MALICK
               (shrugs)
          It could be both…
               (to Lolie)
          You can go play if you want. The
          adults need to talk.

                    LOLIE
          I am a big girl! I can talk, too!

                    MALICK
          I know you are, but this guy
          disagrees…

Lolie chuckles. Darren studies Malick, curious.

                    DARREN
          What's your name again?

                    MALICK
          It's Malick.

                    DARREN
          Right… How old are you?

                    MALICK
               (puffs chest)
          I am eighteen-a man by American
          standards, am I not?

                    DARREN
          Sure… I guess so. Why are—

                    MALICK
          My village was raided by the
          Janjaweed, same as everyone else.

Darren observes the mountain settlement. It resembles a
refugee camp more than a terrorist base.

                    MALICK
          We are not here because we chose to
          be. We were cornered like animals,
          but now we're fighting back.

                    DARREN
               (sighs)
          So I hear… all right, then. Please
          keep Lolie safe, okay?

Darren roams into the camp. Malik and Lolie follow.

> MALICK
> Wait, I need your help. You called
> our abilities "fluxes", no? What
> should I name mine?

> DARREN
> Uh… What?

> LOLIE
> The magic!

> MALICK
> When Muni's evolved, he gave it a
> name. He calls it Vanguard Shear.

> DARREN
> Of course he does—that tool.

> MALICK
> Ms. Amani named hers too, but I do
> not know what to call mine.

> DARREN
> Well, that "evolution" is called a
> Soul Flux, and I haven't heard of
> people naming them until they gain
> theirs. So you have time.

> MALICK
> Soul Flux, eh?

> LOLIE
> What did you name yours?

> DARREN
> I didn't name mine…

> MALICK
> You should! It could be a great
> battle cry during a fight!

> LOLIE
> Just like magic words!

Darren scratches his forehead as he considers it.

MEMORY FLASH: Asa and Darren sit in the cabin in the Congo
village, eating their meals. Asa teases Darren.

Darren smiles.

                        DARREN
              I might have one in mind.

INT. ARJANA - PALACE HALL - DAY

Bia leads Asa down the corridor of a PALACE of even more
quartz. WHITE LIMESTONE covers the walls, filled with ART and
runes that are familiar to us. But this art is not a
reference to anything else. This is the original.

A FRESCO is etched into the ceiling. It diagrams ATLANTIS,
represented by the familiar CREST. An OCTAHEDRON sits in the
center, while NINE JEWELS bedazzle the outermost ring. A
massive MONSTER serpentines around the circular kingdom.

Natural light from the sun illuminates the space. The Palace
itself resembles glass that has been converted into a royal
living space.

Asa, distracted by the FRESCO, rushes to keep up with Bia,
who barely acknowledges her. Bia finally arrives at a wide
DOOR. She places her hand inside three CONCENTRIC CIRCLES.

They light up in response and the door opens. They exit.

EXT. ARJANA - CENTRAL MALL - CONTINUOUS

The door opens to reveal a massive mall. A vast courtyard is
surrounded by giant TREES, while multiple glistening streams
flow through it, straddling the edges of multicolored roads
and sidewalks.

From above, the sidewalks resemble thick threads of webbing
that intersect at many STEPPED PYRAMIDS no more than a few
stories high. Kingdom DENIZENS enter and exit from the base
of the Pyramids.

In the center of the mall towers a colossal OBELISK. Its body
is brilliant white LIMESTONE, while its capstone is a
majestic GOLD.

Asa marvels at Arjana. Her eyes drift from the obelisk back
to the palace. Then she realizes she is being stared at by
the FOUR SPECTRAL GUARDS, dressed in similar splendor to Bia.

Two Guards stand at either side of the Palace entrance.
ZAILA—female, 20s—is the first to speak.

                        ZAILA
              Wow, is that… the invader? They *do*
              look like ghosts!

                    ASA
          Wow… rude.

                    BIA
          Zaila, be respectful!

                    ZAILA
               (straightens up)
          Y-yes, forgive me!

CYMBA, 30s male, leans toward Asa as he inspects her. An
UPWARD BREEZE is the only thing that keeps him from falling.

                    CYMBA
          To be fair, she probably thinks we
          all look like shadows.

                    ZAILA
          Good point, Cymba.

                    ASA
          I've seen black people before!

JAMBI, 40s, a burly man as firmly planted in the ground as
the palace he leans against, inspects Asa.

                    JAMBI
          Princess Bia, would you like us to
          bind her legs so she cannot escape?

                    BIA
          That's enough from all of you! The
          Queen has ordered us to treat her
          like a guest from now on.

The Guards straighten up at the sharpness of Bia's tone.

                    ASA
          So, I'm free to go?

                    BIA
          No.
               (to the Guards)
          Spectral Guard, follow me. Your
          attendance is needed.

The entire group follows Bia through the mall, earning the
attention of multiple Denizens. They arrive at the base of a
wide stepped pyramid on the opposite corner of the mall. This
one's door is already open. The group enters.

INT. ARJANA - TRAINING FACILITY - CONTINUOUS

They enter a chamber as wide as the entire lower level of the pyramid. Dozens of ARJANAN SOLDIERS spar using weapons crafted of metal, and others using various ELEMENTAL tools summoned using their Soul Fluxes. Water, Fire, Wind, and Earth clash and fly until the soldiers notice Bia. They halt.

                    BIA
          All Border Guard training shall
          cease temporarily. This chamber
          shall not be used by anyone for the
          next few days, and we are not to be
          interrupted by anyone unless we are
          being invaded. Please leave.

The Soldiers bow and leave with haste.

Bia leads the group through the facility until they arrive on a square platform an inch off the ground.

                    BIA
          Jambi.

Jambi stomps the ground and the platform rises like an elevator. They ascend to an upper level of the pyramid.

INT. ARJANA - SPECTRUM CHAMBER - CONTINUOUS

They arrive at a chamber filled with natural light from the translucent ceiling. ORBS of floating light occupy separate corners of the room.

                    ZAILA
          Ugh, we are doing this again? It is
          always so tiring!

TYMPANI—40s, female with a grin as energetic as her hairstyle—gives Zaila a pat on the shoulder.

                    TYMPANI
          But it is not often we get the
          chance to exert ourselves so much.
          It will be a good exercise!

                    ASA
          What is this place?

Zaila looks to Bia as if to ask permission to answer. Bia shrugs and walks toward the center of the chamber.

CYMBA
We call this the Spectrum Chamber.
This is where the Spectral Guard—

ZAILA
That is us!

CYMBA
…come to receive specialized
training. However, the only reason
we come here after our initial
training is to practice inducing
the Queen's Spectral Flux.

ASA
The Queen's wha—?

BIA
All of you, gather. We don't have
much time so I will explain this
quickly.

Asa and the Spectral Guard gather around Bia. Asa notices a
pool wrapped around the room and an impressed CRATER beside
them. Four stone COLUMNS are placed around the crater's
corners. Asa also notices Bia's apparent botheration.

BIA
Queen Asase has recognized the
urgency of the current affairs and
has decided on a course of action.

INT. ARJANA - QUEEN'S THRONE ROOM - EARLIER, FLASHBACK

Bia and Anansi are noticeably distressed at Asase's proposal.

BIA
That outsider will solve all of
this… by herself?!

QUEEN ASASE
At the moment, she is the most
informed person here regarding the
state of the outside world. Sending
someone who is already familiar
with this mess is better than
risking our exposure by increasing
the number of parties involved.

BIA
You trust her just because she has
Khadija's Wayfinder?
(MORE)

> BIA (CONT'D)
> It is her adopted son who is
> stealing the Shards!

> QUEEN ASASE
> Her clan may be unorthodox, but
> they were always loyal. If
> anything, this is my fault. Perhaps
> I should have had the boy executed
> when he ran away from the family.

> BIA
> Ugh… fine. Let's assume that we can
> trust this outsider. How is she
> supposed to solve all of our
> problems?! You expect her to deal
> with this "Waalisha" and retrieve
> all the Shards? Anansi, talk sense
> into your mother!

> ANANSI
> Bia is correct. This woman may be
> awakened to Umoya, but she has no
> Soul Flux, by her own admission.
> Even if she is trustworthy, we
> cannot expect her to quell an
> extremist uprising and take down a
> man who potentially possesses two
> Shards. She is not equipped for it.

> QUEEN ASASE
> Then we will just have to equip
> her. Moreover, she will not be
> alone. We will direct her to rescue
> her husband first and enlist him
> for help against the Shard thief.

> BIA
> Bring another outsider in? Mother,
> this is insane! Please think about—

> QUEEN ASASE
> Bia, that is enough!

The Queen's head tilts back, burdened by something unspoken.

> QUEEN ASASE
> This predicament has no precedent,
> so we must resort to unprecedented
> solutions. I am wholly aware of the
> lives hanging in the balance, both
> within and outside the Kingdom. I
> do not treat this lightly. We
> cannot fail, so neither can she.

END FLASHBACK.

INT. ARJANA - SPECTRUM CHAMBER - DAY

All listen as Bia relays the words of the Queen.

> QUEEN ASASE (V.O.)
> Bia, take the Spectral Guard and
> train this outsider as efficiently
> as possible. Do not let her go
> until you are certain she is ready.

Asa is terrified by what she hears.

> BIA
> And I don't intend to.

> JAMBI
> Well, if time is a factor, it makes
> sense why we are here then.

> CYMBA
> I respect Her Divinity's
> flexibility here. This cannot be an
> easy decision.

> BIA
> You can discuss it later. Get into
> position.

The four warriors assume spots atop the four columns. Bia
steps into the crater between them all, looks back at Asa.

> BIA
> Come!

> ASA
> I… I don't know about this. I'm not
> strong enough to do what the Queen
> wants me to.

> TYMPANI
> Be encouraged! Her Divinity has
> tasked you to perform a great
> service.

> ASA
> It's not just that. I don't think
> it's appropriate for me to do this…

                         BIA
          You are correct on both parts,
          outsider, but the Queen has spoken.
          So I will obey.

Asa stands timid on the edge of the crater. Bia grunts, waves
her hand, causes WATER from the pool to rush over. It shoves
Asa into the crater.

                         BIA
          One way or another, you will be
          ready for war by the time I am done
          with you. Let's begin!

The four warriors kneel, place their hands on the columns.
Instantly, their respective elements flood the air. From
Jambi, Earth; Cymba, Wind; Zaila, Water; and Tympani, Fire.

The deluge of Fluxes pour into the air, uniting into one
compacting AMALGAM above the crater. Within seconds, the
amalgam transforms into nothingness. The only trace of its
existence is the extreme invisible pressure SLAMMING Asa into
the floor.

Asa struggles to pick herself up, alarmed and afraid. Bia
also feels the pressure but is not fazed by it.

                         BIA
          Get up.

Asa fights to get to her feet. Then Bia gestures again, pulls
more water into the crater. It coils behind her like a snake
ready to strike.

                         BIA
          Now, block.

                         ASA
          Huh?

The water strikes, blasts Asa back, and lets gravity slam her
into the floor again. Asa is dazed from the attack.

                         BIA
          We will keep going until you do not
          move an inch. Get up!

Asa peels herself off the ground. Bia smirks.

                         BIA
          You see, training with me is its
          own sentence.

EXT. JEBEL MARRA - BASE OF MOUNTAIN - DAY

A TAN SARSAR-1 with a TURRET on its roof creeps to a park. A RSF SOLDIER rises from behind the shield, uses BINOCULARS to scope the mountain.

He sees the refugees, its inhabitants blind to his presence.

RSF Soldier reaches for his RADIO. It clicks on.

                    RSF SOLDIER 1
          General, insurgents in sight.

We pull back to see DOZENS more SarSar-1s creeping into position.

I/E. JEBEL MARRA - SUDANESE TANK - DAY

CLOSE ON the walkie receiving the message. It sits on a chair's arm. A man picks it up, brings it to his face, revealing it to be General Nazeer. His right wrist is a stub.

                    GENERAL NAZEER
          Wait until the fleet is in
          position, then wipe them out.

EXT. JEBEL MARRA - REBEL SETTLEMENT - DAY

A COOK near the perimeter of the settlement fries up kabobs, hands two to Malick. He partakes of one as he walks over to Lolie and Darren nearby.

Darren keeps an eye on Lolie, who blissfully role-plays with her metal TOY ROCKET.

                    DARREN
          I'm surprised you still have that.

                    LOLIE
          You should make one and play, too.

Darren smiles, pats the ground, pulls another lump of dirt that he MORPHS into a mini SPACE SHUTTLE. He blows the dust from the metal model.

                    LOLIE
          You didn't say the magic word!

                    DARREN
          I forgot. I promise I'll say it
          next time.

> MALICK
> Have you eaten, Darren?

> DARREN
> Uhh… don't really feel like it.
> I'll just watch Lolie for now.

> LOLIE
> You don't have to watch me. I'm
> fine.

> DARREN
> (looks at Malick)
> I was thinking the same thing.

> MALICK
> (shrugs)
> Sorry, I am staying close until you
> can be trusted not to leave. You
> may as well get used to me.

Malick offers Darren the second kabob. Darren chuckles, reaches for it, but a THWIP interrupts the handoff. The kabob hits the ground, but so does Lolie…

> DARREN
> L-Lolie!

Her body lies still. Blood pools beneath her head. Darren approaches shock right when another bullet THWIPS into his shoulder, knocks him over.

He groans in pain as the camp becomes filled with SCREAMS. A hail of BULLETS whizzes by, explodes property, mows down Refugees.

> MALICK
> GET DOWN!

Refugees duck, scramble for cover. Malick raises a HUMP of DIRT to protect Darren. He squats behind it.

> MALICK
> Stay down. I will go get Muni!

He runs off, evading the bullets, but Darren stays, his eyes stuck on Lolie. He clutches his arm, but the pain is tame compared to the shock.

The girl's eyes are blank. She never saw it coming. She didn't even have time to drop her rocket.

Darren rises to his knees, stares at Lolie's eyes. They resemble…

MEMORY FLASH: The decapitated ADF SQUAD LEADER; The MASSACRED VILLAGERS of the Congo; The blank face of KHADEEM. The forlorn face of LULA MAE.

Blood drowns his thoughts. Violence plagues, overwhelms him. It's too much.

Tears stream from his face and his teeth grit. As he rips the bullet from his shoulder, SOLDIERS charge into the camp.

INT. JEBEL MARRA - AMANI'S DEN - CONTINUOUS

Amani tinkers with her TESLA COIL, drops it when she hears GUNSHOTS. She looks at Muni for confirmation. He hears it.

Someone BANGS on the door before opening it. It's Malick.

>   MALICK
>   It is the Janjaweed!

EXT. JEBEL MARRA - REBEL SETTLEMENT - CONTINUOUS

RSF Soldiers pour in. They unload their weapons into the dispersing crowd. Most Refugees flee; the few with weapons return fire, but it's not enough. They are run down.

SOLDIER A fires at a FLEEING WOMAN. She takes shelter behind the KABOB TENT. Soldier A aims at the tent, but—

FLAMES torch the Soldier. It's Samba. He exhales another BLAZE onto the Soldier, and he falls over and burns.

Samba moves on, catches another couple Soldiers in his attack, but he is quickly perforated by a hail of bullets from SOLDIER B.

Soldier B steps behind the tent, drags out Fleeing Woman. She screams as she is dragged away, toward the mountain's ledge.

Soldier B halts only when he hears a man's shout. He turns and is met with a BROADSWORD through his chest. He drops the woman. As he slips off the blade, we see its wielder.

It's Darren. He is done with words.

He charges the nearest Soldiers; his speed is hard for them to follow. They fire but miss. They pull MACHETES but get slashed first. They flee but get impaled.

SOLDIER C is the only remainder. Darren sees him. Soldier C runs. He screams into his WALKIE as he bolts for the ledge.

> SOLDIER C
> They are using the witchcraft! Fire
> now!

Darren chases him down, gets close before an ANTI-TANK ROUND
rips up the land before him. He is knocked back. Soldier C is
caught in the explosion.

In the distance, TANKS fire more rounds. They head straight
for Darren—no time to react.

But the rounds explode before reaching him, kicking up dust.
The dust settles, reveals a wall of 9-FOOT **MIDAS SPEARS** that
fence off the camp area. Standing behind the fence, beside
Darren, are Amani and Muni.

> AMANI
> Waalisha! Rise!

The fence allows for a moment of reprieve. Refugees and
Waalisha poke their heads out of hiding. Amani wrangles their
attention.

> AMANI
> As surely as the sun blazes in the
> sky, I tell you the night is
> darkest before daybreak. Right now,
> this darkness clings to our sun,
> desperately trying to snuff out the
> light of our freedom, of our
> revolution. So, I ask you now: Will
> we let our sun burn out?!

Nays roar, and Darren turns to see the growing SCORES of
WAALISHA rising their to feet, entering the frontline.

EXT. JEBEL MARRA - BASE OF MOUNTAIN - CONTINUOUS

General Nazeer steps out of his vehicle, takes the binoculars
of the nearest soldier. He scopes the golden fence, peeks at
Amani through the cracks. His nub wriggles.

> GENERAL NAZEER
> Why did you stop FIRING?!

The Soldiers run to their turrets. The tanks take aim.

EXT. JEBEL MARRA - REBEL SETTLEMENT - CONTINUOUS

Amani helps Darren up.

                        AMANI
          If just for a moment, please be the
          fire that burns with us.

THUNDERCLAPS precede the whistle of approaching anti-tank
rounds. The blasts kick up more dirt as they rip through
parts of the fence. For a moment all is still again.

Then WIND SWIRLS up the dust, funnels it upward before
dispersing, revealing Muni within. SHOTEL in-hand, he swings,
launches a VANGUARD SHEAR that soars toward the Janjaweed.

The Shear hits, bifurcates a Soldier, terrifies the others.
Muni raises his Shotel in the air.

                        MUNI
              ATTACK!

This is the final word needed. WAALISHA GUNMEN climb atop
adjacent HILLS, fire their weapons from there. WAALISHA
FLUXERS move toward the fence but are unsure of what to do.

Amani bends the fence open, allowing her to see her targets.
She outstretches her arm and dozens of MIDAS SPEARS emerge
from the ground. With a shout, the SPEARS launch, shoot into
the sky, rain down on the Soldiers below. They pierce several
vehicles, decommissioning them instantly.

Darren runs toward the Refugees deeper within the camp. He
finds Malick headed toward the battlefield.

                        DARREN
          Where are you going?

                        MALICK
          To fight!

                        DARREN
          You need to stay here and protect
          these people!

A TANK ROUND hits the mountainside above them, killing a
Waalisha Gunman. A ROCKSLIDE ensues. Boulders threaten to
crush Refugees below—they also threaten Lolie's body.

Darren leaps to the Refugees. Lolie is the last thing he sees
before he raises his arms and yells…

                        DARREN
              CRAFTSMAN!

STEEL rises from the earth, forms a GIANT DOME that shelters
them all from the rockslide. None are hurt. Malick and the
other Waalisha are amazed at the structure.

                    DARREN
              (to the Refugees)
         Get out of here!
              (to Malick)
         You take all the Earth and Water
         Fluxers and protect these people!

                    MALICK
         What about the others?

                    DARREN
         They come with me!

Malick ushers the Refugees further into the mountain with
half the Waalisha Fluxers. The other half follows Darren.

They run to the gold fence. On the other side, RSF Soldiers
attempt to climb through.

                    DARREN
         All you Fire people, burn them off
         this gate!

                    WAALISHA FLUXER 1
         But our fire is not strong!

                    DARREN
         Just get mad! Aren't you victims?
              (faces the fence)
         Use all that frustration and
         channel it into the world around,
         then let it manifest!

Darren does likewise, summons another BROADSWORD and stabs
someone through the gate.

                    DARREN
         Come on, already!

The Waalisha Fluxers respond, let their emotions rise and
summon FLAMES that engulf the fence. SCREAMS from the other
side let them know Soldiers are burning.

                    WAALISHA FLUXER 2
         What if we use the wind?

                    DARREN
         Then do the same and blow them
         away!

They obey. Wind WHISTLES as it rips around the fence. Burning
Soldiers cannot resist and are blown off the mountainside.

EXT. JEBEL MARRA - BASE OF MOUNTAIN - CONTINUOUS

FLAMING BODIES bombard the RSF. Demoralization sets in.

General Nazeer evades a falling Midas Spear. He assumes command of a turret, fires at the fence above.

EXT. JEBEL MARRA - REBEL SETTLEMENT - CONTINUOUS

The bullets crack a part of the fence. Muni peeks at the Soldiers and sees something he can't believe.

Amani prepares another dozen Spears for launch.

> MUNI
> Amani, he is here…

Amani peers below. Then she sees him: General Nazeer. Her eyes pierce with rage strong enough to be felt by the General. He meets her gaze.

> AMANI
> Darren, launch me to that tank. The
> same way you did with the Muzungu.

> DARREN
> Are you sure?

> AMANI
> Do it!

Amani prepares DOZENS of MIDAS SPEARS, they sit at the ready. Then she splits open the fence, provides a path for launch.

> DARREN
> *CRAFTSMAN: COIL!*

Darren swats the ground, props Amani onto a STEEL PLATE that sits on a giant LOADED SPRING.

> AMANI
> Now!

The spring EJECTS Amani into the air. Midas Spears follow.

EXT. JEBEL MARRA - BASE OF MOUNTAIN - CONTINUOUS

The barrage of Spears destroys vehicles, impales many from above, and heralds Amani's descent. She lands on the General's tank, adjacent to Nazeer himself.

Their eyes meet again; a reunion a long time coming.

GENERAL NAZEER
Kill her!

He shoots at her, but she evades. She weaves through his fire until she is within a few feet. She pulls a Midas Lance from the ground, prepares to strike, but then—

GENERAL NAZEER
FIRE!

She's in front of the tank's gun. She can't evade.

But then Muni's Vanguard Shear connects with the gun, bends the barrel downward with a descending strike. The gun fires. The explosion disorients Nazeer, but Amani presses on.

She screams with the pain only her heart could feel, causes multiple MIDAS SPEARS to erupt from below. They all pierce Nazeer, elevate him, crucify him 20 feet above ground.

Amani's rage almost subsides, but a bullet grazes her torso. She spots one of many Soldiers—afraid, but willing to fight.

The rage SWELLS again. With a final shout, SCORES of Midas Spears ERUPT from the dirt, throws up dust that screens the battlefield.

There are gunshots and screams. Then there is only silence.

EXT. JEBEL MARRA - REBEL SETTLEMENT - CONTINUOUS

The Waalisha cease their attack at Muni's command. They wait for the smoke and dust to clear.

The lifting dust reveals hundreds of RSF Soldiers suspended on the tips of golden PIKES that have run them through. Some squirm as their life and blood escapes them. The tallest of the pikes hold General Nazeer.

Amani comes into view. She is fine. The Waalisha celebrate in triumph.

But Darren notices Amani doesn't celebrate.

Her heart sears from pain that bloodshed cannot soothe.

                                        FADE OUT.

END OF ACT THREE

ACT FOUR

FADE IN:

INT. ARJANA - SPECTRUM CHAMBER - DAY

WATER coils beside Bia. She points to Asa. It strikes.

Asa takes the hit, holds her ground for a second but is then toppled and slammed into the ground by gravity.

                    BIA
          Again.

Asa rises slowly. She's on her feet, but not for long. Bia strikes and Asa falls. The process repeats. Again. And again.

The final attempt sees Asa lasting for a few seconds. Her eyes pierce forward with purpose… but that purpose vanishes. Bia notices this. Asa falls to the torrent, exhausted.

Bia holds a gesture for a beat.

                    BIA
          Perhaps we should rest.

                    ASA
          Yes! I need a break.
              (pants)
          How long have we been going?

                    BIA
          In here or out there?

                    ASA
          Huh?

The downforce fades and Asa's breath is less labored. She flops over, tries to stand, struggles to find equilibrium.

                    BIA
          Once your bearings return, we will
          begin again. Be quick.

Zaila walks to Asa, hands her a bowl of water.

                    ZAILA
          Here you go… if you aren't tired of
          seeing this by now.

                    ASA
          Thanks!

Asa chugs the water, then studies the crater. Her BODY PRINTS indent the center.

> ASA
> Soul Fluxes really are amazing. I never thought that someone could control gravity with one.

> ZAILA
> A Soul Flux could never do something like this!

> ASA
> Then what's making the gravity stronger—a machine?

> BIA
> You already saw it earlier, do you not remember?

> ASA
> Yeah, when the Queen used it on her arrow guy… That's not a Soul Flux?

Bia sits on the edge of the crater. She studies Asa, contemplates if she should explain more. She caves.

> BIA
> Every person on Earth only has access to a few Fluxes: a Base, a Soul, and a Unity with another person. However, the Royal Bloodline of Atlantis has always had access to one more. This is because only royalty can can use all four elements to 100% capacity. When all four combine, they form a phenomenon called a Spectral Flux.

> ASA
> (studies the chamber; confused)
> But the Queen isn't here now, so what was making the gravity—Oh, was it you?

> BIA
> No, I—
> (uncomfortable)
> I cannot use a Spectral Flux, nor can my brothers…

                    ASA
          But aren't you the princess? How
          come—

                    BIA
          These four were the ones creating
          the gravity field.

Asa has even more trouble hiding her confusion. Bia sighs.

                    CYMBA
          As you have seen, a Spectral Flux
          is more powerful than a Soul by a
          factor of many.

                    ZAILA
          In fact, it was the Spectral Flux
          of the King of Atlantis that caused
          the great cataclysm that
          annihilated it!

                    BIA
          To prevent such a wild abuse of
          power like that from ever happening
          again, the Remnant Kingdom
          commissioned the Spectral Guard:
          four warriors whose elemental
          prowess combine to reproduce the
          ultimate weapon of the throne.

                    JAMBI
          We serve as personal guards to the
          Queen, but also as a check to
          prevent the throne from slipping
          into tyranny.

                    ASA
          That's amazing…

                    TYMPANI
          It seems you have not realized the
          best part yet!

Tympani points at the translucent ceiling. Asa looks up, sees
the sun.

                    ASA
          How is it still daytime? I thought
          we were going for a couple hours!

                    ZAILA
          For us, it has only been 20
          minutes!

>   BIA
>   (grins)
>   Just like any gravitational force,
>   those influenced by it experience
>   time dilation, cursed to feel its
>   weight in slower-then-real time.
>   This is why my mother calls her
>   power **BURDEN**.

Asa is amazed but suddenly spooked by what this means. Bia
gets up and enters the crater once more.

>   BIA
>   This is good, however. We will have
>   plenty of time to work through your
>   insecurities.

>   ASA
>   What am I insecure about?!

>   BIA
>   Well, looks like we will find the
>   answer together then, won't we?

EXT. KIGALI, RWANDA - U.S. EMBASSY - NIGHT, FLASHBACK

The embassy is quiet, still, but it is littered with too many
corpses to be peaceful.

The courtyard is filled with shattered glass from broken
windows, BULLET HOLES through the walls and fences, and ASH
from burned property… and victims.

BUCHU, mid 40s, enters through a BROKEN gate. He is careful
not to interact with the environment, but he does study it.
His Arjanan GOLD EARPIECE crackles with static as an
indiscernible voice speaks to him. He responds.

>   BUCHU
>   They are all Tutsi. They must have
>   broken in when the Americans left
>   and were cornered by the Hutu.
>   (beat; somberly)
>   No. All are dead.
>   (another beat)
>   Understood; moving on.

He starts for the exit before hearing a weak COUGH. He looks
around, spots TUTSI BOY lying on the ground. He is very still
and his breaths are barely noticeable.

Buchu walks over to Tutsi Boy, kneels. The Boy's eyes are
closed. Buchu smiles, speaks with a warm voice.

> BUCHU
> The dead do not cough, young one.

The Boy opens his eyes, trembling. He prepares to run.

> BUCHU
> Easy, I am not here to harm you. Is
> *that* how you survived?

The Boy nods. More static crackles in Buchu's ear. He doesn't like what he hears, but he relents.

> BUCHU
> Understood.

Buchu rises, starts for the exit again.

Tutsi Boy sees the man's back as he leaves. It resembles GLENDA'S back when she left. The Boy curls up, whimpers.

Buchu stops, pauses for a beat before speaking.

> BUCHU
> I cannot do it.
>   (static)
> It does not interfere with anyone.
> The damage is done!
>   (more static)
> I have no problem accepting that
> responsibility…
>   (removes earpiece)
> …even if Arjana will not.

He approaches the Boy again, extends a hand to him, but the Boy backs away.

> BUCHU
> I do not know what horrible things
> you have seen, but if you stay
> here, you may not survive another
> wave of it. You can either stay
> here and try or come with me.

Three HUTU RIOTERS with MACHETES roam into the embassy. They spot the Tutsi Boy and the man kneeling beside him.

> HUTU RIOTER A
> There are two more!

The Hutu sprint toward the two, but Buchu does not waiver. His hand remains, waiting for the Boy to choose. Tutsi Boy's eyes flit between the Hutu and the man before him. He takes Buchu's hand.

                    BUCHU
          Smart choice.

The Hutu close in. Hutu Rioter A swings his machete, but
Buchu conjures a FLAMING BLADE with his free hand, blocks it.

                    BUCHU
                 (to Hutu)
          But foolish of you.

The Hutu are spooked. They drop their weapons, flee.

Then Buchu curves the blade, creates a BURNING BOOMERANG,
tosses it at the Hutu. It spins, rips through the air, cuts
down each of the fleeing attackers. It returns to Buchu,
dissipating as he grabs it.

Tutsi Boy is flabbergasted. He looks at Buchu, then to the
carnage around him. Something perplexes him.

Buchu starts for the exit, beckons for the Boy to follow. He
does.

END FLASHBACK.

I/E. JEBEL MARRA - BASE OF MOUNTAIN - THE TRUCK - NIGHT

Buziba rides shotgun on a small truck driven by Smuggler.
Buziba is unsettled, contemplative, but is pulled from his
thoughts when Smuggler notices…

                    SMUGGLER
          What is this?!

The base of the mountain is covered in trashed tanks, burning
vehicles, and motionless bodies suspended on shiny pikes.

                    SMUGGLER
          Is this… Janjaweed? Oh, no…

                    BUZIBA
          The fighting probably ended a while
          ago. Just keep driving.

The truck proceeds through the battlefield.

EXT. JEBEL MARRA - REBEL SETTLEMENT - GRAVES - NIGHT

FALLEN REFUGEES and WAALISHA are carried to a wide span of
land. WOODEN CROSSES and other STONES reveal it to be a
makeshift gravesite. The fresh bodies are lined up along the
foot of the site. There are dozens. Lolie is among them.

WAILS and SOBS fill the smoky air as all say their goodbyes. Amani presses into the dirt, creating cavities below the bodies. She stands among the crowd and speaks to them all.

> AMANI
> May we never forget the bloodshed
> of the night. As dawn approaches,
> may the bloodstains on our hands
> remind us why we fight.

The living place the dead in the cavities. Darren handles Lolie. As they step away, Amani presses again, and the bodies sink, claimed by the soil itself. Lolie's face is the last to be swallowed.

> AMANI
> They have all earned their rest,
> and so have we.

The crowd of survivors begin to disperse. As Darren walks away, he steps on something. It's Lolie's ROCKET. He picks it up, looks at the grave, but she's already gone.

So he pinches the toy, molds a hole in its nose. He scoops up dirt and transmutes it into a thin steel chain. He feeds it through the nose and puts it on around his neck.

Amani walks over to Darren.

> AMANI
> We could not have won without you.
>   (looks at Lolie's grave)
> I did not want you to get dragged
> into this… or her.

> DARREN
> Then why did you bring us here,
> Amani? Huh? If everything you told
> me about your life is true, how was
> this not bound to happen?
>   (beat)
> You know, I get it. You're all
> caught in some hell-cycle you can't
> get out of. Fine. But this one?
> That girl? That one's on you.

Darren walks away, leaves Amani to chew on his words. They are difficult to swallow.

EXT. JEBEL MARRA - REBEL SETTLEMENT - NIGHT

Malick ushers more injured to the medical tents, and Muni directs drivers of SALVAGED TANKS as they park.

Muni catches a glimpse of a truck parking near the camp entrance. Two people get out of the truck.

Smuggler leads Buziba into the camp. He looks around, spots Muni, points to him.

> SMUGGLER
> He is one of the ones you are
> looking for.

Buziba steps close enough for Muni to recognize him.

> MUNI
> You!

Muni draws his sword, launches a Vanguard Shear from the blade. A COAL WALL rises from below, blocks the attack. Then Buziba leaps from behind it, charges at Muni.

Muni summons a wind that hurls Buziba upward. He prepares another Shear but a COAL COLUMN knocks his sword away, dispels the wind. Buziba lands and immediately summons coal CLASPS to bind Muni. He cannot move.

Buziba gets closer and studies Muni's face.

> BUZIBA
> I remember you.

Buziba leaps back, just missed by the Midas Spears that drop from the sky, separating him from Muni. Amani arrives, frees Muni from his binds.

> AMANI
> Who are you?

> MUNI
> This is the Rwandan I told you
> about. *He* gave me these scars.

> BUZIBA
> It looks like you did not forget me
> either. My name is Buziba.

> AMANI
> What do you want, Buziba?

> BUZIBA
> I am not here to fight. I have a
> question to ask the leader of this
> movement. Is that you?

                    AMANI
          I am who you are looking for, but I
          am not a leader. Just a member of a
          growing body of people.

                    BUZIBA
          Do you serve as the head of this
          body?

                    AMANI
          I do, but I am also the hands or
          the feet, whatever the body needs
          me to be.

                    BUZIBA
          Curious.
               (beat)
          Why would the head take
          responsibilities it is not assigned
          to?

                    AMANI
          Because the entire body is
          important. If the hands are smashed
          and the feet stumble in the dark,
          the head feels that pain. Likewise,
          when the hands are busy, the head
          informs its work, and when the feet
          walk, the head guides its steps.

                    BUZIBA
          You acknowledge the responsibility
          you have, but you still don't call
          yourself a leader?

                    MUNI
          We do not owe this man any answers,
          Amani! Take him out!

                    AMANI
          Why are you asking all this?

Buziba's face mirrors the perplexity of the young Tutsi Boy.

The conversation attracts an audience of distant spectators.
Darren joins them, squints to make out who is talking. He is
incredulous at what he sees.

                    BUZIBA
          Tell me… what would the hands do if
          the feet were under attack. Or,
          what if the left hand is under
          attack by the right… what would the
          head do then?

Amani begins to understand the line of questions.

> AMANI
> If the feet are under attack, then
> the hands will defend. And if the
> left is being attacked by the
> right, the head will broker peace.
> Because we are all members of the
> same body.

> BUZIBA
> And… if a body that is not your own
> attacks another body, then what?

> AMANI
> (smiles)
> Then we will defend those bodies as
> if they're our own. After all,
> multiple members make up a body,
> but multiple bodies make a
> community.

Buziba's face softens. His eyes drift upwards.

> BUZIBA
> I have spent years as a member of a
> selfish body. One that only cared
> for itself, while it idly watched
> the violence of its brothers.

He pulls the FIRE SHARD from his pocket. Its RED GLOW is
visible before it's fully removed. Buziba glares at it.

> BUZIBA
> It sat on tools that could prevent
> bloodshed and assigned its members
> to do nothing but keep them hidden.
> I know how that story ends. I've
> seen it play out continuously. Now,
> I am curious what a more active
> body may do with it.

He walks over to Amani and Muni, offers them the Shard. Amani
is surprised. Muni is confused. Darren is horrified.

Amani takes the Shard. Its power surges, swells around her.
All in the vicinity brace as a FLAMING PILLAR rises, towers
above her, reaches into the sky, briefly paints it orange.

The pillar subsides as Amani lowers the Shard. Its glow
fades. She is now in control.

> BUZIBA
> So, now what will you do?

Amani walks to the side of the mountain. She overlooks the hellish battlefield filled with dead soldiers and machines of war. Her eyes fixate on the fallen General.

                    AMANI
          I will broker peace.

She outstretches her arm and the Fire Shard lights up again. She unleashes a deluge of FLAMES upon the battlefield. The flames are the last thing we see before we…

                              FADE TO BLACK.

                    <u>END OF SHOW</u>

C1GNUS STUD1O

AFROFANTASY

SCREENPLAY BY CHANNING CHEA

Episode 109 – "The Rescue"

Written by

Channing Chea

AFROFANTASY

"THE RESCUE"

<u>TEASER</u>

FADE IN:

INT. ARJANA - SPECTRUM CHAMBER - DAY

The vast chamber feels empty, filled only with the sounds of
CRASHING WAVES and shoes SCRAPING against the concrete floor.

But it's not empty; the SPECTRAL GUARDIANS remain on their
post. Their meditation holds in place the GRAVITATIONAL FIELD
that fills the center of the chamber.

From outside the light-distorting field, we see the source of
the sounds. Water rises, jets, crashes at blistering speed,
and TWO FLURRIES dart around the field like unstable atoms.

We enter the gravity field to see ASA and BIA. They exchange
blows, knock each other back, return for more.

Asa is aggressive, faster than ever. Efficient. She throws a
flurry of punches. Some are blocked, one lands. Bia's balance
fails her.

But water catches her, allows her to recover. With a wave,
Bia manipulates the water. A TENDRIL grabs Asa, throws her up
and away, just far enough for the gravity to catch her, slam
her downward, but Asa lands on her feet.

The attack isn't over. Bia sends a WAVE at Asa. The American
stands her ground, blocks the deluge, doesn't move an inch.
Then with a shout, she spreads her arms as if to split the
wave itself. The water obeys, betrays Bia, leaves her open.
Asa takes the chance and rushes in.

Bia does the same. She fires water at Asa, which Asa dodges
before getting within striking distance. Asa and Bia throw an
elbow, and their forearms connect. The two are locked in a
standoff.

Their eyes meet. Bia struggles to hide the glimmer of pride
in her grin. Her focus is pulled away by a man standing
outside the gravity field. It's ANANSI.

Bia breaks away, signals to the Spectral Guard.

                         BIA
              That is enough for now.

The gravity field drops and Anansi approaches.

                    BIA
          What is it?

                    ANANSI
          The extremists have begun
          campaigning eastward. I suspect
          they intend to take the Capital.
               (beat)
          We are out of time.

                    ASA
          Already? How long has it been?

                    ANANSI
          Two days.
               (to Bia)
          Is she ready?

                    BIA
          No… She still has not found her
          Soul Flux.

                    ANANSI
          She will have to do for now.

TYMPANI steps down from the pillar she sat on and bows.

                    TYMPANI
          Pardon me, Prince Anansi and
          Princess Bia. If neither of you or
          Prince Tano is in a position to go,
          I will happily escort Asa Davenport
          on her mission.

ZAILA steps down as well.

                    ZAILA
          I volunteer as well! Taking down
          those extremists will be easy.

                    BIA
          No. There are currently more
          Fluxers on the planet than there
          have been in millennia, and one of
          them has the Mask. We cannot risk
          Arjana being left without its
          strongest warriors.

                    ASA
          What if I call Khadija and Tau? I'm
          sure they would help.

                         BIA
          With her son dead, Khadija is the
          only one left to guard the West
          Water Shard. And with Acacia's
          death, Tau is the lone guardian in
          Southern Africa. Until something
          directly threatens the Kingdom, we
          cannot risk more Arjanans getting
          involved.

Bia picks up Asa's SHAWL and presents it to her as if to pass
a baton. Asa takes it and throws it on…

                         BIA
          Unless there is someone else you
          trust, this mission is yours alone.

EXT. EAST CONGO COUNTRYSIDE - NIGHT

As Asa overlooks the countryside, we see the new her. She
looks focused, hardened… stronger. CAR HEADLIGHTS illuminate
her from behind. We hear a familiar voice as the driver comes
to meet her.

                         ASA (V.O.)
          I think I might know a guy…

                         KWESI
          The cavalry has arrived!

                         ASA
          Thanks so much for coming, Kwesi.

                         KWESI
          Anything for my favorite Mjingas.

                         ASA
          Things… might get shifty.

                         KWESI
          Nothing would be shiftier than not
          answering a friend's call. Now,
          where are they keeping Darren?

                                        FADE OUT.

                    END OF TEASER

ACT ONE

FADE IN:

EXT. AXUM, ETHIOPIA - STREET MARKET - DAY

The streets of Axum are filled with busy LOCALS and TOURISTS.
Among these tourists is PHARAOH.

He patrons a large TENT filled with many potted plants. He
inspects the variety, calls over an ATTENDANT.

                    PHARAOH
            Which of these flourish in the
            desert?

Attendant ponders, pulls several cactuses and fruits from
behind a shelf, presents them to Pharaoh. Pharaoh approves.

                    PHARAOH
            I will take all of each one.

EXT. AXUM, ETHIOPIA - STREET MARKET LOT - DAY

Pharaoh carries STACKS of SEED SACKS too heavy for the
average person, while the Attendant trails him with a
WHEELBARROW full of the same. They arrive at Pharaoh's JEEP.

As he opens the trunk, Pharaoh's phone RINGS. He steps away
as Attendant loads the seeds. He answers…

                PRESIDENT ZEIN (V.O.)
          (into phone)
            Is this the Zraag with the audacity
            to negotiate Mauritania's aid
            without my input?

                    PHARAOH
          (into phone)
            I presume… President Zein?

INT. MAURITANIA OVAL OFFICE - CONTINUOUS

PRESIDENT IDRISSA ZEIN, 60s, sits anchored to his desk by the
cable of his landline phone. ADVISORS join him in the room.

                PRESIDENT ZEIN
          (into phone)
            So you do know me.
             (MORE)

> PRESIDENT ZEIN (CONT'D)
> Perhaps I should take that as an
> even bigger offense.

INTERCUT:

> PHARAOH
> (into phone)
> It looks like Moustapha reached out
> to you. I meant no disrespect by
> requesting aid on your behalf. I
> only wanted to earn your favor.

> PRESIDENT ZEIN
> (into phone)
> What does my favor grant you?

> PHARAOH
> (into phone)
> Nothing in particular, but I
> suspect we will be working together
> very soon.

> PRESIDENT ZEIN
> (into phone)
> This administration only deals with
> official representatives of
> nations. You, Osas Pharaoh of
> Johannesburg, are not that. In
> fact, media claims you are a
> missing person. Suspicious. Tell
> me—what nation do you represent?

> PHARAOH
> (into phone)
> Not a nation, but a kingdom. One
> that will bring a renewed economy
> to Mauritania. I only ask that you
> be willing to part with the Richat
> Structure in return.

> PRESIDENT ZEIN
> (into phone; scoffs)
> I do not know what is worse: your
> humor or your diplomacy skills.
> Stay out of our affairs!

President Zein hangs up, but Pharaoh is amused. Attendant
finishes loading and waves a farewell.

> PHARAOH
> Oh well. The diplomacy was only for
> your sake anyway.

Pharaoh turns his attention to a CHURCH complex in the distance. As he pockets his phone, the Wind Shard in his pocket GLOWS ominously.

EXT. DARFUR, SUDAN - DESERT ROAD - DAY

Kwesi and Asa drive down the lone desert road. They follow TRACKS that become increasingly prominent and numerous. The Jebel Marra Mountains fill the horizon as they approach. Asa keeps her eyes peeled on the road. Kwesi steals a glance.

                    KWESI
          Aren't you going to ask?

                    ASA
          About what?

                    KWESI
          The stream for Kibera!

                    ASA
          Oh, right! Did you finish it?

                    KWESI
          We are getting close! Many of the
          locals were able to earn enough
          money to buy a bunch of tools. We
          have enough shovels for each of the
          dozens of volunteers to help.

                    ASA
          That's fantastic! How did they earn
          enough money for—

                    KWESI
          Well, after our tussle with the
          Coal Man, he left enough coal
          behind for plenty of people to
          source for their own projects. Some
          used it for cooking and keeping
          warm, and others sold it for money.
          I personally helped the latter set
          up their business endeavors.

                    ASA
          That's amazing, Kwesi. It's super
          impressive that you all got so far
          in a month.

                    KWESI
          A month? It has only been a week.

                    ASA
          Oh… sorry. It's been a long week.

                    KWESI
               (shrugs)
          I saw a gleam of hope in the
          people's eye. It was encouraging.
          For the first time in their lives,
          they had a resource to call their
          own. I cannot wait to see their
          face once we finish the stream. But
          the occasion won't be perfect
          unless you and your husband are
          there.

                    ASA
          We will be there. Both of us.

3-dimensional SHADOWS emerge from the ground, form what look
like palm trees and boulders. As they approach the mountain,
the shadows' true form takes shape. Asa and Kwesi slow to a
crawl as they arrive.

EXT. JEBEL MARRA - BASE OF MOUNTAIN - DAY

The shadowy boulders are revealed to be exploded TANKS and
TRUCKS, burned black by intense fire. The palm trees' trunks
are actually dozens of GOLDEN SPIRES protruding two stories
from the ground, while their leaves are the scorched remains
of crucified corpses.

Kwesi is horrified. Asa is terrified.

She exits the moving car, darts into the burned boneyard.
Kwesi pulls over and follows her.

                    ASA
          Darren! DARREN!!

She runs to each impaled body, inspects its face, searches
for something familiar. Repeats. She cries ever louder.

                    KWESI
          Asa, be easy. He might not be here.

                    ASA
          They said he would be here! He has
          to be here!

                    KWESI
          We do not know that! …They?

Asa falls to her knees, loses her wits.

131

WAALISHA GUARD, 30s, appears from the wreckage. Trains a
RIFLE at the two. He is SWEATY from the desert heat.

> WAALISHA GUARD
> Do not move! Are you RSF?!

> KWESI
> (raises hands)
> Wait! We are not RSF! We are just
> passing through.

> WAALISHA GUARD
> Muzungu, put your hands up!

> ASA
> (cold)
> Where is Darren?

Waalisha Guard prepares to shoot, but his body freezes. He
cannot move, seized by his own sweat.

Asa stands, cuffs her hand as if choking a man. In response,
the sweat on the man coalesces around his neck, lifts him off
the ground. He drops his gun, panics.

> ASA
> I said: Where. Is. My. Husband?

> KWESI
> The American in the green jacket.

One of the Guard's hands clutches at his neck, but his other
gestures, points away. Asa releases him. He chokes for air.

He goes for the gun but is cut off by a burst of FIRE from
Kwesi, who teases with a wink.

> KWESI
> Use your words, Mjinga.

> WAALISHA GUARD
> The American… went with the others…
> To—Khartoum.

> ASA
> Is he ok?

> WAALISHA GUARD
> He is unharmed. Amani wants him
> safe. He helped destroy the RSF!

Asa is relieved, but incredulous. She processes this info.

Amani places the Shard inside and puts on the belt. Then she takes the remaining dirt and layers it over the belt. Within seconds, the belt is glazed with GOLD.

> AMANI
> You see. Now there is no risk of him taking it from me.

> BUZIBA
> Clever. He cannot undo his Soul Flux if yours blocks his access.

> DARREN
> That means you can't get to it either!

> BUZIBA
> I have no need to. The Shard is no longer my responsibility.

> DARREN
> What the hell changed? You chased me and Asa up and down the slums in Kenya just because we *knew* about Umoya. Now, you GIVE AWAY a shard?!

> MUNI
> Consider that recompense for the damage he did to my face!

> BUZIBA
> My duties were my duties. I have nothing to apologize for.

> MUNI
> Then maybe I should cut you up until I make you sorry.

> AMANI
> That's enough, all of you. We should be happy that the family has grown, Muni.

All three men sneer at the thought. Amani sits beside Muni.

> AMANI
> I am curious, though, Buziba. Why is it that only Muni can unlock the abilities of our comrades?

Darren is intrigued.

MEMORY FLASH: Muni BLOWS BACK the RECRUITS in the Congo village. Then the Recruits rise, able to use their Umoya.

                    AMANI
          When these abilities first surfaced
          at Kilimanjaro, we tried to share
          them with as many of our comrades
          as possible, but only Muni was able
          to spread them. …Even if we all
          followed the same steps. Is there
          something special about him?

                    BUZIBA
          You were at Kilimanjaro as well?
          Did you ever touch the Wind Shard?
               (Muni nods; beat)
          There are two ways to awaken Umoya
          within a person. The first is
          through intensive training, but the
          second is to make contact with a
          catalyst—any object with enough
          residual Umoya inside it to trigger
          an awakening.
               (eyes Darren)
          For most outsiders, touching a
          catalyst is the most common method,
          but those lucky enough to touch a
          Shard *become* catalysts themselves.

                    AMANI
          That's fascinating. So exposure to
          that stone was enough to do that?

                    DARREN
          Great! Got any more useful
          information you wanna tell them?

                    BUZIBA
          Do not get the idea I am here to
          help anyone. I am merely a
          spectator in this conflict.

                    AMANI
          I understand, Buziba, thank you.

The DRIVER calls out to Amani. She looks outside the bus to
see the approaching SKYLINE of the capital city.

                    AMANI
          You have already been plenty
          helpful…

EXT. KHARTOUM - DOWNTOWN - DAY

The bus pulls over, and Muni gets out. Amani sees him out and
hands him the gold belt with the Fire Shard.

>   AMANI
>   I'll wait for your signal.
>
>   MUNI
>   You won't be waiting long!

The bus pulls away, reveals the caravan of TANKS and RSF
TRUCKS that follow it. Muni straps on the belt, hops onto the
leading tank.

The bus breaks from the caravan, heads deeper into the city.

ON A NEARBY ROOF:

We see a man observing the caravan from above. It's Anansi.
What he sees concerns him.

The caravan kicks dust into the air that blocks our view. In
a blink, he's gone.

I/E. KWESI'S CAR - ROAD TO KHARTOUM - DAY

Kwesi's Car kicks up towers of dirt as they cruise down the
desert road. Dozens of MINI PYRAMIDS are scattered along the
sand.

Asa is filled with worry, impatience. She checks her phone;
no response to the dozen texts she's sent to Darren.

>   KWESI
>   He was lying—right? Darren would
>   never help the Waalisha, ya think?
>
>   ASA
>   No… maybe. If he was threatened… or
>   someone else was threatened.
>
>   KWESI
>   Hmm. They threaten him, he provides
>   help. Such a bad-faith deal. Even
>   if he is in Khartoum, could we find
>   him?

Asa peers out the window, sees a lone man in the desert sand.
It's Anansi. He gestures down the road, toward the city.

>   ASA
>   He's there. We'll find him.

>   FADE OUT.

                      END OF ACT ONE

ACT TWO

FADE IN:

EXT. AXUM TSION CHURCH - OUTER GATE - DAY

Pharaoh approaches the gate of a massive church plaza. LOCALS
and TOURISTS gather, take pictures of the site.

He takes out the MASK OF ARJANA, and its right corner lights
up, confirms to Pharaoh he is in the right place.

                    ANANSI (O.S.)
          Have you come to worship?

Pharaoh looks over his shoulder to see Anansi dressed like a
priest. He slips the Mask into a POUCH.

                    PHARAOH
          Not exactly. I'm in a period of
          deconstruction, but I hear there's
          something here worth the
          pilgrimage.

                    ANANSI
          Ah, the Ark of the Covenant. It's
          the treasure of Axum.

                    PHARAOH
          Is that the only treasure that is
          here?

                    ANANSI
          What other treasure would there be?

Pharaoh's eyes peer through the gates toward the church.
Anansi studies Pharaoh.

                    PHARAOH
          Maybe another gift from God.
          Something to enable His prophets to
          accomplish miraculous works…

                    ANANSI
          Aaron's rod? Perhaps. They say it
          rests inside the Ark, but none have
          ever seen inside it.

                    PHARAOH
          So they say.

Anansi breaks character, if only slightly.

> ANANSI
> Even if this pilgrimage is
> successful, what would that really
> change for you?

The Shard in Pharaoh pocket GLOWS, and the CLOUDS in the sky
darken and swirl. Pedestrians panic and disperse as a funnel
cloud descends.

> PHARAOH
> It changes nothing for me. It is
> the world that will be transformed.

Anansi, unfazed by the wind, takes a final look at Pharaoh.

> PHARAOH
> The weather is getting bad. You
> should find shelter.

Pharaoh looks back, but Anansi is gone.

A TORNADO descends. Sirens BLARE. All pedestrians and
security disappear to find shelter. Now is the time.

The cloud swallows the complex, provides cover for Pharaoh to
enter the gate. He leaps over it and enters one of the
buildings. As he does, the wind dies.

INT. AXUM TSION CHURCH - ARK CHAPEL - CONTINUOUS

Dying winds whistle through the open orifices of the chapel.
Pharaoh steps deeper inside. Bleeding sunlight guides him.

He approaches an open door, but he's cut off by Anansi, now
wearing his Arjanan wardrobe.

> ANANSI
> You will go no farther.

> PHARAOH
> You are… Arjanan?

> ANANSI
> Osas Pharaoh, if you continue on
> this path, you will create problems
> much larger than you.

> PHARAOH
> This world's problems are already
> bigger than me. But once I get that
> Stone, nothing will be.

                    ANANSI
          If only it were that simple.

A BLAZING ARM fazes through Anansi's body, grabs Pharaoh,
yanks him through an intangible Anansi, into the next room.

INT. AXUM TSION CHURCH - ARK CHAPEL CHAMBER - CONTINUOUS

The arm swings Pharaoh, slams him toward the floor, but WIND
catches him, breaks his fall. Before he breaks free, the
floor beneath him SHIFTS, transforms into a CLAY LION.

The lion bites Pharaoh as it rises from below. It mauls him
like a rag doll until Pharaoh's scream summons an EBONY BOLT.
Black Lightning discharges from him, explodes the lions head.

Pharaoh drops to the floor, clambers to his feet. He clutches
the fang holes in his torso when he notices his pouch fell.

He sees it on the floor, moves to get it, but the BLAZING ARM
punches the pouch, crushes its content. The Mask is gone.

                    PHARAOH
          No!

The arm withdraws, and Pharaoh sees his attackers. JARRAH, a
woman in her 50s wearing priestly garbs, stands stiff as the
arm recedes into her body.

                    JARRAH
          And with that, your treasure hunt
          ends here.

MALVA, male 40s, stands beside her wearing western clothing
covered by a layer of Arjanan Armor.

                    PHARAOH
          Arjanans… Then I am in the correct
          place.

                    MALVA
          This is the last place you want to
          be… or will ever be.

                    ANANSI (O.S.)
          Malva, a barricade please.

Pharaoh finds Anansi to his right, standing before the ARK OF
THE COVENANT. Pharaoh springs toward the Ark, but is blocked
by a rising WALL of CLAY.

Anansi sends a BURST of AIR at Pharaoh, but he fights it,
counters with an Ebony Bolt.

Anansi vanishes in a blink, and the bolt misses. He reappears beside Jarrah and Malva.

Malva makes a chomping gesture with his hands and a CLAY SNAKE emerges from the wall. The snake attempts to swallow Pharaoh, but only succeeds in pushing him to the opposite side of the room before exploding from another Ebony Bolt.

Pharaoh recovers and notices that the Arjanans have moved next to the wall.

> MALVA
> Prince Anansi, no need to strain
> royal hands. Leave this to us.

> ANANSI
> This man holds the Wind Shard; he
> will be a handful. I will assist
> when I can.

> JARRAH
> Another faithless heathen comes to
> see the Ark. Scriptures are never
> enough for your kind.

> PHARAOH
> I do have faith; enough to follow
> the Mask of Arjana to these temples
> and take the Stone for myself.
>   (pats pocket)
> And that faith was already
> rewarded.

> JARRAH
> So, it is greed that brings you
> here. Yet another sin that will
> only earn you death.

> PHARAOH
>   (beat)
> You three… are just like the
> others. So sanctimonious; daring to
> judge me for wanting to fix what
> you refuse to. Only one of you has
> ever dared to question your dogma.

Anansi's eye twitches.

> ANANSI
> This is your final warning, Osas
> Pharaoh. Leave the Wind Shard and
> no more blood will be shed.

Pharaoh clutches his bloody wound. His eyes drift upward.

He sees a vision of his father and friends hanging from the ceiling as they did that fateful night.

> PHARAOH
> Too much blood has already been
> shed. If I need to spill a little
> more, so be it.

EXT. KHARTOUM - CAPITAL - DAY

The Waalisha Bus pulls into the driveway of the CAPITAL BUILDING, where many armed SUDANESE GUARDS stand at-the-ready. The bus catches a few of their eyes.

Amani gazes out the window, past the capital. She waits…

EXT. KHARTOUM - MILITARY BASE GATE - DAY

The Caravan of tanks and combat trucks arrive at a military base, but SUDANESE SOLDIERS are expecting them. Their guns and their own tanks are pointed at the incoming vehicles.

The leading tank halts. The caravan does the same.

INT. INSIDE THE TANK - CONTINUOUS

Muni removes his seat belt and stares off.

MEMORY FLASH: MOTHER and FATHER SULEYMAN's bodies lie motionless and eviscerated on the floor of their home… JOSEPH speaks words of encouragement to a dying comrade…

Muni returns to the moment. His glare burns with anger.

EXT. KHARTOUM - MILITARY BASE GATE - CONTINUOUS

SUDANESE SOLDIER 1 steps to the gate.

> SUDANESE SOLDIER 1
> Get out the tank — NOW!

The tank's hatch opens. Muni climbs out, mounts the tank like he is king of the mountain.

> SUDANESE SOLDIER 1
> Who are you? What is your goal?

> MUNI
> You know well who we are. We are
> here to take back our home.

I/E. KHARTOUM - CAPITAL - INSIDE THE BUS - DAY

Amani rises, heads for the bus door.

                    DARREN
          Amani, wait!
               (she stops)
          I get it—all these people are
          victims, even you. As much as I
          possibly could, I understand why
          you want to do this, but you can't.
          If you lead these people into a
          fight this big, none of you can
          ever go back. You won't be refugees
          anymore. You'll just be terrorists.

                    AMANI
               (beat; processes)
          These people… became more than
          refugees long ago…

                                        INTERCUT:

                    MUNI
          Our innocence was stripped from us
          by you—greedy tools of a corrupt
          state! You destroyed our
          communities, murdered our people,
          and left us with no choice but to
          build something new from the ruin
          you left us in. You transformed us—

                    AMANI
          Into survivors. We've been
          surviving for so long, but now we
          have a chance at freedom. All we
          need is to be willing to dive into
          the savagery we've drowned in for
          years.

                    SUDANESE SOLDIER 1
          You have always been savages!

The FIRE SHARD on Muni's belt glows.

                    MUNI
          No, but here and now… we will be!

Muni stomps on the hatch and the tank FIRES into the
Soldiers. Sudan Tanks respond in kind, blow up Muni's tank.
But FIRE rockets Muni skyward. Then he plummets like a meteor
with a FLAMING TAIL.

He crashes into the formation of Soldiers, ENGULFS them in flames. Instant chaos.

INT. KHARTOUM - CAPITAL - PRESIDENT'S OFFICE - CONTINUOUS

PRESIDENT IBRAHIM sits nervously at his desk, clutching a HANDGUN as if he is alone. He is not. He is surrounded by Sudanese Guards and LIEUTENANT, 40s; all ready for danger.

                    PRESIDENT IBRAHIM
          Where the hell is Nazeer?

                    LIEUTENANT
          Still no response from General—

A TREMOR shakes the office. Lieutenant consults his RADIO.

                    SUDANESE GUARD 1 (V.O.)
               (through radio)
          There was an explosion to the east!
          Base is under fire!

                    LIEUTENANT
          They went for the base first.
          Prepare to move out!

INT. KHARTOUM - CAPITAL - INSIDE THE BUS - CONTINUOUS

Amani sees a PLUME of smoke to the east. That's the signal.

Some Sudanese Guards leave to investigate. Others rally.

                    AMANI
          It is time.

Darren moves to follow her out the bus, but BUS DRIVER points a MACHINE GUN at him.

                    AMANI
               (to Bus Driver)
          Keep him comfortable.

                    DARREN
          Don't do it—Amani!

But she's already gone.

EXT. KHARTOUM - CAPITAL - OUTSIDE GATE - CONTINUOUS

Amani hops on top of the bus, gets a higher perspective. She eyes a familiar area of the building.

With a deep breath she summons 20 MIDAS SPEARS from the
ground. They FLING themselves upward and torpedo down on…

INT. KHARTOUM - CAPITAL - PRESIDENT'S OFFICE - CONTINUOUS

Sudanese Guards clear the office exit as Lieutenant ushers
the President to the door by his arm.

                    LIEUTENANT
          Hurry, sir! We will have you in the
          safe room before they find out—

The gold spears CRASH through the ceiling, impales Lieutenant
as he crosses the threshold. President Ibrahim stumbles back
as more spears create a fence that barricade him inside. The
Guards try to break through the gold bars to no avail.

EXT. KHARTOUM - CAPITAL - OUTSIDE GATE - CONTINUOUS

The outside Guards spot Amani, turn their fire on her. The
bus is sprayed with gunfire, but Amani summons more gold
spears to shield them all from fire.

She hops down, peers through the teeth of fence, takes aim.
With a shout, she hurls more spears through the air and at
the Guards. They hit their targets and the gunfire ceases.

EXT. KHARTOUM - MILITARY BASE - CONTINUOUS

Muni continues to rampage. He SLASHES the Soldiers close to
him with his sword, summons a VANGUARD SHEAR to bifurcate
those at a distance, and drowns the rest in waves of FIRE.

Tanks and turrets attempt to take aim, but they are
interrupted, destroyed by incoming Waalisha-piloted tanks.

WAALISHA FIGHTERS storm the entrance, quickly overwhelm the
remaining Soldiers. Sudanese gunfire is blocked by WALLS OF
EARTH. WIND Fluxers suspend the soldiers in the air, while
Waalisha Gunmen pick them off. FIRE Fluxers burn enemy
vehicles, killing those who cannot escape the explosions.

Muni basks in the devastation and remembers:

MEMORY FLASH: The destruction of his village; the assault on
the refugee camp.

Muni ventures deeper into the military base, leaving only
death in his wake.

EXT. KHARTOUM - CAPITAL - PRESIDENT'S OFFICE - CONTINUOUS

The Presidential Hall is silent, eery. Soldiers in the hall stare down the corridor, waiting for a threat to appear.

President Ibrahim cocks his gun, does the same. He is alone in his office, caged by bars of gold. He watches the door.

Then Amani CRASHES through the ceiling.

She finds the soldiers in the hall. Gold PIKES erupt from the floor and impale them.

Ibrahim takes a shot, misses, but earns Amani's attention. Her eyes meet his; they burn with animosity.

Ibrahim fires again, but Amani doesn't dodge. She blocks the bullets with her forearm, advances toward him. Three bullets in and she grabs his wrist, crushes it. He drops the gun. With a headbutt, she knocks out Ibrahim. The conflict ends.

Amani drops her shield arm, lets blood drip as she begins to pant.

She is exhausted, but not from the battle.

INT. AXUM TSION CHURCH - ARK CHAPEL CHAMBER - DAY

Pharaoh darts around the chapel, evading **CLAYMATED BEASTS** that spawn from the ground. He hurls lighting at HYENAS, destroys them, but a LION forms from their debris, attacks.

Pharaoh wrestles the beast, matches its strength, but he is swatted by a Jarrah's **SABER LIMB.** The limb knocks him airborne, reaches for him, but Pharaoh employs the WIND to swerve away. He flies to avoid the Jarrah's reach.

                    MALVA
          You're quite adept at running away!

Malva pulls dirt from the floor, forms a HAWK. It screeches as it takes flight and pursues Pharaoh.

Pharaoh swats away the hawk. He notices Malva's hands gesture as the animals move.

Pharaoh hurls lightning at the Arjanans, kicking up dust and dissipating the Beasts. But the Saber Limb persists. It snatches Pharaoh from the air and throws him to the floor.

Pharaoh peels himself from the floor as the tile transforms into the mouth of a WHALE. He floats to avoid falling, but the Jarrah's Limb punches down, knocks him into the mouth.

The whale chomps and quickly reverts back into a floor.
Pharaoh is entombed beneath tile. A beat passes.

> MALVA
> Much ado about nothing.

> ANANSI
> It is not over.

The ground crumbles, explodes as LIGHTNING pierces through
the floor. Pharaoh springs from the ground, lands opposite
the Arjanans. He looks worse for wear…

> PHARAOH
> This is why none of you deserve to
> steward the Stone! You just sit on
> this immense power, even as I use
> the same power against you!

> MALVA
> Being a responsible steward is
> knowing when to use such power. We
> won't need it against you.

> PHARAOH
> Surely you needed it when the
> Europeans ravaged our continent!
> Where were you then—when your
> people needed you? Where was your
> responsibility?

> ANANSI
> Our jurisdiction only extends to
> the borders of Arjana and any
> unfortunate soul who stumbles upon
> Umoya. No one beyond that is our
> "people".

Pharaoh seethes. Beat.

> JARRAH
> The people of this world had our
> chance, and we squandered it. We
> were blessed with power, and we
> misuse it time and time again. It
> is the arc of history.

Jarrah points to the wall that shields the Ark.

> JARRAH
> The story of the Ophiuchus Stone is
> the story of the Ark of the
> Covenant, which is the story of
> humanity.

EXT. GARDEN OF EDEN - DAY

We are transported to see the silhouettes of ADAM and EVE as
they stroll in the GARDEN. The SERPENT catches Eve's eye.

It gestures to the FORBIDDEN FRUIT. Eve is entranced by the
LIGHT the octahedral fruit casts.

> JARRAH (V.O.)
> In the beginning, we were blessed
> with everything we needed, but we
> wanted more. More was too much.

Eve plucks the fruit from the tree.

INT. ANCIENT ATLANTIS - DAY

The SHADOWS shift until they become a KING on his THRONE.
Above the throne is a SHINING OCTAHEDRAL STONE that casts
shadows over all in the room.

The King overlooks a MAP of his military conquests. SOLDIER
PIECES cover Africa and parts of Europe.

> JARRAH (V.O.)
> Even if we create paradise by our
> own hand, we lose it through our
> greed.

The King spreads his pieces to the far side of Europe, and
the shadows shift again.

EXT. ANCIENT ISRAEL - THE TABERNACLE - DAY

The shadows spin, form into a FUNNELING CLOUD that
illuminates a massive village. The funnel terminates at the
TABERNACLE.

VILLAGERS within the town lounge, but they are overtaken by
INVADERS. The Invaders pillage the town, come for the
tabernacle.

> JARRAH (V.O.)
> The Almighty Himself could show us
> the way, guide us in the dark, but
> we still find a way to get lost.

CLOAKED SHADOWS enter the tabernacle from the rear. They
emerge with the ARK, and flee in the chaos of the invasion.

The Cloaked Shadows journey through different landscapes
until they arrive at a small chapel…

INT. AXUM TSION CHURCH – ARK CHAPEL CHAMBER – DAY

All shadows fade to reveal the Ark sitting undisturbed behind the stone wall. We enter the chapel to return to the action.

> JARRAH
> The Ark and the treasures within
> are a reminder of the paradises we
> achieved and lost.

> PHARAOH
> So you hide it from the world so we
> can never learn. Let me guess, only
> Arjana can bare that burden, eh?

> ANANSI
> Arjana exists to protect humanity:
> from its own hubris, from the greed
> of nations, and even from the
> indignation of the vengeful.

Pharaoh seethes again.

> MALVA
> There's no use in wasting your
> breath. He will never understand.
> But, of course, it's not his fault…
>   (multiple beasts spawn)
> He is only human.

The Beasts strike. Pharaoh struggles to fight them off. Meanwhile, Anansi fazes through the wall toward the Ark…

Pharaoh fights on. He BLOWS away the Beasts, but they spawn endlessly. He deflects the Saber Limb with his own lightning, but it reforms and returns. It's an onslaught of attrition.

MEMORY FLASH: YOUNG OSAS is brought into KING'S LAUNDROMAT by the WHITE OFFICER. JIBRIL pleads to appease him, while the WORKERS are hiding in the back.

> PHARAOH
> You are running…

The onslaught continues, but Pharaoh is hardened.

MEMORY FLASH: Jibril and the Workers hang from trees outside the laundromat. Young Pharaoh runs away.

> PHARAOH
> All we do… is run…

The Arjanans ignore him. The attack continues.

147

But Pharaoh's Wind Shard glows brighter… his lightning flashes hotter.

MEMORY FLASH: Young Pharaoh punches the wall, shrieks in frustration, battles his own cowardice.

> PHARAOH
> No more running! We—I will fight!

Pharaoh screams! Releases a wave of black lightning that arcs from one beast to the next. They are all gone in an instant.

Then WIND enters the chapel like an inhale, SUCKS IN all windows as it enters. Then an exhaled BURST blasts off the roof, knocks Jarrah and Malva into the wall. An Ebony Bolt ZAPS them both, and they are out of commission.

Pharaoh calms himself. He fires a BOLT at the wall, blasts a hole through it that exposes the Ark. He walks to it.

The Ark of the Covenant is covered in aged gold; a relic of a different millennia; a chest to an even greater treasure.

Pharaoh throws open the Ark, looks inside. There is a GOLD POT of DUST, a DRIED STAFF, and two CRUMBLED STONE TABLETS. But no Shard.

> ANANSI (O.S.)
> Your fight hasn't ended.

Pharaoh turns back to see Anansi standing beside a squirming Jarrah and Malva. Floating above his hand is the EARTH SHARD.

> PHARAOH
> Is it finally your turn?

> ANANSI
> Malva, can you still fight?

> MALVA
> (struggles to stand)
> Do I not have breath?

Anansi nods, motions to hand the Shard to Malva but—

> JARRAH
> Prince, please…
> (beat)
> Do not make us hypocrites.

> ANANSI
> Forgive me, Jarrah, but even the most noble ideals are eventually tainted by hypocrisy.

The Earth Shard floats to Malva, lands in his palm. It GLEAMS a bright GREEN as Malva holds it and shouts.

EXT. AXUM TSION CHURCH - OUTER GATE - CONTINUOUS

The city RUMBLES. As PEDESTRIANS scramble for shelter, the sun is eclipsed. All look up and see the culprit.

A TITANIC CLAY SERPENT towers a THOUSAND FEET in the air. It stares down into the chapel, prepares to strike.

INT. AXUM TSION CHURCH - ARK CHAPEL CHAMBER - CONTINUOUS

Pharaoh gawks at the serpent. Fear and awe battle for prominence in his expression.

                    PHARAOH
          Is this… the Stone's power?

                    MALVA
          Drown in wonder as you meet your
          end.

The Serpent's head strikes, dives like a warhead. It's a dozen feet from PHARAOH before—

Pharaoh SHOUTS, summons a FUNNEL CLOUD to cushion the Serpent's fall. It pushes the beast upward, but it does not give up.

EXT. AXUM TSION CHURCH - OUTER GATE - CONTINUOUS

All living things, people or animal, flee for their lives as a TORNADO wrestles a Titan Serpent. The Serpent is winning…

Its body coils around the chapel, crushes the walls as it finds leverage. It closes the distance to Pharaoh.

I/E. AXUM TSION CHURCH - FALLING ARK CHAPEL CHAMBER - CONTINUOUS

Malva screams his loudest. Pharaoh does the same, but it's not enough. The Serpent approaches. Pharaoh looks up at the descending beast…

MEMORY FLASH: Just as he looked up at his still father…

The fight is not over.

Rage fills Pharaoh, and BLACK LIGHTNING explodes from his body, filling the funnel cloud.

The wind and lightning work in tandem, eating away at the Titan Serpent. With a final scream, the STORM BURSTS and disintegrates the beast.

Malva is only allowed seconds of horror before Pharaoh leaps at him. He punches his chest, sends an Ebony Bolt through it.

The Bolt leaves a hole in his chest. Malva finally collapses, but not before Pharaoh takes the Earth Shard from his hand.

Pharaoh stands victorious, a glowing stone in either hand.

He starts for what's left of the door but Anansi blocks him. Pharaoh chuckles and proceeds, slipping through the intangible Anansi.

> ANANSI
> Even if you restore the Ophiuchus,
> you won't survive to wield it… No
> soul anchored to the world by
> vengeance could endure the trial.

> PHARAOH
> Vengeance never fueled me. It
> simply created me.

He feels a tug on his leg… It's Jarrah.

> JARRAH
> Please… bury it all. Some things…
> should remain—unseen.

Pharaoh's face relents and he finds a mercy within. He nods. Jarrah lets go.

EXT. AXUM TSION CHURCH - OUTER GATE - CONTINUOUS

As Pharaoh walks away, the Earth Shard glows. The earth RUMBLES again. A SINKHOLE opens where the chapel once stood. It swallows the destroyed chapel, the Arjanans, and the Ark.

The sinkhole seals itself as SIRENS blare and people panic. Pharaoh takes his time walking back to his car.

INT. ARJANA - QUEEN'S THRONE ROOM - DAY

Anansi opens his eyes. He is stoic, but concerned. TANO, Bia, and QUEEN ASASE wait for his report.

                    ANANSI
          Osas Pharaoh has acquired the Earth
          Shard. Malva and Jarrah have
          fallen…

                    BIA
          No… they are both gone?!

                    TANO
          Could you not hinder him at all
          yourself?!

                    ANANSI
          My **APPARITION** hardly has enough
          tangibility to hold the Shard.
          Escaping with it was not an option.

                    TANO
          Damnit! Jarrah and Malva were
          gifted fighters. How is this man
          able to beat so many seasoned
          warriors?

                    ANANSI
          His Soul Flux is formidable, and he
          is quite persistent.

                    BIA
          Mother, we need a plan! The
          American will not be enough on her
          own. What should we do? …Mother?

Queen Asase processes, but she has no answer to give.

                                        FADE OUT.

                    END OF ACT TWO

ACT THREE

FADE IN:

I/E. KHARTOUM - DOWNTOWN - KWESI'S CAR - EVENING

Asa and Kwesi drive through nearly deserted streets as
pedestrians scramble for their homes. They peep out their
windows to see the Sudanese Military being routed.

Bloody and beaten soldiers drag themselves down the road.
They are all between spooked and enraged, but none have fight
in them. They are defeated.

The military hogs the road as they flee, forcing Asa and
Kwesi to pull over.

                    KWESI
          We may have to continue on foot.
             (looks down the road)
          If I were to guess, the action is
          probably where they're running
          from. Not sure if we should—

                    ASA
          Then we go that way.

                    KWESI
          Of course…

Asa checks her phone… still no contact from Darren.

                    ASA
             (to herself)
          Please, be safe…

INT. KHARTOUM - CAPITAL - CORRIDORS - EVENING

Malick ushers Darren and Buziba through the capital halls.
Darren keeps his eyes straight to avoid seeing the massacre
of Sudanese Guards. Buziba observes with jaded eyes.

WAALISHA GOONS attempt to remove the corpses from the gold
pikes, as if removing broken scarecrows. Passers-by dip
between the pikes to reach…

INT. KHARTOUM - CAPITAL - PRESIDENT'S OFFICE - CONTINUOUS

Muni helps Amani finish BANDAGING her arm, leaving a bloody
mess on the DESK. She tests her range of motion.

                         AMANI
          Just a month ago, those shots might
          have taken off my arm, but I
          already feel… fine.

                         MUNI
          I know something that will make you
          feel even better.

A beaten man is roped to gold pike on the far end of the
office. He is weary and almost unrecognizable.

                         DARREN
          Is that…?

                         AMANI
          Ibrahim, President of Sudan.

                         PRESIDENT IBRAHIM
               (comes to)
          Dirty *abeeds*.

Muni takes exception to that; slices Ibrahim with his sword.

                         DARREN
          Stop!

                         MUNI
               (sneers; to Goon)
          This might be too much for the
          snowflake American. Send him away.

                         AMANI
          No. He should see this.

                         PRESIDENT IBRAHIM
          I do not know what demon power you
          used, but I should not be
          surprised. It proves the Janjaweed
          should have broken you dogs sooner.

                         AMANI
          Power is a force that corrupts.
          This is merely a gift available to
          all, even us "slaves".

                         PRESIDENT IBRAHIM
          Slaves deserve no such thing!

                         DARREN
          Why are you using that word?

                    PRESIDENT IBRAHIM
          An American slave? At home with the
          dogs of your homeland, I see.

                    DARREN
          Shut up! Why're you—Is the pot
          really gonna call the kettle black
          here? Do you hate you're own—

Ibrahim spits, nearly hits Darren with it.

                    PRESIDENT IBRAHIM
          You dogs are not my people! You are
          the lowest class wherever you go;
          slaves throughout all of history.
          None of you have a place in the
          Arab world, so of course you stole
          it away from us.

                    DARREN
          You are all African! What are you
          talking about?! You're supposed to
          govern for everyone!

Amani watches Darren struggle to process. The contradiction
nearly breaks him. Meanwhile, Buziba's eyes burn quietly.

                    PRESIDENT IBRAHIM
          I govern for my people. Dogs
          deserve no more than crumbs. And
          when there are not enough crumbs, I
          put the dogs down.

                    AMANI
               (beat)
          Our eyes are similar, Darren. We
          both see our own faces on top of
          his, while his eyes force him to
          see opposing shades of the same
          color. His vision only leads to
          genocide. *Our* vision will unite.

Muni clutches his sword. Ibrahim knows his end approaches.

                    PRESIDENT IBRAHIM
          Slave uprisings never last long.
          You will be conquered by the next
          civilized nation and end up just
          like the Tutsi! The Waalisha will
          be nothing more than a shameful
          blot in his—

His mouth his shut closed… by Buziba's hand. Rage bleeds from
his eyes as he squeezes Ibrahim's face.

                    MUNI
          Wait—no!

Ibrahim screams and moans as smoke pours from his mouth.
Buziba lets go and watches as the Curse takes effect. Ibrahim
is soon dead.

                    MUNI
          Who are you to take the spoils of
          our victory, eh?! You did not—

Muni pauses when he sees Buziba's pained expression. Buziba
leaves the room without a word.

                    MUNI
             (sighs)
          He could have at least asked.

Amani somberly watches the life drain from Ibrahim's body.
The longest chapter in her history is finally closed.

                    AMANI
          It is over… almost.

She goes to Darren, who is still vexed by Ibrahim's words.

                    AMANI
          Come with me.

INT. KHARTOUM - CAPITAL - CONFERENCE ROOM - EVENING

Amani welcomes Darren into a large conference room that has
been turned into a makeshift lab. Her TESLA COILS,
LIGHTBULBS, and other tools are strewn about, only half
unpacked. She closes the door behind them.

                    DARREN
          Can you let me go, already? I did
          what you asked for, your people are
          better at using Umoya now. Just let
          me get back to my wife.

                    AMANI
          Your knowledge of Umoya was the
          original reason we… adopted you,
          but soon after, I realized you were
          invaluable in another way.

                    DARREN
          Too bad. I'm done. I don't wanna be
          in the center of a warzone anymore.

                    AMANI
          I understand. I would never force
          people into a situation like this.

                    DARREN
          Oh yeah? Then why did you just
          throw a coup and drag this whole
          country into a dark age?! A
          politician being evil doesn't mean
          governments are useless, Amani!
          They help manage things like the
          economy—

                    AMANI
          And energy. Yes, I know this.

                    DARREN
          So what's your plan, *Leader?!*

Amani tries not to get agitated.

                    AMANI
          Malick and Muni will be in charge
          of law enforcement. The economy is
          already being handled. The energy
          challenge is something I've figured
          out… but I need your help.

                    DARREN
          I'm not running your energy
          department! I'm outta here.

Darren starts for the door but Amani grabs his hand.

                    AMANI
          You are an inventor, aren't you?!

                    DARREN
          I'm… an engineer. How did you—

                    AMANI
          All Soul Fluxes are unique to the
          individual, are they not? Both of
          our abilities allow us to mold dirt
          into metal, but only you can create
          elaborate objects. I cannot come
          close to reproducing your crafts.

                    DARREN
          What's your point?

                    AMANI
          You have an understanding of
          science that I need.
                         (MORE)

                    AMANI (CONT'D)
          Once you help me crack a mystery of
          historical engineering, millions in
          Sudan will have their energy needs
          met! Assist me in this and you can
          go free.

Darren ponders for a beat. Amani's sincerity is certain.

                    DARREN
               (rolls eyes)
          What is it?

Amani moves to a table with an object covered with a cloth.
She uncovers it to reveal a large MODEL PYRAMID made of
actual stone materials.

                    AMANI
          What do you know about pyramids?

                    DARREN
          Umm, tombs. Religious monuments.

                    AMANI
          Is that all?

                    DARREN
          Big.

                    AMANI
          You're correct there, but wrong on
          the first two.

                    DARREN
          What? Literally everybody knows
          they were built to be tombs for—

                    AMANI
          Not a single Egyptian king was ever
          found in a pyramid. But they are
          commonly found only a few miles
          away—in the Valley of the Kings.

                    DARREN
          So you're saying this common
          knowledge everyone knows—

                    AMANI
          Another fabrication by another
          corrupt government, appropriating
          an ancient culture that does not
          belong to them.

157

                    DARREN
              (beat)
          I'll bite. Whose culture is it?

                    AMANI
          The ancient Atlanteans.

Darren pretends to be incredulous. He's not.

Amani goes to sift through DOCUMENTS as she speaks.

                    AMANI
          Everyone knows the story of
          Atlantis, but not many know the
          legend claims that Egypt was an
          Atlantean colony. But this man did…

She plops large, aged packets on the table.

                    AMANI
          Nikola Tesla was inspired by the
          pyramids to create a network of
          wireless antennae that would
          receive energy from a source tower.

Amani plugs in a large Tesla Coil, turns it on. Instantly,
loose LIGHTBULBS around the room start to glow. She slides
over another document.

                    AMANI
          Scientists have already confirmed
          the Great Pyramid of Giza harnesses
          electromagnetic energy naturally.
          We only need to figure out how to
          use it like the ancients intended,
          just like Tesla tried with his
          tower project.

                    DARREN
          I already know about the
          Wardenclyffe Tower. You're
          forgetting one thing: the tower can
          only work if there's infrastructure
          of mini towers to receive the
          electricity. And guess what—Sudan
          doesn't have any.

                    AMANI
          But it does! There are small
          pyramids all over Sudan—more than
          anywhere in the world.

She gets closer to Darren, excitement and zeal filling her.

>   AMANI
>   This is all that's left to do,
>   Darren. If we can realize how the
>   ancients created a power plant with
>   only granite, limestone, and gold,
>   we could supply this nation with
>   all the energy it needs!

>   DARREN
>   It's such a pipe dream… I can't—
>   (beat)
>   Wait… granite and limestone?

Darren pauses, looks at the model pyramid on the table.

>   DARREN
>   (facepalms)
>   Granite is paramagnetic. It can
>   somewhat interact with electricity,
>   while limestone is an insulator.
>   And gold is obviously a conductor.
>   There ya go; mystery solved.

Amani is stunned. She pulls a small GOLD BAR from the ground, puts is on the table.

>   AMANI
>   Test that here! Use the model and
>   this gold.

>   DARREN
>   Don't believe me?

>   AMANI
>   Science is about more than taking
>   one's word.

She exits the room, closes the door behind her. Locks it.

Darren looks at the messy lab, sighs.

>   DARREN
>   Let's get this over with.

He goes to sit, but notices a PHONE CHARGER on the wall. He goes to plug in his dead phone and it CHIRPS to life.

EXT. KHARTOUM - CAPITAL - OUTSIDE GATE - EVENING

As Kwesi and Asa hide behind a building, Asa's phone VIBRATES. She checks it. Kwesi peeks around the corner.

ARMED Waalisha Goons pace around the gate. They have total control. Some experiment with their Fluxes in their leisure.

> KWESI
> These Waalisha are sure thorough. I do not see a way in, assuming Darren is even here.

> ASA
> He's here!

Asa shows Kwesi her phone. Darren's location is pinned on the map of Khartoum. They are right beside him.

> ASA
> His phone has been off for days. Looks like he finally charged—

The pin disappears, with a note that says "Darren has stopped sharing location."

> ASA
> Wha—why?! Did his phone break?

> KWESI
> Maybe he doesn't want you to come.

> ASA
> He's about to be disappointed.

> KWESI
> Do you have a plan?

> ASA
> Find a getaway car and a safe escape route so we can jet when I get back with Darren.

> KWESI
> (looks around)
> Easier said than done. Wait, what do you mean "I"?

Asa is gone. Kwesi looks for her but hides as Goons pass by.

ON THE ROOF

Asa surveys the area, looks for water. The BLUE NILE RIVER is a couple blocks away, but too far to Flux with.

A SUPPLY TRUCK approaches. Asa hops on top of it and stays low as it drives through the open gate. The truck parks next to the building. Asa jumps off and lands on…

EXT. KHARTOUM - CAPITAL - THE ROOF - CONTINUOUS

She stays low and moves away from the ledge.

> WAALISHA GUARD A
> Do not move!

Asa freezes, sees a young Waalisha Guard to her right. They
lock eyes.

> WAALISHA GUARD A
> The Muzungu!

He points to Asa, directs a GUST to blow at her. Asa doesn't
budge. She powers through it to clear the gap between them.
The Guard stumbles, his fall aided by Asa's fist.

Asa stands above him. Water oozes from her HYDRATION PACK.
She dreads this moment.

INT. ARJANA - SPECTRAL CHAMBER - DAY, FLASHBACK

Asa and Bia are flurries within the gravity field. We enter
the field to see…

The two locked in hand-to-hand combat. Bia throws swift
strikes and Asa has trouble keeping up. Asa manages a punch
that Bia blocks, knocking her back, but she stumbles, looses
her footing. She is vulnerable.

Asa moves in to capitalize, but she opens her fist, pushes
Bia over. Bia plops to the ground in disbelief.

Asa grins, proud of herself. Bia is aggravated. She sends a
WAVE of water to wash Asa backward. She falls even harder.

> ASA
> What was that for?!

> BIA
> Mercy in here won't earn you
> favors, and mercy out there will
> get you killed.

> ASA
> So, what, you're saying when I get
> someone on the ropes I—

> BIA
> Kill them. Immediately.

                    ASA
          What… I can't do that! What if I
          could just knock them out?

                    BIA
          And when they wake up, do you
          expect them to be grateful and let
          you live?

                    ASA
          But a lot of those fighters…
          they're kid soldiers… I can't just—

                    BIA
          Anyone who ends another's life
          forfeits their right to be called a
          child.
               (Asa hesitates)
          There is no battle where both sides
          walk away. You either survive or
          you do not.

END FLASHBACK.

EXT. KHARTOUM - CAPITAL - THE ROOF - EVENING

Asa is lost in thought. The Guard reaches into his pocket.

The Guard pulls a knife, hops to his feet, thrusts it at Asa,
but the water blocks the knife. He struggles to get free.

                    WAALISHA GUARD A
          HELP!

The water rushes his face, surrounds his head as if held in
place by an invisible fish bowl. He slowly drowns.

                    BIA (V.O.)
          You decide which side you and your
          husband will be on.

Asa can't watch. She spins the water and twists his neck. The
Guard collapses.

Asa hyperventilates, tries to keep it together. After a
moment, she recalls the water to her hydro pack and moves on.

INT. KIGALI, RWANDA - CABIN - DAY, FLASHBACK

JOHN and GLENDA sit at a table with AMERICAN SOLDIER. They
lean over a MAP of RWANDA. TUTSI BOY sits on a couch,
processing having just witnessed his parents' death.

                    AMERICAN SOLDIER
Most evacuation efforts are
happening at the embassy. If we can
get there, you are home free.

                    JOHN
How far is that?

                    AMERICAN SOLDIER
It's here in Kigali.

                    GLENDA
Will they be able to take all of
us?

                    AMERICAN SOLDIER
Multiple choppers are coming. We'll
have enough room for all expats.

                    GLENDA
And non-expats?

                    AMERICAN SOLDIER
I wasn't given information on—

                    JOHN
     (lowers voice)
Glenda, we got the kid to safety.

                    GLENDA
Dumping him in a war zone is safe
to you?

                    JOHN
I don't want anything to happen to
him either, but we did our part!

                    GLENDA
"Our part" isn't done until we've
done all we can. At least, my part
isn't…

Tutsi Boy overhears the conversation, perks up.

                    AMERICAN SOLDIER
Excuse me, do you know this kid
personally?

                    GLENDA
Do I need to know him to do what's
right?

END FLASHBACK.

INT. KHARTOUM - CAPITAL - LONELY CORRIDORS - EVENING

Buziba's brows furrow, feeling betrayed, even by the memory.
He doesn't notice the breeze from behind him.

                    ANANSI (O.S.)
          You are ordered to answer for this,
          Buziba. Why do you spit in the face
          of the Queen when she spared you,
          brought you into Arjana… showed
          mercy on your pitiful life. Queen
          Asase demands an answer. I demand
          an answer.

                    BUZIBA
               (turns; beat)
          For years, I used to agree with
          you. However, now I question the
          mercy of someone who had the power
          to stop genocide, but chose not to.

                    ANANSI
          So you respond by handing that same
          power to murderers and aide in a
          massacre. How do you stay afloat in
          that ocean of hypocrisy?

                    BUZIBA
          I am not aiding anyone. I want to
          see how an oppressed group would
          correct these wrongs if given the
          tools to do so. Let's see how the
          Shards balance the natural order.

                    ANANSI
          As long as the Shards exist, there
          will never be a natural order.

Anansi's Apparition fades away, leaving Buziba alone once
more. He slips into melancholy. Then he hears a THUD on the
ceiling.

EXT. KHARTOUM - CAPITAL - THE ROOF - EVENING

Asa peers off the roof, sees Muni and Malick talking in the
courtyard. The Fire Shard glows within the belt.

Muni directs Goons to their posts, wrangles others to follow
him as they leave the capital. Malick goes with Muni.

Asa steps away from the ledge and pulls out the WAYFINDER.
She squeezes and the arrow spins erratically. It won't lock
on. Annoyed, Asa puts it away.

                          ASA
               Where are you, Darren?

She roams the roof, searches for a clue. She finds one.

VOICES catch her ear, draws her attention to a HOLE in the
roof. She approaches as artificial light bleeds from the
room. She peeks inside, sees Amani.

IN THE PRESIDENT'S OFFICE

                          AMANI
               Joseph was so much better at
               numbers than me… What did you
               calculate?

Waalisha Nerd, female 40s, crunches numbers with an old
CALCULATOR, PENCIL, and PAPER.

                     WAALISHA NERD
               The global supply has only devalued
               the market by 2 percent.

                          AMANI
               Global? What about in Africa?

                     WAALISHA NERD
               It is hard to say. Politicians are
               tight-lipped, but the media
               mentions panic behind closed doors.

ON THE ROOF

A FLASH of light catches Asa's eye. She investigates.

It leads her to another side of the building… She gets
closer. Another FLASH and a CRACK sound echos from a window.

Asa ejects water from her pack, forms a concave LIQUID
MIRROR. She floats it down to the window.

INT. KHARTOUM - CAPITAL - CONFERENCE ROOM - CONTINUOUS

Darren backs away from the pyramid—astonished.

                         DARREN
               It actually works…

He backs into the wall and notices the window's been opened.
He looks outside just before a water TENDRIL snatches him.

EXT. KHARTOUM - CAPITAL - THE ROOF - CONTINUOUS

The tendril drops Darren. His feet barely touch the ground before Asa rushes in to squeeze him tight.

> DARREN
> Asa?! Babe, how're—you can't be—

Asa hushes him, grabs his hand and leads him away.

EXT. KHARTOUM - CAPITAL - OUTSIDE GATE - EVENING

Kwesi hides in an alley, watches armed Waalisha Goons patrol by. Among them are Muni and Malick.

Sudanese Soldiers ambush, fire at the Goons. Some go down before Malick summons a STONE WALL. The Goons take cover.

Then the Fire Shard glows, and Muni jumps over the wall, BLASTS flames at the Sudanese Soldiers and engulfs the entire street.

After a moment of screams, Muni extinguishes the fire. Most Soldiers are dead, but one survives. Muni inspects him… then calls over Malick.

> MUNI
> End him.

> MALICK
> Sir, he can't fight anymore.

> MUNI
> Call it pity if you need to. As
> long as he ends up dead.
>   (Malick hesitates)
> Not once did they stop to consider
> if any of us could fight back. They
> haven't earned that mercy.

Malick is unsteady. He aims at the Soldier that coughs blood. He takes the shot. The Soldier stops breathing.

> MUNI
> See, was not so bad? Come.

It was so bad, but Malick won't show it. The group moves on.

Kwesi pokes his head out, spooked. He examines the bodies. Darren and Asa enter the alley.

> DARREN
> Kwesi!

                    KWESI
              (notices the couple)
          The well-digger lives on!

                    ASA
          Where's the getaway car!

                    KWESI
          You expected me to hijack a tank? I
          can't surprise any of them since
          their in groups. I do *not* want to
          go up against that!

Kwesi points to burnt bodies in the scorched street.

                    ASA
          What did all that?

                    KWESI
          A guy just passed with a gold belt
          and covered the place with fire!

                    DARREN
          Muni…

                    ASA
          Then he's away from the leader.
          Kwesi, please find *something* by the
          time I get back!

                    DARREN
          Back?! Where're you going?

                    ASA
          I've still got a job to do…

Darren tries to grab Asa, but she jumps, scales the building
with ease. She's gone in a blink. Darren and Kwesi gawk.

                    KWESI
          Since when was she that fast?

                    DARREN
          I was gonna ask you that…

EXT. KHARTOUM - CAPITAL - INSIDE THE GATE - EVENING

Asa zips from vehicle to vehicle, stealths her way through
the courtyard and driveway.

But she catches a Goon's eye. He steps next to a car, checks
for feet underneath—

Then a water tendril grabs his head, SLAMS it against the vehicle, knocks him out. He collapses, and the water drags him beneath the car.

Asa moves on.

EXT. KHARTOUM - CAPITAL - THE ROOF - EVENING

She makes it to the roof, finds the hole to the President's Office again. She eavesdrops once more…

IN THE PRESIDENT'S OFFICE

                    AMANI
          Then, how much more will we need…
          to collapse everything?

Waalisha Nerd processes. Meanwhile, Asa points to Amani from above. Water corkscrews around her arm; a coiling serpent.

The two in the office are completely unaware.

                    WAALISHA NERD
          Umm… historically, 18 tons was
          enough. So it might be smart to
          double that.

                    AMANI
          So about 40 tons, eh?
          That will take time to accumulate…
          but I suppose the battle will be a
          long one.

Waalisha Nerd dismisses herself and Amani is left alone.

Asa has a clear shot. She takes it.

The coiled water strikes, jets at Amani, but it misses, cracks the floor beside its target.

Amani is startled, checks above for the source of the attack. She sees Asa on the roof, but she is not alone.

ON THE ROOF

Buziba clutches her arm. She can't pull away.

                    AMANI
          Buziba, what is—

The water returns to Asa, strikes at Buziba. He disconnects to avoid the attack. He lunges at her, but the water catches him, flings him back and through the hole.

Asa bolts.

IN THE PRESIDENT'S OFFICE

> BUZIBA
> It is the Muzungu!

Buziba leaps out of the office and pursues.

EXT. KHARTOUM - CAPITAL - OUTSIDE GATE - EVENING

Kwesi attempts to hot-wire a TRUCK. The engine TURNS OVER.

> KWESI
> Yes!
>> (to Darren)
> Do you see her?

Darren kneels on the roof of a small building. He squints as he searches for Asa. He finds her.

> DARREN
> Yeah!

But she's in trouble. Buziba is on her tail. She needs help.

> DARREN
> Crap! Asa—JUMP!

She hears him. She leaps off the capital building, narrowly avoiding Buziba's swipe. She falls…

But the ground *shifts* into a metal, SPRING-LOADED PLATFORM. It breaks Asa's fall and launches her toward Darren. He catches her.

They hop off the roof and land on the truck's bed.

> DARREN
> Drive!

Kwesi floors it. They peel away.

Buziba is peeved. He growls as he reaches toward the truck…

I/E. KHARTOUM - DOWNTOWN - HOTWIRED TRUCK - CONTINUOUS

Kwesi swerves through abandoned vehicles as they flee.

> KWESI
> Where are we going now?

>   DARREN
>   As far as possible!

>   ASA
>   Look out!

A HOT COAL BARRICADE rises from the road. Kwesi swerves left onto a new street.

>   KWESI
>   Was that more coal?!

>   DARREN
>   He can Flux from that far away?

>   ASA
>   Another one!

Another coal barricade rises. Kwesi turns left again.

>   DARREN
>   Don't go in a circle!

>   KWESI
>   Would you like to drive?!

A third barricade. Kwesi turns right and speeds up.

They approach an intersection. This time a COAL WALL blocks off every exit.

>   DARREN
>   Don't stop!

Kwesi is uneasy but proceeds. Darren reaches for the wall…

>   DARREN
>   *CRAFTSMAN: RAMP!*

A STEEL INCLINE rises from the road, fixes itself atop the barricade. The truck drives up the ramp.

But a MIDAS SPEAR plunges into the ramp's apex, plants itself. The truck CRASHES into the spear and it barrels out of control. The passengers are ejected.

They slowly get up, try to keep moving. Soon they reach…

EXT. KHARTOUM - BRIDGE OVER THE NILE - CONTINUOUS

They approach a bridge that crosses over a quickly flowing Nile River.

                    ASA
          I can carry us if we jump in! Come—

GUNSHOTS spark on the bridge. The three retreat behind a
STEEL DOME Darren raises. It blocks more bullets.

Another MIDAS SPEAR falls from the sky, this one carrying
Amani. She lands beside the crashed truck as more Waalisha
Goons make it to the site.

                    AMANI
          Hold your fire!

The gunfire ceases.

                    AMANI
          I would have let you go free, but
          you are choosing to be an enemy!

                    DARREN
          You're the one making enemies.

                    AMANI
          You know that isn't true! We are
          the only thing the people of Sudan
          have that could end—

                    BUZIBA (O.S.)
          WHY ARE YOU HERE?!

Buziba finally arrives. He is Angrier. Confused. Indignant.

                    BUZIBA
          Muzungu!

Asa steps forward, as if to guard Darren.

                    ASA
          Because my husband was in trouble.
          Why else?

                    BUZIBA
          He must have something valuable. Or
          maybe your pride was so wounded
          that you came to avenge it. Yes…

                    KWESI
          Why does a wife need a reason to
          rescue a her lover?

                    BUZIBA
              (recognizes Kwesi)
          You… and you! Why?

                    KWESI
          Does a man really need a reason to
          help friends?

Buziba has trouble processing. This only makes him angrier.

Kwesi notices the Waalisha close in. He glances as Asa and
Darren.

                    KWESI
          You two should be ready to escape.
          I will stay and teach this Mjinga a
          lesson.

                    DARREN
          Without you—are you crazy?!

MEMORY FLASH: Kwesi gets down on one knee, presents a RING to
JINA. She hesitates…

                    KWESI
          Maybe I am.

Buziba calms himself, walks toward the trio.

                    BUZIBA
          Kenyan, you are just a dog to these
          foreigners. Leave their lap!

                    KWESI
          A dog, eh?

Kwesi raises his arms. The Waalisha take aim, Buziba braces.
Kwesi reflects for a beat, before a BALL of FIRE appears in
his hands.

                    KWESI
          What is so wrong with that?

He hurls the fireball. It misses all people, but hits the
crashed truck. The truck EXPLODES, knocks the Waalisha around
it off guard, disorients Buziba and Amani.

The flash blinds the Americans. Kwesi grabs them both.

                    KWESI
          We always knew I was the Mjinga!

Kwesi shoves them off the bridge. They plummet into the Nile
and get washed down the river.

Buziba notices. He rushes at Kwesi, but Kwesi is ready.

>   KWESI
>   Funny thing about dogs, Coal Man…

Kwesi raises his arm again. Around it, fire swirls until it forms a FLAMING BOOMERANG. It SIZZLES in the air as Kwesi grips it.

>   KWESI
>   They are loyal!

He flings it toward Buziba. He evades, but it sears multiple Goons as it flies by.

It's trajectory arcs toward Buziba again. He raises a COAL WALL to block, but then its trajectory shifts—changes direction completely. The boomerang targets more Goons, bounces between them. Panic ensues.

Buziba finds Kwesi, notices him controlling its path. Buziba rushes him.

But Kwesi throws a second boomerang. Buziba dances to evade, charges forward. Kwesi loses ground. He recalls both boomerangs and sends them at Buziba again.

Buziba jumps, twists impossibly, dodges the attack, makes it to Kwesi. He snatches Kwesi's face, and the boomerangs dissipate immediately, just before they hit Amani.

Buziba grips and Kwesi screams. Smoke pours from his mouth.

>   BUZIBA
>   Death is what you earned, and for
>   complete strangers! Is this what
>   you wanted? Was it worth it?

Kwesi claws to get free, tears streaming from the pain, but his body eases as his eyes drift upward.

MEMORY FLASH: Jina sees the sincerity in Kwesi's eyes, and the reservations in her own vanish. She takes the ring…

Buziba stares into Kwesi's eyes, demands an answer to his questions. Kwesi's eyes glaze over. His body goes limp as he peacefully fades. Buziba lets go and sees a small grin.

Buziba receives his answer. It leaves him confused.

>   FADE OUT.

                         END OF ACT THREE

ACT FOUR

FADE IN:

EXT. KHARTOUM - DOWN THE BLUE NILE - NIGHT

Asa and Darren wash ashore. They cough up water, get their
bearings. The Khartoum skyline is upstream.

                    ASA
          Idiot… why did he—AGH!

                    DARREN
          Babe…

                    ASA
          Why would he do that?! We need to
          help him! Let's go—

                    DARREN
          Asa!

Darren grabs her shoulder. They lock eyes for a beat,
confirming what they both already know. Kwesi is gone.

                    DARREN
          Come on. It's not safe here.

Asa takes one last look at the city before following Darren
into the desert.

EXT. KHARTOUM - CAPITAL - COURTYARD - NIGHT

Malick trails Muni as they rush through the busy courtyard.
Burned and injured Waalisha Goons seek medical attention.
Amani coordinates the efforts.

That's where Muni finds her.

                    AMANI
          Where were you?!

                    MUNI
          I was patrolling the city. What
          happened?

                    AMANI
          We were attacked. Darren escaped.

                    MUNI
          Attacked by whom?

                    BUZIBA
          The Muzungu.

Buziba studies Kwesi's corpse as if waiting for it to speak.

                    BUZIBA
          And a stranger.

                    MUNI
          You can't be serious. Three people
          did all this? Sudan's entire
          military barely inconvenienced us.

                    AMANI
          Enough, Muni! Where are our
          soldiers now?

                    MALICK
          They are posted around the city…

                    AMANI
          Call them back.
               (Muni protests)
          We cannot lose the capital after
          coming this far!

                    MUNI
          So we will sacrifice the city we
          claimed for our people?

                    AMANI
          It cannot be helped. We are
          stretched too thin as it is.

                    PHARAOH (O.S.)
          Then I suppose my timing could not
          have been better.

The Waalisha frantically search for the source of the voice.
The try every angle except…

                    BUZIBA
          Above.

They look up to see Pharaoh floating. Muni grabs his sword
and Amani summons a Midas Spear.

                    PHARAOH
               (descends)
          I mean no harm. I have only come to
          negotiate.

Pharaoh lands. Amani gets a better look at him.

                    AMANI
          I know your face, Osas Pharaoh. I
          remember the public statements you
          made about the Waalisha Khufu and
          the adversarial legislation you
          proposed. What do you want?

                    PHARAOH
          Your conquest today was all over
          the news. The media has no idea how
          a small rebel group could rout
          Sudan's forces.
                    (glances at Buziba)
          But when I saw footage of that
          brute summoning fire from a glowing
          stone, I developed a theory.

                    MUNI
          Just like a politician to
          acknowledge the downtrodden when it
          benefits him.

                    PHARAOH
          Perhaps, but I think this
          discussion benefits you as well.

Pharaoh pulls the Wind and Earth Shards from his pocket. All
present are amazed, including Buziba.

                    PHARAOH
          As you can imagine, obtaining these
          was not easy. So you can imagine
          how disappointed I was when I
          realized I cannot use either stone
          to their fullest capacity.

                    MUNI
          Why not?

                    PHARAOH
          It's a hunch. Either way, I'd feel
          much more comfortable if I owned
          the Fire Stone you currently have
          instead.
                    (Muni braces)
          Like I said, I'm here to negotiate.
          Here is my offer: I will give you
          these stones that control Wind and
          Earth, in exchange for yours.

ON THE ROOF

Anansi's Apparition watches. He is in shock.

                    ANANSI
          No…

ON THE GROUND

                    AMANI
          Why would you make such an
          obviously foolish trade?

                    PHARAOH
          The Waalisha has lofty goals and so
          do I. This trade would empower us
          both.

Amani hesitates. She looks at Buziba, who inconspicuously
notices Anansi.

                    BUZIBA
          Only a spectator…

                    MUNI
          A sure thing is better than a
          gamble. We will be fine.

                    AMANI
          Muni, give him the stone.

                    MUNI
          You cannot be serious!

                    AMANI
          I am deathly serious. Do it.

Muni relents and removes the Fire Shard from the gold belt.
Pharaoh grins, employs WIND to levitate his two shards.

They count to three and make the exchange. Muni holds the
Wind Shard, Amani the Earth Shard, and Pharaoh the Fire.

                    MUNI
              (to the Shard)
          This time, I won't let you go.

Pharaoh clutches his shard and ELECTRICITY builds around his
body. His smile becomes crazed.

                    PHARAOH
          That would be smart. Next time I
          won't be so diplomatic.

A massive black LIGHTNING BOLT descends on PHARAOH. He
vanishes with the thunderclap.

                    MALICK
               (to Buziba)
          Did you know that man?

                    BUZIBA
          No.

Amani inspects the Earth Shard in her hand, in awe.

                    AMANI
          He is a problem for another day.
          Right now, we have work to do.

ON THE ROOF

Anansi is disgusted by what he sees.

                    TANO (PRE-LAP)
          He did nothing?!

INT. ARJANA - QUEEN'S THRONE ROOM - NIGHT

Tano, Bia, and Queen Asase listen to Anansi's report.

                    TANO
          Three of the Shards were in the
          same location, and Buziba did not
          even attempt to collect them?

                    ANANSI
          That is correct. He practically
          gave both parties his blessing as
          they made the exchange. Buziba has
          defected from Arjana.

Queen Asase processes. The burden weighs on her shoulders.

                    TANO
          Buchu should have left him to die
          in Rwanda. It was a mistake to let
          him inside the kingdom.

                    ANANSI
          Do not imply Her Divinity has made
          a mistake in her presence.

                    TANO
          But she has! You have, Mother.

                    BIA
          Stop it, Tano, you are not helping.

                    TANO
I could have helped. That is my
duty, after all. Instead, Mother
left our fate to an orphaned
outsider and a trespassing Muzungu.

                    BIA
Anansi, what is Asa's status?

                    ANANSI
She successfully rescued her
husband, but Buziba interrupted her
mission to kill the Waalisha
leader. The Americans fled. I am
still locating them.

                    TANO
That makes two out of two outsiders
that have failed us.

                    QUEEN ASASE
Very well, Tano, what do you
propose we do?

                    TANO
Your Divinity, I will lead a small
team to take back each of the
Ophiuchus Shards. We will leave at
once!

                    BIA
The Americans are still alive.
Perhaps they could—

                    TANO
Bia, I admit you did well training
the Muzungu. If what Anansi said is
correct, her attack would have been
a success if not for Buziba.
However, there are too many factors
at play for us to take any more
risks. Besides, we do not know
where they are.

                    ANANSI
Found them.

                    QUEEN ASASE
     (beat)
Let me speak to them.

EXT. SUDAN DESERT - NIGHT

Fire CRACKLES from Asa's hand, ignites a tiny PYRE in a
makeshift pit. Asa takes a seat beside it.

Asa stares into it, blank. She retreats into the light.

> ASA
> I shouldn't have asked Kwesi for
> help… I should've come alone… then—

> DARREN
> Then we'd both be dead.

> ASA
> It's still my fault.

> DARREN
> He chose to help you. He chose to
> save our lives.

> ASA
> Yeah, he did.
> (beat)
> What do we do now?

Darren's expression also blanks. As he formulates a response,
the fire births an Apparition. Queen Asase appears.

> QUEEN ASASE
> Hello, Asa. And you must be Darren.

> DARREN
> Who're you?!

Asa yanks Darren down to a kneel, like her.

> ASA
> Be respectful. It's the Queen!

> DARREN
> Queen of what?

Darren examines Asase, the Arjanan wardrobe gives her away.
He bows his head.

> DARREN
> (to Asa)
> You actually found it?

> QUEEN ASASE
> Stand. No need for formalities.

The couple rises.

EXT. SUDAN DESERT - NIGHT

Fire CRACKLES from Asa's hand, ignites a tiny PYRE in a
makeshift pit. Asa takes a seat beside it.

Asa stares into it, blank. She retreats into the light.

                    ASA
          I shouldn't have asked Kwesi for
          help… I should've come alone… then—

                    DARREN
          Then we'd both be dead.

                    ASA
          It's still my fault.

                    DARREN
          He chose to help you. He chose to
          save our lives.

                    ASA
          Yeah, he did.
               (beat)
          What do we do now?

Darren's expression also blanks. As he formulates a response,
the fire births an Apparition. Queen Asase appears.

                    QUEEN ASASE
          Hello, Asa. And you must be Darren.

                    DARREN
          Who're you?!

Asa yanks Darren down to a kneel, like her.

                    ASA
          Be respectful. It's the Queen!

                    DARREN
          Queen of what?

Darren examines Asase, the Arjanan wardrobe gives her away.
He bows his head.

                    DARREN
               (to Asa)
          You actually found it?

                    QUEEN ASASE
          Stand. No need for formalities.

The couple rises.

> ASA
> Your Divinity, I'm so sorry, I
> tried to take out their leader—

> QUEEN ASASE
> I know. Anansi saw the whole thing.

> ASA
> I can still do it! Just give me
> more time and I—

> QUEEN ASASE
> Your mission is no longer to
> assassinate Amani Suleyman. You're
> only assignment is to return home.

> ASA
> Huh?

INT. ARJANA - QUEEN'S THRONE ROOM - NIGHT

Tano and Bia listen to the Queen's address. She sits on her throne, while Anansi kneels beside her, holds her hand.

> QUEEN ASASE
> Osas Pharaoh has acquired the Wind
> and Earth Shards and traded them
> for the Fire Shard in the
> Waalisha's possession. Both parties
> are now deadlier than they were
> before. The restoration of the
> Ophiuchus Stone may be imminent.

EXT. SUDAN DESERT - NIGHT

The couple is horrified.

> QUEEN ASASE
> Arjana will act to prevent this at
> all costs, but if we fail, the
> resulting conflict could endanger
> the entire continent.

> ASA
> We can help! We've fought the
> Waalisha multiple times! We can—

> QUEEN ASASE
> No. We do not even know what the
> Waalisha's next move will be. We
> cannot guarantee your safety.

                    DARREN
          Cairo…
               (Asase waits for more)
          Amani mentioned wanting to use the
          Giza pyramids like a power plant.
          She thinks they're some old
          Atlantean technology. I think
          she'll go there next.

                    QUEEN ASASE
               (alarmed; nods)
          It was naive of me to allow you
          into this conflict. This is a
          problem created by Arjana and we
          will solve it. You both have served
          us generously. We will not allow
          you to get caught up in the
          consequences of our negligence.

                    ASA
          We can't just leave when so many
          people are in danger! Darren and I
          will handle it with you, right hun?

Darren appears drained, but oddly at peace.

                    DARREN
          Ma'am, thank you for your concern.
          We will do as you ask… and go home.

                    ASA
          Darren!

Queen Asase nods, smiles. Her burden gets a little lighter.

                    QUEEN ASASE
          Thank you. Farewell, Davenports.

The Apparition fades away. The couple is alone again. Asa
turns to Darren, demands an explanation. Darren's face wears
exhaustion and indifference.

                    DARREN
          Asa, we've been here long enough.
          Let's go home.

                              FADE TO BLACK.

                    END OF SHOW

CIGNUS STUDIO

110

AFROFANTASY

SCREENPLAY BY CHANNING CHEA

AFROFANTASY

110 - "The Pyramidion"

Written by

Channing Chea

AFROFANTASY

"THE PYRAMIDION"

ACT ONE

FADE IN:

EXT. SUDAN DESERT - NIGHT

A CAMPFIRE burns, the only natural illumination in the
desert. KHARTOUM's city lights pollute the rest of the
darkness in the distance.

MINI PYRAMIDS sprinkle the desert void like pimples on flesh.
The only living creatures in sight are DARREN and ASA.
Darren's eyes drift down, while Asa's attempt to wrangle his
attention. He is weary. She is befuddled.

                    ASA
          What did you say?

                    DARREN
          We don't have to do this anymore.
          Let's go home…

                    ASA
          You really just… wanna leave? Just
          like that?

Darren perks up, as if to convince himself.

                    DARREN
          We've had enough adventures, right?
          We went through a lot; saw a lot.
          We checked off our bucket lists a
          dozen times over! That's why we
          came here, right—to see and learn
          new things?

                    ASA
          No… that's—

                    DARREN
          They've probably missed me at work.
          I have plenty of design ideas to
          show them. I can help someone else
          finish the project so—

                    ASA
          That's not why we came here!!!

Darren freezes, as if exposed.

187

MEMORY FLASH: LULA MAE lies on her death bed, her eyes fade.

                    ASA
          I know you didn't forget! You're
          really gonna pretend like you don't
          know why you traveled halfway
          across the world?!

Anguish fills Darren's face; a look similar to Lula Mae's.

                    DARREN
          I didn't forget…

                    ASA
          So… did you get what you came here
          for?

                    DARREN
          No.

                    ASA
          Then what's your deal?

                    DARREN
          I'm tired, Asa, and I was wrong. I
          can't get what I came here for, so
          there's no point.
               (beat)
          It was pointless to come here.

                    ASA
          You're really gonna give up? You
          pushed so hard, fought so many
          people—*helped* so many people, and
          after all that you're just going
          home?

                    DARREN
          That's right.

                    ASA
          WHY?!

                    DARREN
          Because none of this is worth it!
          I'm tired of seeing all this death
          over something that doesn't matter!
          It's been the same thing ever since
          we got here. It's all too much…

Darren squats as the weight falls on his shoulders. It's all
he can do to stay upright.

> DARREN
> I saw innocent people die. I saw
> guilty people die. People who were
> victims became killers and created
> more victims… and for what? All
> these people with the same skin,
> finding ways to hate each other
> because someone decided they were
> different. But I can't tell them
> apart. They all look the same to
> me; they look like me. It's stupid.
> Maybe it's always been stupid, and
> I was too busy chasing a fantasy to
> notice that none of this matters.
> I was so excited that I became a
> human 3-D printer that I didn't
> realize I was wasting my time. I
> don't have a traceable lineage. It
> got wiped out by centuries of
> violence, before and after the
> slave trade. I don't have a reason
> to be here anymore. So please, Asa,
> let's just go home.

Darren finds strength to stand. He walks away, passes Asa.

> ASA
> Fine, then go. I'm staying.

> DARREN
> What?

> ASA
> I didn't get what I came for
> either, but I'm close. I'm so
> close, but if I run away now, I'll
> never get to make things right.

> DARREN
> Asa… babe, just stop it, already.

> ASA
> I need to know who I am, too. I
> just wanna prove I'm better than
> who everyone thinks I am.

Darren looks his wife over. He finally understands.

> DARREN
> Staying here won't make you a
> better person. I don't even know
> why you care.

                    ASA
          'Cause I'm tired of everyone
          thinking so little of me because of
          stuff I didn't do! No one ever
          looks at me and sees me! They just
          see their own trauma. Pharaoh did.
          Your grandma, too.

                    DARREN
          Why do you care what she thinks?

                    ASA
          Because you do.

                    DARREN
          But she didn't marry you.

                    ASA
          Wha…

                    DARREN
          Pharaoh didn't marry you; Buziba
          didn't either. I did.

                    ASA
          But it still hurts…

                    DARREN
          I love you because I know you, Asa.
          So please take my word for it when
          I say I know who you are, and you
          are good.

Darren pulls her in, embraces her. Asa's eyes fill with
tears, and she lets them fall. He pulls away, takes her hand.

                    DARREN
          There, now you've gotten what you
          came for. Now we can go.

He turns, scoops dirt with his power, throws it on the flame.

                    ASA
          Ya know, I wish you would've just
          taken my word for it, too. I
          could've told you things about
          yourself whenever.

                    DARREN
          Yeah? I'm listening.

He throws more dirt on the flame, but it triggers—

MEMORY FLASH: The Earth swallows LOLIE's face as she sinks into the ground.

The image haunts him. He shakes his head.

                    ASA
          You're kind.

Darren gazes at the stars. He recalls Lolie pointing to a satellite in the sky. Asa notices the TOY ROCKET dangling from his neck. She touches it.

                    ASA
          You're creative.

The memory hurts. He must escape. Darren walks away, runs into a mini pyramid beside them. He gazes at it… recalls the electric flash from the model pyramid in Amani's lab.

                    ASA
          You're smart.

Darren shakes the idea from his head, turns around again.

                    ASA
          You're always thinking ahead.

                    DARREN
          No, we were told to leave. That's
          what we should do.

                    ASA
          And you also have a hard head.

Darren wrestles with his thoughts, revisits images we don't see.

                    DARREN
          This stuff isn't our fault… it's
          not our responsibility to fix. We
          tried to fix enough.

                    ASA
          Maybe… but that never stopped us
          before.

Eventually, he calms down, wipes the conflict from his face to leave nothing but resolve.

                    ASA
          So, what do you want to do?

EXT. DARFUR VILLAGE - NIGHT, FLASHBACK

DARFURIAN VILLAGERS gather around a BONFIRE—a festive night.

Among the many families is a familiar one. FATHER SULEYMAN
sits with CHILD MUNI, while MOTHER SULEYMAN holds BABY
JOSEPH. CHILD AMANI plays with the baby.

The bonfire grows weak, Child Amani notices. She sets off for
firewood. Child Muni assists.

The two gather sticks, but Muni gathers more. They both start
for the fire, but Child Amani trips, drops her wood. Child
Muni walks over, offers a hand to help her up, but she
doesn't acknowledge him. She's already up.

She collects her wood and continues, drops it in the fire.

Child Muni is emasculated. His father notices, and he walks
over to him.

> FATHER SULEYMAN
> She is a strong one, but you will
> be stronger still.
>> (points to Baby Joseph)
> You will lead them both one day
> when you are big and strong.

Child Muni's eyes are hopeful. His father smiles back.

> FATHER SULEYMAN
> That's what big brothers do…

END FLASHBACK.

I/E. CARAVAN BUS - ROAD TO CAIRO - DAY

MUNI opens his eyes. Sunlight bleeds through the window,
blinds him into consciousness.

> FATHER SULEYMAN (V.O.)
> They lead.

The bus stops abruptly. Muni moves to the front, sees AMANI
already gazing through the windshield.

Dozens of EGYPTIAN TANKS and VEHICLES barricade the road,
halts the Waalisha CARAVAN of commandeered Sudanese vehicles.

> AMANI
> We were expected.

EGYPTIAN SOLDIER barks orders via MEGAPHONE into deaf ears.

>   MUNI
>   We were underestimated.

Muni grabs his SHOTEL. A GOLD SPHERE covers the pommel, glows WHITE from the Wind Shard within.

>   MUNI
>   Never again.

Muni exits the bus, walks toward enemy lines. WIND swirls around him, envelops his sword. The clouds themselves contort at his presence. He prepares to swing…

The Egyptian military prepares to rain fire upon them, then—

GOLDEN OBELISKS erupt from the earth. They skewer the tanks, elevate the vehicles, eviscerate the soldiers' bodies. The landscape itself shifts to a field of sky-scraping spires.

The Earth Shard fixed into Amani's gold belt dims, powers down. She calls out from the bus.

>   AMANI
>   We don't have time to waste. Let's
>   get going.

Muni powers down as well, but emasculation haunts him. He steps back onto the bus.

The gold obelisks open, clear space for the caravan to pass through. They proceed.

As they drive, MALICK gazes at the obelisks as blood drips down the lustrous metal. The carnage gives him pause.

EXT. EGYPTIAN DESERT - ROAD TO CAIRO - DAY

The sun shifts in the sky. Time has passed, but the tracks of the caravan remain, winding through the golden obelisks.

A BLUE BLUR passes—hardly perceptible—and kicks up the sand. It follows the trail to Cairo.

EXT. CAIRO - DOWNTOWN - DAY

LOCAL EGYPTIANS bustle through sidewalks, scramble for nearby apartments and shelters. They carry whatever food and belongings they can. SIRENS BLARE.

The military hogs the roads. TANKS and HUMVEES cruise through as soldiers shepherd Locals into their homes.

Standing on one of the balconies is PHARAOH. He observes the chaos. He looks up to see FIGHTER JETS soar overhead. They fly past the GIZA PLATEAU.

                    PHARAOH
          They are moving quickly.

EXT. GIZA PLATEAU - DAY

The fighter jets fly in formation around the plateau. On the ground, the Egyptian MILITARY barricades the entire plateau with soldiers and vehicles. The palisade of military might only widens as more units continue to pour in from the city.

EGYPTIAN GENERAL climbs an erected WATCHTOWER. He peers into the desert with BINOCULARS. A long caravan of Sudanese vehicles kicks up sand as it slithers closer.

                    EGYPTIAN GENERAL
          At-the-ready!

The soldiers take aim.

I/E. GIZA PLATEAU - CARAVAN BUS - CONTINUOUS

Amani keeps her eyes on the road. So does Muni.

                    AMANI
          Whenever you are ready.

A grin cracks Muni's face as he shouts into a RADIO.

                    MUNI
          NOW!

EXT. GIZA PLATEAU - CONTINUOUS

EXPLOSIONS catch the General's ear, but they are from behind him. He turns toward Cairo. What he sees floors him.

EXT. CAIRO - DOWNTOWN - CONTINUOUS

Locals flee from buildings that burst into FLAMES. The earth rumbles as BOOMs fill the air and winds GUST on queue. As locals pour into the street, they are chased by WAALISHA FLUXERS. Some of them are teens. Some are young adults. All of them have Umoya.

Soldiers in the city rush to respond, but they are felled by the Fluxers. Chaos breaks out.

EXT. GIZA PLATEAU - CONTINUOUS

Soldiers in the barricade break away, rush toward the city.

> EGYPTIAN GENERAL
> Do not break ranks! Let the
> militia—

A SHADOW falls over the General as something blots the sun.
He looks up to see a GOLD OBELISK descend…

Several obelisks crash into the ranks of the military,
skewering vehicles, crushing soldiers and the General. They
scatter like ants.

But some hold their ground. They take aim, unload their
weapon into the Waalisha forces. They do not stop until a
massive WIND SHEAR rips through swathes of soldiers. Their
bodies fall to pieces.

Muni laughs, withdraws his sword, then points to his enemies.

> MUNI
> Go! Take back the freedom that was
> stolen from us!

Waalisha Fighters charge—on tanks, on foot, on purpose. They
almost reach the Egyptians before—

MISSILES rain from above, whistling as they fall. Waalisha
are caught in the blast, but Amani raises giant GOLDEN WALLS
to shield her people.

Fighter jets pass overhead. They circle back.

> MUNI
> Go on! I will handle them…

Muni raises his sword and the pommel gleams. A TORNADO
swallows him and he is gone…

EXT. GIZA PLATEAU - A THOUSAND FEET UP - CONTINUOUS

PILOT A looks out the window, notices a tornado ascending. It
cuts him off.

The jets climb, attempt to escape. Some do, but Pilot A
doesn't. The tornado sucks the jet into a sandstorm. Flames
and flashes from within signal its destruction.

The fleet doubles back. They fire endlessly into the tornado.

The funnel cloud vanishes as the jets pass. The Pilots search for Muni, but he finds them first. He appears on PILOT B's wing.

He employs a VANGUARD SHEAR to slash away the wing. The jet plummets. He takes out the remaining jets, and they leave black CONTRAILS as they fall.

EXT. GIZA PLATEAU - CONTINUOUS

Muni returns to the ground. His victory galvanizes the Waalisha. Earth Fluxers block bullets with earthen walls and launch boulders into the enemy. Wind Fluxers toss soldiers around, Fire Fluxers burn them and their vehicles, and Water Fluxers drown who's left.

BUZIBA steps from the caravan bus, watches Muni and Amani lead the charge through Giza. They rout and destroy all they see. The destruction is familiar.

MEMORY FLASH: TUTSI's flee as they are slaughtered by HUTU MILITIAs in Rwanda. The bloodshed is one-sided.

                    BUZIBA
          Is this different?
               (beat; introspective)
          Is this… better?

I/E. CHARTERED CESSNA - A MILE UP - DAY

Darren and Asa observe the landscape from a CESSNA SKYHAWK. The Giza Plateau has become a broken battlefield. PLUMES of smoke climb to meet the clouds.

CESSNA PILOT scans for a place to land.

                    ASA
          No… are we too late?

Darren looks at the Great Pyramid. It is untouched.

                    DARREN
          Not yet…

INT. CAIRO - DOWNTOWN CAFE - DAY

Blood drenches the floor of a cafe, spilled from the bodies of Locals who could not escape the gunfire of the Waalisha.

BLACK ELECTRICITY arcs off the bodies of two WAALISHA FLUXERS, who could not escape the lightning of Pharaoh. They join their victims on the floor.

Pharaoh peers out the window, gazes at the pyramids.

The streets have calmed as most chaos has passed. He leaves the cafe and starts for the Giza Plateau.

EXT. GIZA PLATEAU - EXECUTION TRENCH - DAY

A dozen GUNSHOTS fire in unison. Their echoes drown out the sound of falling bodies.

Defeated EGYPTIAN SOLDIERS are immobilized in a wide trench. MOUNDS of DIRT clasp their limbs. They watch as their comrades' bodies are dragged away by Waalisha.

Muni reloads a RIFLE, hands it to Malick.

> MUNI
> Just like that.

Malick is horrified. He almost forgets to take the gun.

> MUNI
> (to everyone around)
> Everyone fires at Malick's command.

The Waalisha reload. They wait for their signal. Muni grabs his sword. The pommel glows as wind levitates him.

> MALICK
> Sir, they're beaten… and unarmed.
> Can't we just show them mercy?

> MUNI
> (frowns)
> No such thing.

Muni flies off into the plateau.

All eyes are on Malick. He clutches the rifle, takes aim.

> MALICK
> Ready!

The Waalisha aim. The rifle trembles. So do the Egyptians. Malick closes his eyes.

> MALICK
> Fire!

Bullets fly—then stop. Waalisha gasp. Malick opens his eyes.

A wide MUD WALL covers the Egyptians. The Waalisha search for the culprits. They find no one, until…

The mud transforms from a wall to a WAVE. It swallows the Waalisha gunmen and hardens, locks them in place. Now the culprits are visible.

Darren and Asa stand together, locking fingers with one hand and controlling the mud with their other. They release each other and the remaining mud subsides.

                    DARREN
          I thought you were better than
          this, Malick.

Malick drops his head.

                    ASA
          Darren, the hostages.

Darren stamps the ground and the dirt mounds recede. The Egyptians are released.

                    ASA
          Get as far from here as you can!
          Things are only gonna get crazier.

They grab the rifles they can find and flee. The only ones left are the trapped Waalisha and the Americans.

                    MALICK
          Amani said you betrayed us.

                    DARREN
          I was never on your side. I just
          didn't want you idiots to get
          massacred. Look where that got us.

                    ASA
          Where are the Suleymans?

                    MALICK
          Going to the Great Pyramid. She's
          going to restore—

                    DARREN
          I know.
               (gazes at pyramid)
          That won't turn out the way she
          thinks…

Darren shoots a stern look toward Malick, then he stomps. The dirt around him falls away. He is free.

                    DARREN
          Don't ever let me catch you in the
          Waalisha again. Got it?
               (Malick is incredulous)
          Maybe there is such a thing as
          mercy.

Tears of gratitude fall. Malick nods his farewell to the couple and runs off. The remaining Waalisha grumble angrily.

                    ASA
          What about the others?

                    DARREN
          I doubt they'll be as reasonable.

                    ASA
          Probably not. Welp… are you ready?

                    DARREN
               (nervous)
          I don't know…

                    ASA
               (takes Darren's hand)
          It's okay, I believe in you.

                    DARREN
          I believe in you, too.

                    ASA
          Then what else could we need?

Her words earn a full smile from Darren.

                    DARREN
          I guess you're right. Let's go.

The couple starts for the pyramid.

EXT. GIZA PLATEAU - PANORAMIC POINT - DAY

Hundreds of Waalisha Fluxers and Gunmen regroup. They move the enemy's fallen and heal their own. Amani directs available hands to assist where needed. Buziba observes.

Muni floats down, lands near Amani when a coughing man gets his attention. DYING WAALISHA, 30s, is bloodied and on his last leg. He is cradled in another's arms as he calls out to no one and everyone.

                    DYING WAALISHA
          Did I do it?! I cannot go until I
          am done!

Amani starts for the man, but Muni grabs her shoulder. He
walks to the man instead. Silence befalls all present.

                    DYING WAALISHA
               (sees Muni)
          Sir, help me up so I can keep
          working. They won't be able to stop
          until it is all done. Please—

Muni gently holds him down.

                    MUNI
          The hard work has been done. We can
          finish what's left ourselves
          because of you… You can rest now.

This calms him. He gazes through tears into the ether. Muni
takes his bloodied hand.

                    DYING WAALISHA
          Will *they* be able to rest now?

                    MUNI
          They received their rest the moment
          you buried them—your first family
          and your new one. Now, you have
          earned yours as well.

Dying Waalisha accepts this. He allows his head to fall.

                    DYING WAALISHA
          The family grows…

                    MUNI
          It does.

The man fades. Muni releases his hand and he his carried
away. Muni is solemn as he turns away and sees Amani's face.

She smiles at him with an acknowledgment we have not seen
before. Muni has not seen it either.

                    BUZIBA
               (to Amani)
          What is your plan now?

                    MUNI
          The Egyptians will send
          reinforcements. We will handle them
          when they come.

                    AMANI
          And in the meantime, I will do what
          I came here for. What about you?

                    BUZIBA
          I think I will have the best view
          if I join you.

                    AMANI
               (nods)
          Muni, I don't know how long it will
          take to restore the pyramid, so I
          am counting on you to give me time.

                    MUNI
          I know. Your elder brother will not
          let you down.

Amani smiles and the Earth Shard glows. A GOLD SPIRE with
PEGS forms from the sand below them. Amani and Buziba grab a
peg, and the spire launches toward the Great Pyramid.

                    MUNI
               (to the Waalisha)
          We do not have time to lose. Get
          ready for the next wave!

EXT. GIZA PLATEAU - GREAT PYRAMID - TOP - DAY

The gold spire reverts to sand as it approaches the pyramid,
and Amani and Buziba land on the pyramid's apex.

                    AMANI
          Have you seen this work before?

                    BUZIBA
          Arjana does use similar technology.
          I don't understand how it works, so
          I cannot guarantee that this will.

                    AMANI
          Then hopefully I can surprise you.

Amani raises her arms and the Earth Shard GLOWS. In response,
TONS of SAND rises around the necropolis and orbits the
pyramid. It bends to Amani's command.

                    AMANI
          For the first time in thousands of
          years, the world will see the Great
          Pyramid in its full glory. Let's
          make it a show.

                    DARREN (O.S.)
          WAIT!

The distant shout gets Amani's attention. She moves the sand
to search for the source. She sees two specks on the ground.

EXT. GIZA PLATEAU - NECROPOLIS - CONTINUOUS

Darren and Asa run through the necropolis, approach the
pyramid. Darren pulls earth from the ground, forms it into a
GIANT METAL MEGAPHONE and shouts into it.

                    DARREN
          Amani! I know what you're trying
          but it won't work—not like you
          think it will! It's too dangerous!

                                        INTERCUT:

                    AMANI
          Darren?!

                    BUZIBA
          The Muzungu?!

                    DARREN
          The pyramid *will* produce
          electricity, but there's nowhere
          for all that energy to go! If you
          do this, you'll just create a power
          plant that's outta control!

Muni hears Darren's voice and locates him. He launches
himself with a GUST of wind.

                    AMANI
          I already told you how I will
          harness the energy. Why come all
          this way to stop me?

                    DARREN
          It's too much! It's not the sa—

Muni CRASHES into the necropolis, blasts Asa and Darren back.

They tumble as Muni prepares a swing. His sword glows as he
strikes at Darren, but Asa shoves them both out the way.
Muni's strike creates a hundred-foot scar on the earth.

                    MUNI
          This is the day your luck expires!

                         ASA
              Muni, we don't want to fight! Tell
              your sister to stop so no one—

Another horizontal swing. Darren's dirt pillars eject the two
from the strike's path. Muni follows with a typhoon, blowing
the Americans a couple hundred feet back.

The couple tumbles. As they recover, bullets WHIZ by them.
Darren raises a STEEL DOME to block. Asa uses WATER to block
FIREBALLS that rain from another angle. They're successful
until Muni's Vanguard Shear hits Darren's dome and knocks the
couple back again.

Amani shakes her head in pity. She turns her attention to the
sand. It clumps, coalesces, transforms into LIMESTONE and
takes the shape of a SURFACE TILE. The first tile plants
itself at the pyramid's base, and others follow it. They wrap
the monolith one tile at a time.

Meanwhile, the Americans are dazed. The Waalisha Fluxers
close in. Muni closes in.

Muni prepares a vertical swing. His sword extends with 100
feet of condensed WIND. The blade cuts the air itself.

                         MUNI
                    (to himself)
              Now you can rest too, Joseph.

He brings his sword down.

But a translucent FORCEFIELD blocks the blade! It nearly
cracks before a colossal GEYSER of water gushes from below,
disperses the blade.

Muni and the Waalisha are pushed back by the dispersing
blast. As sand, water, and wind settles, three individuals
come into view.

TAU, KHADIJA, and BIA stand around the Americans.

                         BIA
              You Americans really don't like
              following orders.

                         TAU
              Believe me, Princess, that is
              nothing new.

                                        FADE OUT.

                    <u>END OF ACT ONE</u>

<u>ACT TWO</u>

FADE IN:

EXT. GIZA PLATEAU - GREAT PYRAMID - TOP - DAY

Amani is distracted. Buziba peers below, suspicious.

                    AMANI
          What is happening down there?

EXT. GIZA PLATEAU - NECROPOLIS - DAY

Water pools as sand and debris cloud the area. Muni searches
for his opponents as the Waalisha regroup.

Meanwhile, Tau helps up Darren and Asa.

                    KHADIJA
          Pardon our delay. We came as soon
          as we received word.

                    ASA
          How did you—?

                    BIA
          When we figured out the Waalisha's
          plan, Mother dispatched Tano and a
          small platoon. They will arrive
          soon, but I went on ahead.

                    TAU
          I plan to have this packaged-up
          before they even get here!
               (eyes metal dome)
          Is that… your Soul Flux?

                    DARREN
          Yeah. It's kept me alive 'til now.

                    TAU
          What?! It only took you a month to
          achieve yours?!

                    ASA
               (to Khadija)
          But if you're here, who's guarding
          the Water Shard?

Khadija smiles, pulls the WATER SHARD from her pocket.

                    KHADIJA
          What use is a guardian that does
          not guard?

                    BIA
          I had a similar thought.

She looks at the Great Pyramid's apex and glares at Buziba.

EXT. GIZA PLATEAU - GREAT PYRAMID - TOP - DAY

Dust clears, allows Buziba to peer through the sand. He sees
Bia glare at him. His heart drops, but he steels himself.

EXT. GIZA PLATEAU - NECROPOLIS - DAY

Muni begins to see his targets. He wrangles his troops.

Asa looks at the water that begins to flood the necropolis.

                    ASA
          Where'd all this water come from?

                    DARREN
          There's an ancient aquifer beneath
          the pyramid.

                    BIA
          Focus! We have a traitor to kill.

Waalisha Fluxers step into view. Some with guns in hand,
others armed with their Fluxes.

                    MUNI
          The little shepherd boy is back!
          Looks like I'll get to bury all of
          my enemies in a single week.

A figure plummets from the pyramid. A COAL PILLAR erupts from
below, catches the figure. It's Buziba.

                    BUZIBA
          Why am I not surprised to see you
          here, Tau?

                    TAU
          You… helping outsiders? After all
          you did to me—my family—this is
          what you're doing?!

                    BUZIBA
          My duty bound me to violent tasks,
          but I am not bound to that duty
          anymore.

                    BIA
          I cannot wait to hear the story of
          your treachery. We can discuss it
          over your extended execution.

                    BUZIBA
          I intend to see this path through
          to the end, wherever it goes.
               (points to Asa)
          But first, I have one more Curse to
          deliver.

                    ASA
          I was hoping you'd say that!

                    MUNI
          So these are the Arjanans, eh?
          Then, let's make a sport of it!

Muni calls to the Waalisha; points with his sword.

                    MUNI
          50 points to whoever kills the
          shepherd; another 50 for the old
          hag. Capture that "Princess" and
          you can take her as a wife! 100
          points to kill the Muzungu, and if
          you decapitate Darren… you win!

There's laughter among the Waalisha. GREEDY FLUXER steps
forward, eyes Bia.

                    GREEDY FLUXER
          May I go first, Captain?

                    MUNI
          Be my guest.

The Waalisha cheer him on as he steps forward. Bia hardly
acknowledges him.

Greedy Fluxer lifts water by his feet. It squashes as if
ready to pounce Bia. She doesn't move.

The water strikes but halts mid-air. Bia waves and the water
returns to Greedy Fluxer. It coils around him, binds him. He
panics.

Bia twirls her finger and the water transmutes into a green ACID. It spins, melts, EVISCERATES the man instantly.

His unrecognizable remains spill onto the wet sand. All are horrified, but Bia doesn't bat an eye.

                    MUNI
          Kill them!

Every Waalisha launches attacks of either BULLETS or FLUXES.

The Water Shard GLOWS, and all the water around them gathers to form a SPINNING WALL to protect them.

                    ASA
          Did you need to be so harsh?

                    BIA
          He is fortunate I made it quick.

The aquatic wall is bombarded with FLUXES, but it holds.

                    KHADIJA
          Excuse my haste, Your Divinity, but
          we need a plan.

OUTSIDE THE AQUATIC WALL:

Waalisha Fluxers spit FIRE, throw BOULDERS, blast WIND into the towering defenses to no avail.

                    MUNI
          Do not let up! Make them all
          suffer!

Buziba watches from atop his pillar. He notices someone escape from behind the wall. Asa sprints away from the field.

She looks back, sees Buziba, dares him to follow.

He takes the bait. He leaps from the pillar and pursues her.

                    MUNI
               (notices)
          Where is he going?

The aquatic wall twists, expands. It pushes the Waalisha away, halts their assault. It also spits Darren out. He sprints to the pyramid. The Water Shard glows in his pocket.

Muni spots Darren, prepares to swing, but his strike is interrupted by the BEAMFORM extending from Khadija's cane.

>   KHADIJA
>   Pardon, dear, but you still have
>   business here.

Bia watches Darren run away with the Water Shard.

>   BIA
>   Are you two sure we can trust him?

>   TAU
>   Wouldn't be the first time!

>   KHADIJA
>   Her Divinity certainly trusts Asa.

>   BIA
>   She can take care of herself.

EXT. GIZA PLATEAU - PYRAMID OF MENKAURE - TOP - CONTINUOUS

ANANSI stands atop the Menkaure Pyramid and gazes at the
battlefield. He speaks to no one present.

>   ANANSI
>   Yes, I see them all. The battle is
>   about to begin.

INT. ARJANA - SPECTRUM CHAMBER - DAY, FLASHBACK

Asa pushes water at Bia like a JET STREAM. Bia blocks with
her hand, studies Asa as she struggles.

WIND and FIRE attempt to merge with the stream, but no Soul
Flux appears. The stream only weakens.

Asa pushes harder, shouting as she forces a new effect to
emerge… nothing happens. She grows exhausted and drops to her
knees. Bia drops her guard, walks over.

>   ASA
>   How do you do it? How did Darren do
>   it? We've been at this for weeks
>   and I still can't get it!

>   BIA
>   Everyone's awakening is different.
>   In truth, there is less skill
>   involved than people think.

>   ASA
>   I need to get better! Be honest… do
>   you think I can get good enough?

Bia studies Asa as a depression falls over her.

                    BIA
          It may not be about getting better.

END FLASHBACK.

EXT. GIZA PLATEAU - THE SPHINX - DAY

Asa jumps into the impressed yard of the SPHINX. She lands in
front of it, splashes as water from the flooding necropolis
pools into the area. The base of the monument is submerged.

                    BIA (V.O.)
          Maybe it comes from already being
          good enough.

Buziba arrives. He stands on the Sphinx's head, looks down on
Asa. She meets his gaze. It peeves him.

                    BUZIBA
          I do not see anyone to help you.
          Are you dumb enough to think you
          can fell me by yourself?

                    ASA
          If I can't, all those days in the
          Spectrum Chamber would've been a
          major waste of time!

                    BUZIBA
             (beat; contemplates)
          I was planning on executing you and
          your pet husband, but if you accept
          this offer, I will let him live and
          only kill you.

                    ASA
          That sounds like a bad deal.

                    BUZIBA
          Rescind your love for him, and
          admit it was false all along.
             (beat; Asa is shocked)
          There is no one around but the two
          of us. You can speak the truth
          without anyone else hearing—

                    ASA
          Weird… Bia told me you were smart,
          but you've gotta be pretty stupid
          if you think I'd *ever* do that.

                    BUZIBA
          You can drop the facade. You will
          earn my respect if you tell the
          truth before you face your death.

                    ASA
               (laughs)
          Wanna know something? There's only
          one person's respect I need, and
          it's not yours.

                    BUZIBA
          Then I will tell him—

                    ASA
          And it's not Darren's either.

Water WHIRLS at Asa's feet. Waves rise and circle her.

                    ASA
          And by the way, you're gonna regret
          calling him a pet.

EXT. GIZA PLATEAU - NECROPOLIS - DAY

Bia's ACID WATER catches, melts bullets that fly at the
Arjanan trio. BOULDERS that hurdle toward them are sliced by
Khadija's cane. FIRE and water are halted by Tau's SKY-BLOCK.

The Waalisha Fluxers are sloppy but not uncoordinated.

Bia's eyes are pulled toward Muni, who stays back.

                    BIA
          Why isn't the one with the Wind
          Shard fighting?

                    TAU
          I'm not complaining…

                    KHADIJA
          Waiting for an opportune moment?

Muni shouts and the Waalisha launch a coordinated strike. The
earth below the trio rumbles, erupts into spikes. They avoid
by jumping upward.

The Waalisha summon wind to blow them away. But Tau summons a
PLATFORM—an invisible wall to provide footing in the air.

Muni's sword glows. He prepares to launch an attack, but
Khadija's BEAMFORM extends, forms a long spear, knocks the
sword from Muni's hand.

The wind stops, and the Arjanans return to the ground. Bia creates space by throwing acid over the nearby enemies. Screaming ensues. Muni recovers his sword.

> BIA
> The one with the Shard is coordinating their attacks. We need to separate them. You two go and retrieve the Shard.

> TAU
> Why us?!

> BIA
> You both are Aerofluxers. Your skills will allow you to counter him. You'll also be most adept at using the Shard after securing it.

> KHADIJA
> Will Her Divinity be fine alone?

Bia raises her hand toward the Waalisha and they flinch.

> BIA
> I am not the one you should worry about.

> KHADIJA
> As you wish. Tau, shall we?

Muni growls. He summons another HUNDRED-FOOT WIND BLADE.

> MUNI
> Think you have time to chat?!

He swings horizontally, and the trio jumps to evade.

Khadija's Beamform shifts into a pole, and she vaults toward Muni. The pole shifts mid-air into a blade. She downswings.

Muni blocks, but it leaves him open. Tau swoops through like a missile, punches Muni in the gut. Muni goes flying away from this section of the battlefield. Khadija and Tau follow.

The Waalisha are shocked, but coalescing water wrangles their attention back to Bia.

> BIA
> What's wrong? I thought we were still playing a game.

EXT. GIZA PLATEAU - NORTHERN NECROPOLIS - CONTINUOUS

Muni recovers airborne by flying. Tau leaps into the air, kicks off of multiple Sky-Blocks until he closes in on Muni.

Muni catches Tau with a GUST and launches him back toward the ground. He summons a massive VANGUARD SHEAR and shoots it toward Khadija and Tau. They evade it, but it leaves another scar on the earth.

Dust covers the ground, cloaks Tau and Khadija. Muni attempts to fly back to the battlefield, but he runs into an invisible wall. He turns around just in time to evade another strike from Khadija's extending cane.

> TAU
> What's the rush? Afraid your
> friends will be bested by a woman?

> MUNI
> I know what you're doing—trying to
> separate us! I will not leave my
> comrades alone.

He turns away, but before he can depart, a Beamform HOOK snatches him, hurls him into the ground.

> KHADIJA
> That is very responsible of you.

> TAU
> Too bad your hands are knotted!

Muni rises from the dirt. His anger seeps through his words.

> MUNI
> What do you know of responsibility?
> Do your shoulders carry the weight
> mine do?

> TAU
> Well, my head isn't that big, so…

> KHADIJA
> (contemplative)
> What responsibility burdens you?

> MUNI
> Leading my comrades—my family—out
> of the hell a corrupt world threw
> us into. What would you know of
> that burden?!

Sand swarms around Muni as a mini TORNADO lifts him skyward. Tau braces himself, but Khadija is introspective—ashamed.

> KHADIJA
> Perhaps… more than I should.

EXT. GIZA PLATEAU - GREAT PYRAMID - BASE - DAY

Darren arrives at the base of the Great Pyramid. Floating SAND coalesces above him, forms giant limestone plates that line the monolith one-by-one. The lower third of the obelisk has already been restored. It glistens a brilliant white.

Darren begins his climb. He sprints up its side.

EXT. GIZA PLATEAU - GREAT PYRAMID - TOP - CONTINUOUS

Amani meditates atop the pyramid; her attention fully focused on the restoration. The Earth Shard gleams.

> DARREN (O.S.)
> Amani! Stop it now!

Her focus breaks. She spots Darren halfway up the pyramid.

> DARREN
> It's too dangerous! If you finish,
> you're gonna get more people
> killed!

> AMANI
> You were the one who proved this is
> possible. Why should I stop when I
> can provide energy for everyone?

> DARREN
> This pyramid hasn't been used for
> thousands of years! The
> infrastructure to control it is
> gone. If you activate it, the
> energy that's been building all
> that time will discharge too fast!

> AMANI
> Then I will rip off the bandage.

A limestone tile forms above Darren. It drops, almost smashes him, but he escapes. More follow suit, chasing him around the monolith's surface.

213

Darren dashes to Amani. Before he reaches her a gold PIKE erupts from the stone beneath her, pummels Darren. He falls back, tumbles down the pyramid.

He catches his footing, starts to climb again, but small MIDAS SPEARS form from the airborne sand. Darren struggles for his life as he is bombarded from above.

Amani is satisfied with this. She returns her focus to the restoration…

EXT. GIZA PLATEAU - THE SPHINX - DAY

WATER TENDRILS satellite Asa—a kinetic weapon and shield.

Buziba leaps from the Sphinx's head, lands on a STONE BLOCK that emerges to meet his foot. He charges at Asa, each step supported by a small platform. She runs to meet him.

The water tendrils strike. Buziba contorts to avoid, bypasses them and throws a punch—but it's blocked by a liquid barrier. Another tendril comes to successfully slap him away.

Asa strikes again. Whipping tendrils smash from above. Buziba blocks, and Asa closes the gap. She throws a punch, but it's blocked. Peeved, Buziba shoves her away.

Asa prepares to rush again, but her feet are caught. She looks down: a COAL MOUND holds her in place. STEAM evaporates from the water that rushes over it.

Buziba capitalizes, rushes in and throws a flurry of strikes. Asa blocks many, but not enough. She takes a beating until…

A GEYSER bursts from beneath them, pushes Buziba away, rips Asa from the mound. She is free but worn down. Buziba resumes his attack.

Punches and kicks from an ancient martial art are thrown at Asa. She recognizes them, dodges some. She loses ground. She BLASTS Buziba with another WAVE to clear some distance.

He flies through the air, but a wall of COAL breaks his flight. He returns to the ground, hardly shaken. Steam and vapor continue to SIZZLE off the hot coal he's summoned.

Asa catches her breath, gazes up at the coal wall that towers behind Buziba. It brings back a memory…

INT. SECK RESIDENCE - LIVING ROOM - NIGHT, FLASHBACK

We are briefly returned to Khadija's home. Empty tea cups sit on a table as Khadija reflects upon her life.

> KHADIJA
> …It never feels like enough. It is like the more deeds I stack in hopes of climbing over that wall of shame, the higher it gets.

> ASA
> Then maybe it's not meant to be climbed! If it's a wall, then it should be broken down!

END FLASHBACK.

EXT. GIZA PLATEAU - THE SPHINX - DAY

Asa points her finger like a gun, cradles it with her second hand. WATER, FIRE, and AIR crackle at her fingertip.

> KHADIJA (V.O.)
> Do you have something strong enough to do that?

> ASA
> I do now…

Buziba squints suspiciously at the American. He notices the steam and vapor in the vicinity begin to swirl, coalesce at a Asa's fingertip.

The condensed vapor illuminates as Asa aims at Buziba. Then she releases her Soul Flux: **VAPOR BULLET.**

The BULLET whizzes past Buziba's head. He hears an explosion behind him and turns to see what happened.

The Bullet RIPS clean through the coal wall. It leaves a seared hole. This is the first time we see Buziba SHOCKED.

> ASA
> You won't be cursing anyone ever again.

Asa fires more rounds, Buziba hurdles out of their way, and they rips through the rest of the wall. It slowly tumbles.

> BUZIBA
> What trick is this?

215

He charges, zig-zagging as he dodges Asa's shots.

                    ASA
          There is no trick. I'm real!

Buziba slams the ground through the layer of water, resulting
in a massive COAL BOULDER catapulting toward Asa. Asa
unleashes a flurry of Vapor Bullets, obliterating the rock.

Buziba's angers and confusion are hard to contain. He rushes
her, opts for hand-to-hand combat again.

                    BUZIBA
          Then what Arjanan knowledge did you
          steal to get this power?

                    ASA
          It's a Soul Flux, you idiot!

Asa has trouble evading. She fires into the ground, the HEAT
from the bullet creating enough steam to separate them.

Asa knocks on her chest.

                    ASA
          Maybe all it took was a little
          heart the whole time.

                    BUZIBA
          Heart?! Heart for what—for WHO?!

                    ASA
            (winks)
          I think you know the answer to that
          one.

Buziba holds his forehead, tries to keep his composure. He's
failing.

MEMORY FLASH: TUTSI BOY watches his fallen FATHER shrink as
he plummets off a cliff. He sees his MOTHER float lifelessly
in the water as GLENDA pulls him onto a RAFT. He watches
Glenda fly away as the U.S. HELICOPTER ascends.

Each memory ends with a lonely and scared Tutsi Boy.

He hyperventilates as the images repeat.

                    BUZIBA
          You lie. It is not true… not real…
          They all *abandoned* you…

Buziba is erratic. Asa is confused but on guard.

                              BUZIBA
                       YOU ABANDONED ME!

Buziba slams the ground. An earthquake ensues. The Sphinx
court erupts with dozens of GIGANTIC COAL PILLARS in all
directions. Coal BARRICADES enclose the space.

Asa ascends, lifted by a pillar, but she calls the water to
follow her. Buziba gets to her first…

He tackles her off the pillar and they both crash into the
coal-blackened water below.

Asa employs water to eject her from the space, but Buziba
chases. He swipes at her with desperate ferocity. She rides
the water to just barely escape his pursuit.

A coal COLUMN rises behind Asa, and she runs into it. Buziba
doesn't stop. He thrashes her into the pillar and it
collapses atop them both.

Asa hacks debris, regains her bearings. Buziba is already up.
His eyes bleed from pain, but not from the fight.

                              BUZIBA
                 How far will this facade take you?!

He reaches for her face, but Asa fires another Vapor Bullet,
point-blank. It hits his chest, sends him flying back with a
concussive burst.

He lands 20 feet back, but on his feet. Asa gets to her feet,
rapid-fires at her opponent.

The Bullets ravage his body, but the only pain is internal.

He screams as he slams the ground again. From it, a COAL
PILLAR emerges and RAMS Asa into the foot of the Sphinx.

The impact sends a CRACK up the monument until its neck
crumbles. The Sphinx's head begins to fall—

But ASA clenches her fist, fires a LARGER bullet at the head.
The blast pushes it up and away, above Buziba. Then another
rapid flurry of normal Vapor Bullets annihilates the head.

The debris plummets over Buziba, knocks him over. But he
doesn't stay down.

He rushes Asa a final time. He summons FOUR BLACK WALLS that
enclose around Asa, trapping her. But the box doesn't hold.

Vapor Bullets blasts through the walls, slice it open like a laser. The walls fall, and Asa searches for Buziba… but he's already in front of her.

He reaches, grabs her face, and slams her into the Sphinx's body. COAL CLASPS pin her to the monument.

Asa squirms to get free. It's no use…

                BUZIBA
     ADMIT IT!

Buziba faces the ground as his fingers dig into Asa's face.

                ASA
     Admit what?! AGH!

Buziba's fingers sear the flesh on Asa's temples.

                BUZIBA
     Do it, and you both can live!

His eyes meet Asa's and she sees the tears and desperation bleeding from his face. He can barely keep himself together.

                BUZIBA
     Admit that your love is all a lie,
     and I let you both go free… Please…

Asa's expression softens. She finally sees the truth.

                ASA
     I can't do that, because it's not a
     lie. I love Darren. The only reason
     I've been able to push this far is
     because that love is real. *Our*
     love… is real.
        (beat)
     I'm sorry if you've never had that
     for yourself.

Buziba withdraws, steps away as anguish pierces his heart.

                ASA
     I don't know what you've been
     through, but I'm not like whoever
     hurt you before. I'm my own person.

Buziba is silent, expressionless as he kneels. A beat passes.

A SANDSTORM blows by, sucks sand toward the necropolis. Asa turns, sees a FUNNEL CLOUD descending from above.

She groans, yanks with all her might and breaks free of the
clasps that bind her. She starts for the necropolis but looks
back.

Buziba does not react. He remains stationary.

>   ASA
>   Buziba, I'm sorry, I really am… but
>   I refuse to be guilty.

She leaps away from the Sphinx's desolated courtyard and
rushes toward the necropolis.

EXT. GIZA PLATEAU - NECROPOLIS - DAY

BOULDERS fly through the air; they aim for a single target.
But a spinning wheel of acid slices them all, deflects them
away from Bia.

She jumps, cleanly avoids a large WAVE that crashes beneath
her. While airborne, the WIND blows her off her axis. She
falls to the sand, recovers quickly enough to evade the
FLAMES being blown her way.

Bia moves like a flowing stream, evading Waalisha attacks
while landing her own. Her movements are hard to follow.

But they are precise. She maneuvers behind an unsuspecting
dozen, slices them with an **ACID WHEEL**, moves along. The lucky
Waalisha not caught in her attack are spooked but keep
attacking desperately. Bia is not amused.

She recalls her Acid Wheel. It floats around her like a
deadly shield. It constricts, ready to strike again, but a
SANDSTORM blows over the necropolis. Even the Waalisha halt
their fighting to take cover.

Bia's eyes follow the sand to see where it leads. It is
sucked into the sky until it becomes a descending TORNADO.

GIZA PLATEAU - NORTHERN NECROPOLIS - CONTINUOUS

Muni ascends until his body vanishes into the funnel cloud.
Then the tornado drops, falls right on Tau and Khadija.

We peer through the sand to see Tau's forcefield holding off
the tornado, cracking as the pressure builds. It's too heavy.

>   TAU
>   I can't keep this up!

           KHADIJA
Drop your barrier and run as fast
as you can.

           TAU
What about—!

           KHADIJA
I will be fine.

The tornado breaks through. It blows dirt everywhere as it bores into the ground.

           MUNI
You Arjanans fight us for
what—because you were told to? I've
been fighting for my life for my
entire life! What do you know of
that?

Muni pulls back the tornado, assesses the damage. A CRATER is bored into the ground along with a small HOLE, but no bodies.

He is concerned, but he soon sees Tau zipping around. Muni points and the tornado hones in on the shepherd, chases him around the necropolis.

           MUNI
Look! You are chased by a threat
bigger than you and you run! I was
never able to run—I had to fight!

The tornado closes in on Tau. It almost swallows him when—

Khadija BURSTS from the ground beneath Muni, her cane's Beamform in the shape of a DRILL. It shifts into a BLADE as she approaches him…

Muni notices and hardly blocks in time with his sword. The impact sends him flying into the ground again.

The tornado dissipates. Tau rushes back to Khadija.

           KHADIJA
Fighting alone does not make you
noble.

Her eye sees the Wind Shard in Muni's Sword. Her Beamform shifts into a CLAW, reaches for it.

Muni recovers and slashes the claw away. The Wind Shard glows as he prepares another 100-foot slash. The blade drops, but Tau swoops Khadija out of the way. Muni leaves another scar on the earth.

                    MUNI
You have no right to judge my
fight! I can look at you and tell
you never faced hardships like us.
A shepherd in a Lesotho blanket and
a woman wearing traditional
clothing in a war.

                    KHADIJA
What is your point?

                    MUNI
You're privileged to even be able
to represent your own culture. I
had to fight to keep mine alive,
while my government tried to wipe
it out! Do you know what that's
like… to have your culture and
bloodline wiped out?

Wind flares up in response to Muni's rage.

                    TAU
          (to Khadija)
I'm running out of ideas…

                    KHADIJA
          (beat; to Muni)
You are right. I do not know what
that is like… not from your
perspective.

Tau is confused. Muni is off guard. Khadija is introspective.

                    KHADIJA
I have seen people who's cultures
were taken from them. There is a
void in their eye that they try to
fill with sights of the past, but
it is too late for them to fight
back. What they lost was taken from
them before their birth. So, I
fight on their behalf.

                    MUNI
How do you fight for them if the
damage is done?

                    KHADIJA
Retroactively, I work to reverse
the damage. If I can weaponize the
privilege afforded to me through
generations of bloodshed, perhaps I
can make a difference.
                    (MORE)

KHADIJA (CONT'D)
Perhaps I can even sway those like
you from their destructive paths…

Muni's expression softens.

MUNI
You want to restore what was taken…
So do I. The world took everything
from my family, and I will give it
all back to them in the best way I
know how. I'll lead us down
whatever path it takes.
(beat; to himself)
Because that is what elder brothers
do.

KHADIJA
If giving requires you to take from
someone else, then it is not true
restoration, is it?

MUNI
(scoffs)
Giving freely must be so easy for
the privileged, but they've never
given their all like the less
fortunate have to every day. Tell
me, Arjanan, have you honestly
given everything for your
restoration?!

Muni ascends into the sky as the clouds swirl around him. He
enters the eye of a birthing HURRICANE.

KHADIJA
(introspective)
No, I suppose I haven't… yet.
(to Tau)
We won't be able to beat him by
normal means.

TAU
No kidding! We'll have to regroup—

KHADIJA
But we *will* defeat him.

Tau glances quizzically at Khadija, sees her clutch her cane.
Her face shows a haunting resolve.

KHADIJA
I am going to use a Soul Transfer.
That will give us the edge we need
to finish this.

                    TAU
              (beat; somber)
         We'll only have one shot.

                  KHADIJA
         Then I will make this life count.

EXT. GIZA PLATEAU - GREAT PYRAMID - TOP - DAY

The final limestone panel covers the last uncovered spot of
the pyramid. The restoration is almost complete.

                   AMANI
         Finally.

The remaining sand that orbits the pyramid coalesces above
Amani. It forms an amorphous blob of GOLD. As more gold
appears, it slowly takes the shape of a COLOSSAL CAPSTONE.

Wind WHIPS across Amani, almost knocks her off the top. She
gazes into the sky as clouds blot out the sun.

                   AMANI
         Muni, what are you doing?

Darren sneaks higher up the pyramid, avoiding obstacles that
fall his way. He checks the battlefield and sees Tau and
Khadija. LIGHT appears to emanate from the latter…

EXT. GIZA PLATEAU - NECROPOLIS - DAY

Bia notices the forming hurricane. She is worried.

Then a Waalisha Fluxer sneaks behind her, shoots FIRE at her.

The fire almost connects, but a WAVE rises and blocks the
flame. When the water falls, it reveals Asa on the other
side. She unleashes a Vapor Bullet through the man's chest.

Bia catches the end of the exchange. She is surprised.

                    BIA
         Is Buziba…?

                    ASA
         He won't be a problem. What's
         happening?

Bia and Asa fire their Fluxes into the Waalisha. This attack
and the wind causes them to pull back a bit.

223

                    BIA
          I am fine, but the others need
          help. I should not have sent them
          alone. They are not strong enough
          to—
                (sees Khadija)
          No…

Asa catches Khadija glowing in the distance.

EXT. GIZA PLATEAU – NORTHERN NECROPOLIS – CONTINUOUS

Khadija's body GLOWS almost as bright as a SHARD. She clasps
her cane tightly.

                    TAU
          Are you sure this will work?

                    KHADIJA
          I am certain it is worth trying.

Muni hovers high into the sky.

                    MUNI
          It is time to claim this land for
          the community…
                (glimpses Amani; she
                 glimpses back)
          …for the family.

Shearing wind extends his sword once more. He aims at Tau and
Khadija below and swings, releasing a giant VANGUARD SHEAR.

Tau speeds away, but Khadija remains. Her body's glow moves
into her arms. She looks up and swings…

Her own BEAMFORM energy transforms her cane into a fifty-foot
SABER. It DEFLECTS Muni's Vanguard Shear, swats it away.

Muni's Shear splits the clouds as it returns to sender. He
gazes in disbelief at Khadija. Her hair grays by the second
and her skin pales. Her smile invites.

An aggravated Muni descends like a missile, swings at
Khadija. She blocks the strike; the impact quakes the earth.

The two cock their empowered blades once more and swing
again. Their blades collide. The hurricane falls upon them as
a struggle ensues.

The wind and their clash shakes the entire Giza Plateau.

Tau anchors himself with his own Sky-Block.

Asa and Bia keep low to the ground.

Darren hugs the pyramid to keep from blowing off.

BY A NEARBY MONUMENT:

And hiding behind a monument nearby, Pharaoh peeps his head out to view the action. He sees Khadija in the distance. Something about what he sees softens him… He's without words.

IN THE NECROPOLIS:

Khadija's eyes remain forward, but she smiles, as if she sees Pharaoh—impossibly. A tear falls from her cataract eye.

                    MUNI
          You will fall—I will make you! It's
          my responsibility to make you!

Muni screams in desperation. The wind weighs Khadija down like gravity itself. Her knee touches the ground.

                    KHADIJA
          I won't fall…

Khadija shifts her grip, finds new leverage. Muni is slightly off balance.

                    KHADIJA
          There is still a wall I must climb…

She shouts. Her graying hair flashes white, her skin drains of color, but her Beamform EXPLODES in glory.

GUSTS funnel around them as Khadija's leverage gains. Muni loses his balance… and his grip. He slumps back too far.

Then Khadija swings forward until Muni's body is within the BLAZE of her Soul Flux.

Muni cries as his body is ravaged by Khadija's attack; as his pride is ravaged by failure. He loses his grip on his sword.

He drops his sword. It and the attached Wind Shard go flying. Tau leaps after it, catches it before it's swept away.

The remaining details of Muni's body fade from existence, burned away by Khadija's attack.

The hurricane subsides. Khadija's Soul Flux vanishes… and her body is still for a beat before she falls to the ground.

Her eyes are clouded by cataracts, wet with tears, and smiling with peace. A final breath escapes her lungs…

                                        FADE OUT.

                        <u>END OF ACT TWO</u>

ACT THREE

FADE IN:

EXT. GIZA PLATEAU - GREAT PYRAMID - TOP - DAY

The wind dies down. Amani searches for Muni, but she cannot find him. She nearly panics until she finds…

Muni's sword, Wind Shard attached, in Tau's hand. He runs over to Khadija, checks on her.

                    AMANI
          Muni… brother?

Amani cracks… her eyes flit with madness. She outstretches her arm.

Below, an obelisk-sized MIDAS SPEAR ejects from the ground. It floats by Tau and Khadija, aims for them.

                    AMANI
          You dogs can all di—!

Darren's fist connects with Amani's face, his momentum knocking them both off the pyramid's apex. They tumble down its side.

The Midas Spear falls, leaving Tau unharmed, but so does the gold capstone. It escapes Amani's influence and drops onto the rest of the pyramid, shaking the earth as it connects.

Darren breaks his fall, but not soon enough to evade Amani's charge. She tackles him and they both tumble to the bottom.

EXT. GIZA PLATEAU - GREAT PYRAMID - BASE - CONTINUOUS

Darren kicks a rabid Amani away as they hit the ground.

                    DARREN
          Knock it off, Amani! It's—

                    AMANI
          You took them both away!!!

Amani struggles to refrain from burying her face in her hands. Darren hesitates, fazed by her near hysteria.

                         AMANI
            All I had were my brothers… and you
            killed them, my baby brother… my
            older brother… you killed them
            both! What makes you think I will
            let you walk away—

A blinding FLASH and THUNDER quakes the plateau.

They glance at the Great Pyramid, notice STEAM sizzle from
the SPARKING PYRAMIDION's surface. Then it happens again…

The capstone lights up, discharges a COLUMN of LIGHTNING that
shoots into the clouds, splitting into hundreds of bolts that
web across the sky.

A haunting serenity and relief falls over Amani.

                         AMANI
            It wasn't for naught…

                         DARREN
            No…

Darren rushes away, leaves Amani to gawk in awe.

EXT. GIZA PLATEAU - NORTHERN NECROPOLIS - DAY

Tau cradles Khadija as Asa and Bia make their way over.

The Waalisha gawk at the sky, in awe of the sight. Until…

Lightning falls, rains upon the necropolis. Multiple Waalisha
are struck, burned, annihilated by it. Panic ensues and they
all run for their lives.

                         BIA
            Tau, restrain them and cover us!

Tau looks hesitantly at the Wind Shard in the sword, but he
grabs it, lifts it up. He activates his Soul Flux and the
Shard GLOWS.

A forcefield covers the entire battlefield, boxing in the
Waalisha, protecting everyone from the lighting.

Meanwhile, more lightning rains from the sky, strikes
military vehicles, blasts buildings in the city. Chaos
spreads as blackouts roll.

Darren arrives by Tau, takes cover under his forcefield.

                    DARREN
          You've gotta get outta here, now!

                    BIA
          This shelter is the safest place we
          can be for now.

                    ASA
          What's happening?

                    BIA
          The Great Pyramid was a prototype
          for the energy tower used in
          Arjana. It has been decommissioned
          for millennia, but the electric
          energy has been building up that
          entire time.

The pyramid releases another blast that recharges the sky.
More lightning rains upon the region.

                    DARREN
          The lightning's gonna keep arcing
          everywhere unless we insulate that
          pyramid.

                    TAU
          How do we do that?

                    DARREN
          I should be able to, but first…

Midas Spears CRASH through Tau's forcefield, scatters the
group among the sand.

Amani stands in the necropolis: the sole obstacle between
them and the Pyramid. Darren stands and walks toward her. He
gives Tau a nod, and he understands. Tau closes the
forcefield again, this time leaving Darren outside.

                    AMANI
          My family gave everything for this.
          The fruit of our labor is all I
          have left of them. You will die
          before I let you take that away
          from me.

                    DARREN
          That's ALWAYS been your issue!
               (grips rocket necklace)
          You never think about how many
          innocent people will get caught up
          in your stupid, dangerous plans!

                    AMANI
          I do. But I think on the
          benefactors of my deeds more. That
          makes it all worth it.

                    DARREN
          No bloodshed is ever worth it.

                    AMANI
          Yours will be.

DOZENS of MIDAS SPEARS erupts from the earth, jet toward
Darren. He slaps the ground, creates and ejects himself with
a COIL SPRING. He flies out of harms way.

But the Spears keep coming. Amani hurls an endless hoard of
golden javelins at Darren, who dodges them all by hopping
from one spring-loaded platform to another.

He shifts directions, B-lines straight for Amani, but a GOLD
COLUMN erupts from below, smacks Darren into the air. She
follows with another barrage of giant javelins.

Darren is airborne. He shakes the hit off, notices the NILE
RIVER in the distance and the aquifer water below. He reaches
into his pocket…

The javelins get mere feet from Darren before a TSUNAMI
BLASTS them away and floods the Giza Plateau. Amani braces as
she sees…

A SWIRLING TOWER of water defends Darren. The Water Shard is
in his hand. He pulls dirt from the earth, fashions a metal
belt and places the Shard inside. Fire is in his eyes. A
battle of Titans begins.

He bounds forward, skiing across the wet surface of the
necropolis as a TENDRIL of water boosts him from behind.

Amani hurls more Midas Spears at him. He skims the water,
evading every projectile, getting with arm's reach.

He clotheslines her, sends her flying back, skipping over the
water itself. Darren follows by sending a TSUNAMI at her, but
she recovers and blocks with a golden WALL.

Amani screams and dozens of 10-story PIKES erupt from the
ground, blast through the water. Darren rides more water to
evade but it's too much. He gains some distance.

Amani notices his retreat. With another shout she launches
the PIKES skyward, jumps onto one herself, and rains them
like missiles upon the battlefield.

Darren skims the water at high speed to avoid the onslaught, while Amani hops from one falling pike to the next as she pursues him. The chase takes them through the necropolis, many fleeing Waalisha becoming collateral.

Darren approaches the Menkaure Pyramid, treats it as a ramp and boosts himself skyward, away from Amani's immediate range. Amani lands and perches atop the pyramid.

Darren overlooks the plateau, gets his bearings.

> DARREN
> This sucks! I can't get to her if she can use the whole ground as a weapon!

He glances at the Great Pyramid as more lightning discharges from it.

> DARREN
> But that might help…

Something catches his eye. He throws himself higher with water up to evade chunks of pyramid flying his way.

Amani rips more pieces from the Menkaure Pyramid and launches them at Darren.

Darren calls the waters to meet him in the sky.

> DARREN
> CRAFTSMAN: *CLUB!*

Water forms a hundred-foot CLUB. Darren grabs it, swings, bats away the incoming projectiles, returns them to sender.

The projectiles bombard Amani on the pyramid, and she tumbles down.

She reaches the bottom, rage filling her. The Earth Shard glows fiercely. TONS of sand and stone accumulates onto Amani, creates a humanoid suit. The suit turns Gold: It becomes the **MIDAS GOLEM.**

The Golem charges at Darren as he returns to the ground, and he charges to meet her as well.

UNDER TAU'S FORCEFIELD:

Tau focuses on keeping his barrier up. Asa cradles Khadija's body, now drained of any sign of life.

Bia assesses the damage dealt to the plateau as golden spires and water destroy the landmarks as the two battle.

The Midas Golem crashes into monuments, splits the land with each step, and the once desert floor is flooded by living waves that flush the bodies of fallen Waalisha and Egyptian Soldiers into the fissures.

> BIA
> Centuries of secrets just for it to all come undone.

> TAU
> (to Asa)
> Now you know why I tried so hard to keep you all away from Umoya. I should have tried harder…

ON THE BATTLEFIELD:

Darren breaks away from the exchange of blows. He fires a jet of water at Amani's head, but he misses. The water hits the Great Pyramids golden capstone instead. The lightning pauses, but Amani doesn't notice.

Darren mobilizes himself once more with the water. He rushes toward the Great Pyramid, scales it. Before he reaches the top, the Golem grabs him, slams him against the limestone. Darren is pinned just below the capstone.

> AMANI
> No more running.

Darren tries to yank loose. It's no use. Amani presses, crushes him against the limestone.

> AMANI
> I welcomed you into a new family, and you spurned us, instead fighting to preserve a world of corrupt powers. That world ends with you.

The Golem reaches with its free hand, yanks the Water Shard from Darren's belt. Its glow ceases…

Then, a thick layer of water drains from the capstone. It envelops Darren as he holds his breath.

> AMANI
> That will not help you.

SPARKS fly from the capstone. It shoots LIGHTING into the sky, but the lightning returns. It BLASTS the Midas Golem!

The Golem releases its grip on Darren. Amani drops the Water Shard, and Darren catches it. Its glow returns.

Darren slides down the pyramid, then summons water to propel him back up. His fist catches Amani's face with enough force to rip her from the Golem. The Golem goes limp; they go flying.

EXT. GIZA PLATEAU - A THOUSAND FEET UP - CONTINUOUS

Amani is dazed. She somewhat comes to in time to see Darren soaring above her in the sky, lighting arcing behind him.

The only thing separating them is twenty feet of space and Darren's rocket necklace that dangles in front of his face. He glances at the necklace before he holds the Water Shard up once more and shouts…

                    DARREN
          CRAFTSMAN: *ROCKET!*

All water in and around the plateau meets Darren in the sky. It envelops him and takes the shape of a life-size ROCKET. He merges with its nose. The rocket points down.

With a final shout, water EJECTS from the "thruster", propels Darren into Amani. They plummet like meteors toward Earth.

The impact quakes the Giza Plateau like nothing before. Sand and water cloud the vicinity…

EXT. GIZA PLATEAU - BROKEN NECROPOLIS - CONTINUOUS

As debris blows over the forcefield, Asa lays Khadija down.

                    ASA
          Let me through.

Tau drops the forcefield and Asa runs toward the point of impact.

She arrives at a deep CRATER. Dust screens the two figures at the bottom.

IN THE CRATER:

Amani lies beaten in the center of the crater. She is barely conscious, her body twitching from residual electricity. Her eyes stare off into the sky, searching for answers.

Darren stands above her, searching for breath.

                    DARREN
          Surprised?

233

He reaches for her belt and strips the Earth Shard from it.

>   DARREN
>   People don't know this, but when
>   it's purified, water is a horrible
>   conductor of electricity—bad enough
>   to be an insulator—while gold
>   happens to be one of the best.

Amani's consciousness fades.

>   DARREN
>   But you already knew that last
>   part.

EXT. GIZA PLATEAU - NECROPOLIS - LATER

The Earth rumbles as WHITE LIGHTNING arcs from the pyramid
and into the sky.

Tau keeps his Soul Flux active, subjugates the remaining
Waalisha under his FORCEFIELD. Some try to escape in vain
while others are demoralized. About 100 men remain.

Darren and Asa approach Tau and Bia, an unconscious Amani in
tow. She is bound by STEEL CUFFS. They drop her there.

>   BIA
>   Is she dead?

>   DARREN
>   Just unconscious.

>   BIA
>   And the Shards?

Darren pats his pockets. The Shards' glow penetrates through.
Asa's attention moves to Khadija.

>   ASA
>   I don't understand… what happened?

>   TAU
>   She Soul Transferred—sacrificed all
>   of her life force energy to power
>   her last attack. She really… gave
>   her all.

Asa kneels beside Khadija's body, notices her faint smile.

>   ASA
>   (somber; to Khadija)
>   I guess you found your own way
>   through that wall, huh?

>   BIA
>   Khadija sacrificed herself to
>   protect the Ophiuchus Stone Shards,
>   as was her duty. Her clan will be
>   properly recognized for her deeds.
>   (looks at Darren)
>   But you Americans… Both of you had
>   nothing to gain from helping us.

>   DARREN
>   I wouldn't say 'nothing'. We
>   couldn't let the Waalisha run
>   rampant. They've already done so
>   much killing.

>   BIA
>   The Queen ordered you to return to
>   your home so you would be safe, but
>   you intervened anyway. There was
>   nothing you wanted in return?

>   DARREN
>   (shrugs; glances at Asa)
>   Maybe it's just… who I am.

Unbeknownst to all present, the arcing lightning turns blue…

Footfalls signal someone's arrival. They turn to see who it is and are surprised to see…

>   BIA
>   Buziba!

Buziba approaches but doesn't get too close. He is somber, defeated. Bia summons an Acid Wheel.

>   BIA
>   I should cut you down here!

Asa touches Bia's shoulder. This pacifies, but confuses her. Asa approaches Buziba, who stands lonesome.

A beat passes, then Asa extends her hand. Buziba is vexed. He stares at her hand before—

A **GLEAM DART** bursts from the ground, punctures his leg from behind, then circles around and threatens his face.

EARTHEN MOUNDS erupt from all over the necropolis and bind the remaining Waalisha forces. A mound also binds Buziba.

100 ARJANAN SOLDIERS rush into view. They form a perimeter around the necropolis, subjugating the Waalisha they see.

One man lands above Darren and friends, standing on Tau's forcefield. It's TANO.

> BIA
> Tau, drop your Soul Flux.

He does so. The barrier disappears and Tano lands on the ground, joins the group.

> TANO
> Buziba, you are seized for
> committing treason against the
> Throne of Arjana. You will be tried
> once we return to the Kingdom.

Buziba winces from pain, but remains silent.

Tau bows. Asa follows his lead.

> TAU
> Welcome, Prince Tano.

> ASA
> Hello, Prince Tano!

> TANO
> Tau. Muzungu…
> (scans the plateau)
> What happened? This place has been
> devastated.

> BIA
> Her name is Asa, and they were both
> integral to the Waalisha's defeat.
> As was Darren and Khadija. They are
> all due the recognition of the
> Throne, Tano.

Tano glances at Asa, tries to hold his disdain.

> TANO
> Is that so? Well, Tau and… Asa…
> well done.

Asa grins at the acknowledgement. All the while, the lightning shifts to violet…

Nearby, ROWDY WAALISHA causes a raucous. He blows FIRE into the dirt mound he's in, attempts to escape his bonds.

Tano glances over. His Gleam Dart leaves Buziba, soars over to Rowdy Waalisha, impales his chest, and returns to Buziba. Rowdy Waalisha is dead.

Tano calls out to ARJANAN SOLIDER 1.

> TANO
> Gather them all and prepare for a
> swift return. Search for deserters.

> DARREN
> It might be worth checking the
> city, too.

Tano sizes up Darren.

> TANO
> (to Arjanan Soldier 1)
> Take a team to search Cairo.

> ARJANAN SOLDIER 1
> Yes, Your Divinity.

Arjanan Soldier 1 points to a few other Soldiers, and they start for the city.

Tano walks closer to Darren.

> TANO
> You are the Muz—Asa's husband?

Asa walks over and hugs Darren's arm.

> ASA
> He sure is!

> TANO
> I see.
> (beat; takes a bow)
> Khadija Seck, Tau Lane, Darren
> Davenport, and Asa Davenport, the
> Throne of Arjana recognizes your
> service and is indebted to you.
> (rises again)
> Now then, where are the Shards?

> DARREN
> Oh, right here.

Darren pulls out the Shards. Tau fails to remove the Wind Shard from the sword's pommel, so he hands over the sword.

237

Tano takes the sword. Darren steps forward, motions to hand over the Shards…

But Tano checks the sky. The lightning has turned nearly black. He spooks, SHOVES Tau and Darren away, right as—

A GIANT, BLACK LIGHTNING BOLT strikes, EXPLODES onto the necropolis, blasts Tano. Its shockwave knocks the group back.

Asa, Darren, Bia, and Tau gain their bearings. They check for Tano, and they find him: motionless, burnt, lifeless inside a small crater of sand and fresh GLASS. The three dropped Shards lay next to him.

                    BIA
          T-Tano!

Bia crawls toward her brother, but another dark LIGHTNING BOLT hits the crater again. This one delivers a man.

Pharaoh stands next to Tano's body, grasps the FIRE SHARD.

                    DARREN
          Pharaoh?!

                    BIA
          You… YOU!

Bia lashes, summons an ACID WHEEL and strikes at Pharaoh, but he blasts it with an EBONY BOLT, vaporizes it instantly. He kneels, reaches for the other shards…

                    DARREN
          Don't let him grab them!

Darren summons a STEEL DOME to cover the Shards. Asa, Tau and Bia shoo Pharaoh away with their fluxes, but he evades by jumping high.

His Fire Shard glows and he redirects LIGHTNING from the pyramid. It CRASHES upon the necropolis and the shockwave knocks the group back once more.

He lands, kicks away the steel dome. His eyes glisten at the sight…

                    PHARAOH
          Finally…

ARJANAN SOLDIER 2 flings dozens of PORCELAIN SPIKES at Pharaoh, but a GUST catches the spikes. Pharaoh is touching the Wind Shard in the sword…

The wind escalates, throws back the spikes, impales Soldiers.

The onslaught begins. Arjanan Soldiers from every angle launch Soul Fluxes of every variety at Pharaoh at once. None reach him. His foot is on the WATER SHARD.

He combines the wind and water to create a WATER SPOUT. He sweeps the necropolis, washing away every Soldier he sees.

                    DARREN
          Asa!

                    ASA
          Got it!

Darren slams the ground, forms a STEEL CANNON that he stands on. Asa places her hands inside barrel from the back.

The cannon fires a massive VAPOR CANNONBALL. It almost connects before Pharaoh summons a STONE WALL to deflect. His foot is now touching the Earth Shard.

He scans for the culprits, spots Darren on the cannon. With a stomp, Pharaoh hurls stone PROJECTILES from the ground, scatters them in all directions. One flies at Darren—

But Asa tackles him, and they both narrowly avoid the projectile. *Buziba notices this.*

With a SHOUT from Pharaoh, the entire Giza Plateau RUMBLES. The ground fissures, the water spout expands, and lighting inhabits a funnel cloud as it descends on the plateau.

Everyone on the plateau desperately hunts for shelter. The earthquake breaks many free from their earthen bonds, but they are sucked into a FUNNEL CLOUD above.

All of Cairo is veiled by the darkness of the storm.

The only light visible are the glimmering Shards. They orbit Pharaoh, gleaming and shaking like unstable subatomic particles. Pharaoh is their nucleus.

Their luminance increases as they move closer together. Pharaoh guides them with his hands. Their differing colors blend into a vibrant prism as…

The Shards merge.

A SHOCKWAVE repels everyone in the area as the prism's blinding light dispels the darkness.

But the shockwave reverses, except it only pulls in one man: Pharaoh. He panics, struggles to escape its influence. He screams as his body is pulled inside completely.

And then nothing.

The air is clear… still. All that can be seen is a vibrant, OCTAHEDRAL GEM that floats above the ground: **THE OPHIUCHUS STONE.**

The plateau is in shambles, only the pyramids remain intact. Bia is the first one up.

> BIA
> All on your feet! Pick up your
> comrades.

She takes stock of the situation. Many Soldiers are hurt, others are worse.

A STEEL DOME falls over, reveals Tau, Darren, and Asa on the other side.

> DARREN
> You both all right?

> ASA
> I think so.

> TAU
> I am still only down one limb, so
> that's good news.

> ASA
> What happened?

They all look around. Buziba and Amani are gone, but so is Pharaoh. Darren walks to Bia.

> DARREN
> Where is Pharaoh?

Bia sighs, approaches the Ophiuchus Stone.

> BIA
> It does not matter. He is gone.

A WAIL echoes from the Stone. Bia flinches, steps away.

> BIA
> No…

The Stone seemingly opens, becomes a portal for a GODLIKE FIGURE to pull itself out. The Figure glistens with the same glory of the Stone itself. It emerges completely and we see its face.

It is Pharaoh.

He is still. Just long enough for Asa to fire a Vapor Bullet at his face, but his head hardly budges.

He is reminded of her existence, looks at her, smiles.

Pharaoh's finger twitches and the earth responds. METAL CLAWS spring from the ground, grabbing Asa and Darren.

> PHARAOH
> I would like you to see this.

Pharaoh ascends with the terrifying grace of a deity. The Ophiuchus Stone follows him. It floats above his head.

> PHARAOH
> Purge. This. Continent.

The Stone glows violently.

So do Asa's eyes and mouth…

> DARREN
> Asa, what's wrong? Do you hear me?!

She doesn't. Her orifices illuminate, and a STREAM of LIQUID LIGHT spills out of her, pours upward.

EXT. JOHANNESBURG - DOWNTOWN - DAY

A CAUCASIAN FAMILY drives down the street. CAUCASIAN FATHER appears sick… he tries to pull over before he vomits, but he can't in time.

He vomits his own soul through his orifices. He crashes into a light pole. His head is embraced by the AIR BAG.

BLACK OFFICER rushes to the crash scene. He goes to check on the driver, but he is spooked as everyone in the car falls victim to the same phenomenon.

SCREAMS echo throughout the city as thousands more CAUCASIAN CITIZENS suffer the same ailment. All of their souls soar upward and to the North.

INT. NAIROBI AIRPORT - DAY

Every Caucasian Citizen and TOURIST in sight is stripped of their soul, while everyone else hides.

The victims are suspended by their faces as their souls are extracted. The souls fly North again.

EXT. CAIRO - DOWNTOWN - DAY

Arjanan Soldiers and straggling Waalisha panic as LOCAL
EGYPTIANS are also effected.

MILLIONS of souls soar upward, toward the Giza Plateau.

EXT. GIZA PLATEAU - NECROPOLIS - DAY

Countless souls swarm the plateau. They are sucked into the
Ophiuchus Stone with the sound of a wailing wind.

Finally, the stream of souls ends.

Asa's eyes lose their light as the last of her soul is
siphoned away. She is deathly still. Her body goes limp.

                    DARREN
          Asa?! ASA!!

The Stone dims as Pharaoh grabs it. He is satisfied.

Without a word, he soars into the sky, jets westward. A SONIC-
BOOM heralds his exit.

He leaves the plateau in ruin. The survivors contemplate,
attempt to make sense of what happened.

The only audible sounds are Darren's cries as he attempts to
wake a corpse.

                                        FADE TO BLACK.

                    END OF SHOW

AFROFANTASY

SCREENPLAY BY CHANNING CHEA

AFROFANTASY

111 - "The Risen City"

Written by

Channing Chea

AFROFANTASY

"THE RISEN CITY"

<u>TEASER</u>

EXT. OUTER SPACE - EARTH - DAY

                                    FADE IN:

…To reveal EARTH hanging in the silent void of space. It
spins to reveal Africa.

As the continent comes into view, the SCREAMS of a terrified
populace pierce the silence. We zoom into Africa, landing on…

EXT. JOHANNESBURG - DOWNTOWN - DAY

SMOKE clouds the skies of JOHANNESBURG, rising from crashed
vehicles that litter the streets in all directions. CAUCASIAN
CORPSES fuel the flames as they burn.

BLACK OFFICERS direct GOOD SAMARITANS to help address the
carnage. They pull WHITE DRIVERS from their vehicles, attempt
to revive them with CPR, protect them from…

LOOTERS dig through the pockets of the fallen. Good
Samaritans fight to drive them away, but there are too many.

FIREFIGHTERS battle the fire that spreads through leaking
gasoline all over, but it's a losing battle. Only a third of
their men are available. Another third attempts to revive the
fallen Caucasian third, but the RIOTERS do not make it easy.

EXT. MASERU, LESOTHO - SETSOTO STADIUM - DAY

A SOCCER STADIUM is transformed into a makeshift clinic as
dozens of Caucasian TOURISTS and CITIZENS are wheeled in on
stretchers. They are guided into position by KING KOPANO.

                KING KOPANO
          Keep the children with the adults
          they were found with! Place them
          beneath the tents!

He follows them to a TENT. Nearby, GERALDINE sits across from
a SHAKEN WOMAN, 40s, who holds a White man's pale hand.

                GERALDINE
          What do you mean? Please explain it
          once more…

245

                    SHAKEN WOMAN
          He was lifted off the
          ground—floating like he was
          possessed—then the light stopped,
          and his body fell over… He just
          went cold. He won't wake up…

Shaken Woman breaks down, realizing the truth of her own
words. Geraldine and King Kopano exchange glances.

                    KING KOPANO
               (stares into distance)
          Tau, were you too late?

EXT. NAIROBI, KENYA - AIRPORT - DAY

FLAMES burn from either end of a runway from botched takeoffs
and landings. The remaining gates are filled, and the tarmac
is loaded with jets that have been grounded.

INT. NAIROBI, KENYA - AIRPORT - TERMINAL - DAY

The terminal is empty. An emergency message plays over the
P.A. SYSTEM, but the only audience are the White corpses.

EXT. KIBERA, KENYA - DAY

The bodies of HUMANITARIANS are placed on a hill by LOCAL
KENYANS. The bodies appear to be lounging. The Locals can
only hope to keep them comfortable.

A Local carries almost-clean water from a nearby stream,
gives it to HERALD. She places a wet cloth on a
Humanitarian's forehead. It's all she can think to do.

EXT. CAIRO - DOWNTOWN - DAY

CAIRO is a ghost town. The streets are painted by the carnage
of the earlier siege, but there are plenty of bodies that
have not been touched by bullets or weapons. ARAB EGYPTIANS
sprawl about the city with the same still lifelessness as
their Caucasian counterparts.

EXT. GIZA PLATEAU - NECROPOLIS RUINS - DAY

LIGHTNING arcs through the sky, rumbles the earth. It's the
only sound that interrupts the cries of a morning husband.

TAU and the ARJANAN SOLDIERS pick themselves up, observe solemnly as Darren demands a response from Asa. He seems to be the only person who has not accepted the obvious.

BIA cradles TANO's body. Tears stream down as she struggles to stay strong in front of her Soldiers.

ANANSI is not far away. His Apparition stares at his siblings. He is in a trance.

> ANANSI
> So much life… in a single swoop…

> QUEEN ASASE (V.O.)
> Anansi. ANANSI! Report.

He breaks from his trance.

INT. ARJANA - QUEEN'S THRONE ROOM - DAY

QUEEN ASASE sits on her throne, her face more stern than we've ever seen it. She asks merely to confirm what she already knows.

> QUEEN ASASE
> What has happened?

JAMBI, CYMBA, ZAILA, and TYMPANI stand around the Queen's throne. They are all concerned, curious. They all wait for Anansi's reply.

He finally musters the strength to answer.

> ANANSI
> The Ophiuchus Stone has been restored.

FADE OUT.

<u>END OF TEASER</u>

ACT ONE

FADE IN:

EXT. SAHARA DESERT - RICHAT STRUCTURE - A MILE UP - DAY

Sand clouds blow over the EYE OF THE SAHARA. From above, we
see the peaks and valleys that form concentric circles on a
massive geological scale. It is the fossil of a nation.

PHARAOH floats into view. His body SHIMMERS with light
visible even in the sunlight. He observes the land, hovers in
meditation as the OPHIUCHUS STONE floats above him. DOZENS of
SEED SACKS orbit him. A beat passes, then…

Pharaoh roars over the land. The land hears him.

A shockwave ejects dusts from newly forming cracks and
crevices in the ground as the Richat Structure rumbles. It's
structure seemingly renovates itself.

Valleys flatten. Mountains rise. The land levels, and massive
reservoirs form to hold absent water.

Pharaoh twirls his fingers. The land responds. The cracked
and hardened surface breaks, turns itself until it forms a
soft SOIL.

The seed sacks explode. HUNDREDS OF THOUSANDS of seeds rain
from the sky and plant themselves on every inch of elevated
land. IRRIGATION CHANNELS form as the soil hugs the seeds.

Pharaoh roars again, straining as if to lift something heavy.

EXT. MAURITANIA - ATLANTIC COAST - CONTINUOUS

LOCAL MAURITANIANS mind their business until a TSUNAMI
catches their eye. The ocean itself recedes and a MONSTER
WAVE swiftly approaches the shore. The Locals panic, almost
lose their minds until…

The Wave leaps over them all, stretching like an aquatic
rainbow over the entire city. The water blots out the sun.

EXT. TUNISIA - MEDITERRANEAN SEA COAST - CONTINUOUS

TUNISIANS run for shelter, brace as the earth quakes. All are
thrown off balance as the ground is RENT, creating a vast
trench for the Mediterranean Sea itself to pour into. The
city is split as a new RIVER is born.

EXT. OUTER SPACE - EARTH - CONTINUOUS

Water from the ocean and sea flow from their home and toward
the Richat Structure. The very geography of West Africa
changes before us.

EXT. SAHARA DESERT - RICHAT STRUCTURE - CONTINUOUS

The waters roll in, fill the valleys and trenches carved for
them. They trace the outlines of past ancient rivers and fill
irrigation channels throughout the land.

The rings of the Richat Structure are now separated by mile
wide chasms of water. Rivers from northern mountains flow
into the chasms and empty into a southern mouth that leads to
the ocean. But the structure is still only water and sand.

Pharaoh descends into the center island of the Eye. A TEMPLE
forms around him as he does, sheltering him. The Ophiuchus
Stone follows him. It lands in his hand. He admires it.

                    PHARAOH
          A new Capital is birthed!

He slams the Stone into the temple floor and a surge of LIGHT
floods the building, extends into the entire region.

The light touches the land and water, merges with it. Within
seconds, every seed in the region germinates.

A MILE UP:

The drenched desert structure is transformed into a lush
grassland with plains and rivers throughout. This is no
longer the Eye of the Sahara. It is now ATLANTIS.

INT. ATLANTIS - TEMPLE - CONTINUOUS

The light from the Stone subsides. It rests, planted inside
the foundation of the temple. Pharaoh's divine light also
fades and a CRYSTALLINE THRONE catches him as he falls back.

He smiles as he overlooks the Risen City.

                    PHARAOH
          Baba, I have found our nation.

EXT. CAIRO - DOWNTOWN ALLEY - DAY

A few Non-Arab Egyptians roam the streets, search for
survivors. They are terrified at the mountain of corpses.

Meanwhile, AMANI drags herself down the alley. She is worse for wear, barely holding on. She leans against a building as tears escape her eyes.

A shadow reveals that someone approaches. It's BUZIBA.

> AMANI
> I wanted to stop it from ever
> happening again… what happened to
> us. Maybe I was naive to think I
> could topple power without my own.
> (beat)
> Please, do not let me live with
> this failure.

Buziba steps closer, reaches for Amani's face, but he stops. Dissatisfaction is written on his face.

> BUZIBA
> I have been responsible for enough
> death.

He walks away, leaving Amani alone in her failure.

EXT. CAIRO - VACANT BUILDING - DAY

The remnants of a devastated ARJANAN ARMY gather themselves before a damaged building. They await direction from BIA, who holds TANO's lifeless body. Anansi delivers a message before his Apparition disappears.

> BIA
> (to the army)
> Return to Arjana at once. We will
> regroup and assess damages.

The Arjanans begin to move, but TAU approaches the princess.

> TAU
> Pardon me, Your Divinity, but I
> volunteer to stay with the
> American.
> (Bia considers it)
> With the Waalisha defeated, Darren
> is the only involved party aware of
> Umoya. And… I think he could use a
> friend right now.

> BIA
> If you think Kopano can manage
> without you, then I approve.

She takes a last look at Asa's corpse through the open
doorway before leading the Arjanans away.

ON THE ROOF

Buziba watches the Arjanans depart, sees Tau enter the
building.

INT. CAIRO - VACANT BUILDING - CONTINUOUS

Tau enters a small building with a single room. To the left,
Khadija's body lies on the floor. Before him, Darren kneels
before Asa's body, pleading silently for it to wake.

>   DARREN
>   (to Asa; somber)
>   You know, I think I figured it out:
>   who I am, why I'm here. I never got
>   to tell you, but I promise I will
>   if you just wake up. Please…

Tau moves to sit beside Darren… when Buziba enters the room.

Tau hops up, blocks his path to the Americans. Darren doesn't
even acknowledge him.

>   BUZIBA
>   I am not here to fight. I no longer
>   represent Arjana.

>   TAU
>   Then why are you here?!

He doesn't know how to answer, so he doesn't.

>   BUZIBA
>   Your wife… resembles the others
>   throughout Cairo. Whether Muzungu
>   or Arab, all of them have been
>   stripped of their souls.

>   TAU
>   Are you serious? Well, that's not
>   too far off from what King Kopano
>   said. Even Lesotho was effected.

>   BUZIBA
>   Then all of Arjana's tales of the
>   Ophiuchus Stone's power were true.

>   DARREN
>   What's your point?

                    BUZIBA
          Your wife gave me a new perspective
          when we fought. So out of
          gratitude, I would attempt to
          return the gesture as much as
          possible.

                    DARREN
          Swell. And how the hell do you plan
          on doing that?

                    BUZIBA
          By telling you how to bring her
          back.

Darren swings around, faces Buziba for the first time.
Desperate intensity burns in his eye.

                    DARREN
          Do not screw with me!

                    BUZIBA
          It is not a lie. You can do so
          using the same method Khadija used
          in her battle.

                    TAU
          A Soul Transfer?

                    BUZIBA
             (nods)
          Khadija knew she had no chance of
          outpowering the Wind Shard in what
          was basically a one-on-one fight,
          so she employed a Forbidden Flux to
          accomplish her goal.
          A Soul Transfer is similar to a
          normal Flux in that the user moves
          his or her spiritual energy into an
          element. However, a Transfer
          expends the entirety of one's
          spirit. This has two results:
          First, the user can empower
          themselves to temporarily achieve
          feats on par with an Ophiuchus
          Stone Shard.

Buziba's eyes fall on Khadija's body.

                    BUZIBA
          And second, this ability, without
          fail, will result in the user's
          death. This is why it is Forbidden.
             (beat as they process)
                    (MORE)

                    BUZIBA (CONT'D)
          High-ranking Arjanan warriors are
          taught how to execute this Flux as
          a final resort. Khadija used it to
          fulfill her duty. It is the only
          time using such a Flux is
          acceptable.

                    DARREN
          I don't need a power-up! I need to
          bring Asa back to life! Will it
          still work that way?

                    BUZIBA
          As far as I know that hasn't been
          attempted, but it is said that
          miraculous wonders have resulted
          from a Soul Transfer. It is up to
          you if it is worth the risk.

Darren's eyes drift over to Asa once more.

                    DARREN
          Why are you telling me this?

                    BUZIBA
          Would that answer change your
          decision?

                    DARREN
               (beat)
          I'll do it.

                    TAU
          Darren, hold on, we don't know if
          this would work.

                    DARREN
          Only one way to find out.

Darren kneels beside Asa and holds her hand. Buziba
hesitates.

                    BUZIBA
          You… may be dead before you see the
          results of the Transfer. Are you
          certain—

                    DARREN
          I don't need to see her alive, I
          just need her to *be* alive. Now,
          show me how to do this.

Buziba is filled with a simultaneous fascination and sadness.
He steps closer to Darren when—

                        PHARAOH (O.S.)
              Let's not be so hasty.

Pharaoh stands in the doorway looking as an average man. All heads snap to see him, in shock.

                        PHARAOH
              I'm certain there's another—

In a blink, the three rush him, instantly summoning their Soul Fluxes and directing it toward Pharaoh's neck.

They each connect, and Pharaoh's head flies off, rolls on the ground. His body flops over.

But within seconds, the head and body crack like ceramic and sink into the ground. A beat passes. The light in the building shifts until it takes a familiar shape again. It turns into an APPARITION of Pharaoh.

                        PHARAOH CLONE
              I suppose something intangible will
              have to suffice for this
              conversation.

Darren strikes again, swings a SWORD through his neck, but it slips through him. Rage bleeds through Darren's teeth.

                        DARREN
              Stop the damn tricks and fight me
              yourself!

                        PHARAOH CLONE
              You know that wouldn't be smart for
              either of us.

INT. ATLANTIS - TEMPLE - DAY

Pharaoh sits on his throne and overlooks the lush forestation of the landscape.

                        PHARAOH
              I'm afraid I've made too many
              enemies too quickly to make a
              personal appearance…

                                  INTERCUT:

                        PHARAOH CLONE
              …so we'll make due with a call.

                        BUZIBA
              How are you doing this?

                    PHARAOH CLONE
          It's a trick I picked up.

                    DARREN
          What makes you think I have
          anything to say to you?!

                    PHARAOH CLONE
                (sighs; observes the room)
          I understand there is a lot of
          hatred in this room. Toward each
          other… toward me. My goal from the
          very beginning was to make us—the
          ones who remain—whole again.

                    DARREN
          You expect me to believe any of
          your shit? You just took everything
          from me.

                    PHARAOH CLONE
          I suppose it is hard to hear when a
          vengeful heart is screaming at you…

The clone lifts a hand slowly. Those in the room brace.

Back in Atlantis, a WIND HOWLS through the Temple and a
single SOUL bleeds from the floor, shoots out of the window.

                    PHARAOH CLONE
          So allow me to quell the noise.

The soul descends, enters the Cairo building, fills the space
before finding its vessel. It pours itself into Asa's body.
Within seconds her cheeks blush red. Her eyes crack open.

Darren rushes to her side, cradles her as she slowly wakes.

Pharaoh then outstretches his arm to Tau, who is too floored
by a resurrection to notice. In response, a group of ELEMENTS
converge on Tau's nub, begin to merge, shift into flesh…

Tau pulls away from the elements to reveal a new human ARM.
He is an utter shock, awe. Tears start to well.

But Pharaoh waves his arm again, this time over Khadija. A
beat passes… He looks away, sad. *Buziba notices.*

                    ASA
          Wha— happened?

> DARREN
> (sobbing)
> It's okay, babe, everything's fine!
> You don't have to get up.

Asa scans the room until she sees Pharaoh.

A fire lights in her eyes. She swings her legs beneath her,
points her finger like a gun, aims at Pharaohs head, then…

Nothing.

She tries again. Same result.

> PHARAOH CLONE
> Olive branches are most effective
> when pruned.

Asa gets lightheaded, starts to fade. Darren catches her.

> DARREN
> Asa!

> ASA
> I'm fine… so tired.

She faints.

> DARREN
> (to Pharaoh)
> What did you do?

> TAU
> He fixed me…

Darren notices Tau's new arm. The two are indistinguishable.

> PHARAOH CLONE
> Made you whole, just as I said.
> Hopefully that was enough to earn
> some of your time.

Darren, Buziba, and Tau exchange looks, silently agree to
disarm.

> DARREN
> What do you want?

> PHARAOH CLONE
> In a word: help.

INT. SENEGAL PRESIDENTIAL PALACE - PRESIDENT'S OFFICE - DAY

PRESIDENT MOUSTAPHA sifts through NOTECARDS as a MEDIA TEAM sets up a camera. A TELEVISION plays the news, distracts Moustapha with images of fallen Caucasians.

>   MOUSTAPHA
>   Are we ready?

The media team ushers him into place. They begin a countdown when LAMINE, female 40s, barges in with a note.

>   LAMINE
>   Wait! More news from the Institute
>   of Geology.

>   MOUSTAPHA
>   I'm not revising this address
>   again. That will have to wait—

>   LAMINE
>   (hands him the note)
>   It's about Mauritania…

The media team waits impatiently as Moustapha scans the note. His face shifts from botheration to frightened incredulity.

>   MOUSTAPHA
>   Call them in.

LATER:

The President's office is filled with teams of scientists and a media team that's dozing from another delay.

The blank, white wall becomes the canvas for a PROJECTOR. It displays a map of West Africa. GEOLOGIST A, female 50s, directs to the area above Senegal.

>   GEOLOGIST A
>   Sensors detected seismic activity
>   just north of the border, abruptly
>   followed by the rapid sea level
>   decline. This activity took place
>   only moments after the phenomenon
>   with the Europeans.

GEOLOGIST B, male 50s, mans the projector, switches slides.

>   GEOLOGIST B
>   This is the geography of West
>   Africa as we know it, and this…
>   (switches slides)
>   (MORE)

                    GEOLOGIST B (CONT'D)
          …is the current view from
          satellites.

The images show TWO long RIVERS that stretch from the Pacific
and the Mediterranean Sea and meet at the Eye of the Sahara.
Moustapha gawks at the map of the transformed Mauritania.

                    MOUSTAPHA
          It must be… coincidence…

                    PHARAOH CLONE (PRE-LAP)
          The ground work has been laid.

INT. CAIRO - VACANT BUILDING - DAY

Buziba, Darren, and Tau listen to Pharaoh, on guard.

                    PHARAOH CLONE
          The Ophiuchus Stone granted me the
          power to terraform the Sahara
          Desert. I've simultaneously
          resurrected the fallen city and set
          the foundation for something new!

                    BUZIBA
          "Fallen city"? Did you really…?

                    PHARAOH CLONE
          That's right. Atlantis has been
          resurrected. Of course, granted the
          Stone's power, the resurrection was
          always going to be the easy part.
          The true challenge comes in
          populating the space. This is where
          you come in. Help me build a new
          nation!

                    DARREN
          Nope.

                    PHARAOH CLONE
          No?

                    DARREN
          I've heard that phrase too many
          time in the last month to act like
          I don't know what comes next.

                    PHARAOH CLONE
          I'm sure you have, and that's why
          I'm inviting you. Think of the
          perspective you can offer.
                    (MORE)

> PHARAOH CLONE (CONT'D)
> An American engineer removed from
> his heritage. A Rwandan abandoned
> by his people twice over. A Basotho
> who once walked with the disabled.
> And I, a man whose childhood was
> robbed by the evils of Apartheid.
> In one way or another, we've all
> lost our identity, forced by the
> world to live without one.

Pharaoh lifts his arm in a welcoming embrace
indistinguishable from a T-pose.

> PHARAOH CLONE
> But we will form a new identity. We
> will plant seeds in the soil of a
> new Pan-Africa, and the trees that
> sprout forth will be rooted in a
> new ideal—a new world!
> (beat)
> Darren, create the nation your
> grandmother always deserved.

Something seizes Darren. He can't tell if it's rage or grief.

> BUZIBA
> Give us one day and you'll have
> your answer from us.

Pharaoh looks at all in the room, nods. He turns to exit.

> PHARAOH CLONE
> That's a fair request. When you are
> ready to give your answer, just
> call my name…
> (clone fades away)
> I will hear you.

The group waits to ensure they are alone before they speak.

> TAU
> I'd say that's a new low for you,
> Buziba. The Waalisha were beaten
> for less than a day before you
> jumped to the next winning team.

> BUZIBA
> Watch your tongue before you lose
> your arm again.

> TAU
> Just try to take it.

                    BUZIBA
          (scoffs)
     Since I clearly have to explain it
     to you, I am only stalling until we
     devise a plan. The answer was
     always going to be "no".

                    TAU
     "We"?

                    BUZIBA
     He poses a threat to more than just
     the Muzungu now. At the very least,
     I can point the fools willing to
     oppose him in the right direction.

                    DARREN
     I guess that's a compliment.

Darren lays Asa down, blankets her with her shawl.

                    DARREN
     But even I'm not that crazy. You
     saw what he did to Arjana's
     soldiers with that Stone. The
     Waalisha routed multiple armies
     with a fraction of that power. Now
     Pharaoh has the whole thing and
     he's resurrecting ancient cities.

                    TAU
     He's got the power to rip souls
     from people's bodies! That's not
     the same as staring down a bullet.

                    BUZIBA
     Yes, but you fools are both missing
     an important detail.
          (points to Asa)
     He has not done the same to us.

                    TAU
     Just because he *has not* does not
     mean he *cannot*.

Darren stares as Asa for a beat. The lightbulb goes off.

                    DARREN
     Either way, we are still here, and
     I can probably guess why.

Darren faces Tau and Buziba, studies their expressions.

                         DARREN
          Of course, the only sure-fire way
          to keep him from doing it again is
          to take the Stone from him.

                         TAU
          Is that even possible? How would we
          even get that close to him?

                         BUZIBA
          I think you already know the answer
          to that.

INT. ATLANTIS - TEMPLE - DAY

Pharaoh reclines in his throne as his PHONE RINGS. The caller
ID reads: Moustapha.

                         PHARAOH
          Looks like he's pieced it together.

He hears a VOICE echo in his head…

                         DARREN (V.O.)
          Pharaoh, I'm ready.

                         PHARAOH
          And just in time, too.

EXT. CAIRO - VACANT BUILDING - DAY

Darren steps away from the building and waits. Tau and Buziba
watch from the door, but do not join him.

Light shifts before Darren, forms another Apparition.

                         DARREN
          I'll do it.
             (Pharaoh scans for others)
          It'll just be me… for now.

                         PHARAOH CLONE
          Well, you have great timing. We
          have work to do.

The Apparition snaps and a BUBBLE of WIND lifts Darren from
the ground. In a flash, Darren is launched into the sky. He
flies West at hypersonic speed.

                                        FADE OUT.

END OF ACT ONE

ACT TWO

FADE IN:

INT. SENEGAL PRESIDENTIAL PALACE - PRESIDENT'S OFFICE - DAY

Moustapha paces in his office while the voice of Mauritania
PRESIDENT ZEIN blasts through his phone.

                    PRESIDENT ZEIN (V.O.)
          This was your doing, wasn't it?!

                    MOUSTAPHA
          Of course not, Zein. How could I
          possibly—

INT. MAURITANIA - GRAY PALACE - OVAL OFFICE - DAY

Multiple teams of ADVISORS in crisis management mode surround
President Zein. They have their own calls and conversations
vying for Zein's attention, but he is doing his own digging.

                    PRESIDENT ZEIN
          Years without a natural disaster,
          and the week after a neighboring
          country offers aid, the Sahara
          floods! What am I expected to
          think?

                                        INTERCUT:

                    MOUSTAPHA
          I understand how it appears, but
          how could any nation cause what
          happened? It's not just Mauritania
          that's reeling at the moment.

                    PRESIDENT ZEIN
          Did the ocean leap into the sky to
          cross any other nation, or was that
          just us? Thousands have been
          displaced from their homes so far.
          You are only dealing with a few
          lightheaded tourists!

                    MOUSTAPHA
          It is hardly that simple.

A SONICBOOM rattles the Presidential Palace windows.
Moustapha checks out the window to see Darren kneeling on the
ground and Pharaoh glancing at the window. He sees Moustapha.

                    MOUSTAPHA
          Mr. Zein, I will have to call you
          back. Please let us know if we can
          aid you.

                    PRESIDENT ZEIN
          I do not want your a—

Moustapha hangs up, places a WALKIE in his pocket, exits.

EXT. SENEGAL PRESIDENTIAL PALACE - COURTYARD - DAY

Darren catches his breath, shaken from the trip.

                    PHARAOH
          I thought you would be more
          exhilarated by that.

                    DARREN
          Don't do that again… Where are we?

                    PHARAOH
          Senegal.

                    DARREN
          Senegal? Why are we here?

                    PHARAOH
          Diplomacy.

Moustapha joins the two alone.

                    PHARAOH
          Good to see you again, my friend.

                    MOUSTAPHA
          Osas… please don't tell me you are
          connected with these catastrophes.

                    PHARAOH
          Why wouldn't I tell you? I'm here
          to bring good news, after all.

                    MOUSTAPHA
          Osas, millions all over Africa are
          dead! What kind of weapon did you
          get your hands on? How is this
          possible?

                    DARREN
          It's a lot to take in…

                    MOUSTAPHA
          And who are you?

                    PHARAOH
          This is Darren Davenport, the first
          cabinet member in Atlantis' new
          administration.

                    MOUSTAPHA
          Atlan—What are you on about?

                    PHARAOH
          I suppose it is indeed a lot to
          process. So, let me show you in
          greater detail.

Pharaoh raises his hand and summons another bubble that
seizes Darren and Moustapha. They are launched into the sky.
Then Pharaoh disappears—another Apparition.

INT. CAIRO - VACANT BUILDING - DAY

Asa's eyes peel open. She slowly gets to her feet.

                    TAU
          Finally awake, eh? It's good to
          have you back, my friend!

                    ASA
          Back? Where did I…

                    TAU
          For a couple hours you were… dead.

                    ASA
          Dead? Wait, where's—Darren!

                    BUZIBA
          At the moment, with your killer.

Buziba raises his arms in submission, disarming Asa.

                    ASA
          With Pharaoh? What's he doing?

                    TAU
          Same as usual: fixing issues that
          are not his own.

                    ASA
          He went to fight Pharaoh…
               (punches Tau's shoulder)
          And you didn't go with him?!

                    TAU
          Hey, I just got this arm…

Asa gasps, finally noticing the arm.

                    BUZIBA
          That man, Pharaoh, wanted your
          husband's help, so he revived you
          and restored Tau's arm. So, in
          return, your husband obliged.

                    ASA
          So… did he go fight or help him?

                    BUZIBA
          Both.

EXT. ATLANTIS - TEMPLE - DAY

Moustapha and Darren stare out into the Atlantean landscape,
awestruck. Pharaoh sits on his throne.

                    DARREN
          How is *this* the Sahara?

                    PHARAOH
          I believe you engineers call it
          "terraforming".

                    MOUSTAPHA
          All the aid you asked me to provide
          for Mauritania was not for them… it
          was for this.

                    PHARAOH
          Mauritania is welcome to the funds
          if President Zein is willing to
          work with Atlantis.

                    MOUSTAPHA
          Why would he be, Osas? Millions are
          dead because of your actions.
               (beat)
          Was that truly you?

                    PHARAOH
          I had to make room.

                    MOUSTAPHA
          For whom?

                    PHARAOH
          The return of the diaspora.

The two's eyes connect and Moustapha's fears are confirmed.
Moustapha looks away; a man betrayed. A man in disbelief.

> MOUSTAPHA
> How do you expect me to be a part
> of this?

> PHARAOH
> Because being an ally of Atlantis
> is in your people's best interest.
> It is certainly better than the
> alternative.

> MOUSTAPHA
> Are you threatening my people?

> PHARAOH
> Only giving you the verbiage to
> negotiate with Zein.

> MOUSTAPHA
> What would Khadi—

Pharaoh summons another WIND to pick up Moustapha.

> PHARAOH
> I already told you what Atlantis
> needs. Please advocate for that
> along with anything else you feel
> would be wise.

The wind ROARS and Moustapha is launched westward before he
can respond. He fades into the distance.

Pharaoh's head hangs almost imperceptibly.

> DARREN
> You know, the dumbest part of your
> plan was thinking you'd find people
> who'd think it's good idea.

> PHARAOH
> He will come around, as will you.
> (beat)
> Oh, yes. I should probably send
> Atlantis' ambassador to be a part
> of the discussions. We can discuss
> infrastructure and domestic matters
> when you return.
> (Darren is silent)
> Come now, we are making history. We
> are making the future! Think of how
> proud your grandmother would be.

> DARREN
> Probably more so than Khadija would
> be of—

Pharaoh's fist meets Darren's gut with the force of a train.
He collapses.

Another wind bubble swoops Darren up.

> PHARAOH
> Assist Moustapha. I will check your
> progress later.

Darren is sent soaring through the sky as Moustapha was.

As he soars, he looks back at the shrinking Atlantean Temple.
What did he get himself into?

INT. CAIRO - VACANT BUILDING - DAY, FLASHBACK

Darren, Tau, and Buziba huddle in the room.

> DARREN
> I do know, but a plan like that
> still equates to overthrowing a
> god. I can't go in without having
> some idea of what he's capable of.
> You Arjanans are the experts,
> right? What do you know?

> TAU
> My father never told me anything
> about the Ophiuchus Stone outside
> of the legends. Arjana doesn't like
> keeping records about it.

> BUZIBA
> More records enable outsiders to
> stumble upon the information, which
> only invites more conflict into the
> world. That was my job to prevent.

> DARREN
> So I have to go in blind?

> BUZIBA
> No. In the brief time he spoke with
> us, I noticed a few significant
> details.

> DARREN
> I'm listening.

                    BUZIBA
First, it seems that he can create
limbs and body parts on a whim,
even for those he has never met.

                    DARREN
         (to Tau)
How does that arm feel?

                    TAU
Like it's always been mine…

                    BUZIBA
This not only reveals the molecular
accuracy at which he can Flux, but
it suggests decapitation may not be
an effective method of killing him.

                    DARREN
Well, it's worth a try. What else?

                    BUZIBA
When he spoke to us, he used an
Apparition.

                    TAU
Isn't that the name of the Soul
Flux the Prince of Arjana uses?

                    BUZIBA
Yes. He must have crossed paths
with Prince Anansi when he was
collecting the Shards. That means
he must be able to reproduce the
Soul Fluxes of other people.

                    DARREN
So, not only can he make new limbs
for himself, he can copy anyone
else's Flux, too?

                    BUZIBA
It seems so. But here is where we
find our first good news.

                    DARREN
Still listening…

                    BUZIBA
The Ophiuchus Stone cannot
resurrect the dead.

                    DARREN
          What are you talking about? He just
          did that with Asa.

                    BUZIBA
          But not with Khadija…
               (beat)
          When he appeared earlier, he waved
          his hand toward your wife. That was
          when she breathed again. He then
          waved over Tau and gave him a new
          arm… but he also waved over
          Khadija's body. However, she did
          not respond at all.

                    TAU
          That doesn't mean he tried to
          revive her. He doesn't know her…

                    DARREN
          Actually… yeah, he does. Khadija
          was basically his adoptive mother.
          Maybe he did try…

                    BUZIBA
          But he failed to do so. This tells
          us two things. First, there are
          indeed limits to the Ophiuchus
          Stone's power. And second—

                    DARREN
          All of the lives he specifically
          took with the Stone can be brought
          back!

                    BUZIBA
          If those souls are only locked away
          and not lost, then perhaps.

Darren glances at his sleeping wife once more. Sighs temper
his excitement.

                    DARREN
          Still, he knows I really don't have
          a choice. Whether we try to stop
          him or not, I was always gonna go.

                    TAU
          How could he know that?

                    DARREN
          'Cause he has a hostage.

END FLASHBACK.

INT. CAIRO - VACANT BUILDING - DAY

Asa hangs her head.

                    ASA
          Me.

                    BUZIBA
          More accurately, he has millions of
          them but only one that flips the
          scale in his favor. Your husband
          will search for the Ophiuchus
          Stone, but even if he finds it, he
          will need an army to take it back.

                    TAU
          That's where we come in.

                    ASA
          All right. Then besides us three,
          who else do we—

Asa tries to stand, but stumbles over, her body weakened.

                    BUZIBA
          Without your Umoya, you will not be
          of much value in this fight.

                    ASA
          I don't need my Umoya to be
          valuable.
               (smiles)
          All I need is to make a call.

EXT. MAURITANIA - GRAY PALACE - DAY

Moustapha smoothes his clothing ruffled by flight. He finds
his poise as a SCREAM from above signals Darren's descent. He
lands in a well-groomed courtyard.

Wind cushions Darren's fall as his feet touch the ground.

                    DARREN
          That's not getting easier…

                    MOUSTAPHA
          So Osas sent his shoulder devil.

                    DARREN
               (notices Moustapha)
          You're blaming me for him a being
          mass murderer? I thought you know
          him.

                    MOUSTAPHA
The man I grew up with would never
have become this! I know his mother
and brother; they were my family
too. No murderer could ever come
from relatives that loving.

                    DARREN
You knew Khadija and Khadeem?

                    MOUSTAPHA
Of course! She was my second
mother, and Khadeem a close friend.
        (beat)
Why do you say "knew"?

Darren hesitates as marching footsteps interrupt them. Dozens
of MAURITANIAN AGENTS storm the courtyard, surround the two,
GUNS drawn.

Darren finally notices the GRAY PALACE nearby. In the window,
President Zein stares at the visitors.

INT. MAURITANIA - GRAY PALACE - OVAL OFFICE - DAY

Darren and Moustapha sit at a large conference table. More
Agents surround them. Zein paces around the table.

                    PRESIDENT ZEIN
First, you offer aid as if I am the
President of a third-world nation,
then you show up to my doorstep
uninvited demanding an audience. It
is as if you do not respect the
sovereignty of this office.

                    MOUSTAPHA
Zein, it is nothing like that. An
old political advisor suggested I
offer aid, but now I see why.

                    PRESIDENT ZEIN
Osas Pharaoh? I told him the same
thing I told you: stay out of
Mauritania's affairs!

                    DARREN
You know Pharaoh, too?

                    PRESIDENT ZEIN
You will stay out of this too,
American! I have enough people
butting into my business.

                        DARREN
             I'm here to help! I'm pretty sure I
             know more than anyone in the room
             about what's going on.

                        PRESIDENT ZEIN
             Splendid! You can gather your
             thoughts in detention.

Zein snaps and an Agent yanks Darren up, attempts to remove
him from the room. It is not easy.

                        DARREN
             Knock it off and listen to me!

                        PRESIDENT ZEIN
             You and this "Pharaoh" will learn
             to respect my authority in my
             country. If he is not here to
             learn, you will be an example.

Darren earns more guns trained on him as he tugs away. The
Agents shout commands at him, but Darren is fed up.

                        DARREN
             That's it… *CRAFTSMAN—CUFFS!*

Each gun in the room DEFORMS, wraps itself around the wrist
of its Agent. Panic ensues as BULLETS drop to the floor.

Darren BANGS on the table, wrangles everyone's attention.

                        DARREN
             Listen up! Everyone in this room is
             a hostage—including me! I'm here to
             prevent as many people from dying
             as possible. So are you gonna work
             with me or find out exactly how
             dangerous the guy who threw your
             country into chaos really is?

Moustapha finds his poise again. Zein reluctantly tempers his
rage, takes a seat at the head of the table.

                        PRESIDENT ZEIN
             The floor is yours.

EXT. ARJANA - INNER GATE - DAY

Bia leads a her soldiers through the open gate. They are
greeted with a community of Arjanans prepared to mourn.

Foremost among them is Queen Asase. She hobbles, assisted by wind, to embrace Bia. A hovering GURNEY floats to a stop beside her. A face imprinted through cloth is all she needs to see.

She leans on the gurney, allows tears to soak the cloth.

INT. ARJANA - QUEEN'S THRONE ROOM - DAY

The royal family and the Spectral Guard are the only ones in the throne room. The Queen makes her way to the throne.

> BIA
> Tano will receive a prince's
> burial, but first we will bury his
> killer!

The Queen mounts her throne. She stares off, her face blank.

> ANANSI
> A search party is locating Osas
> Pharaoh as we speak. They are
> instructed to report the moment he
> is found.

> BIA
> We will mobilize the full force of
> Arjana's might with your blessing!

Asase's gaze drifts upward as her shoulders are weighted by an invisible burden.

> BIA
> Mother… do we have your blessing?

> QUEEN ASASE
> You have always had my blessing,
> Bia, but our castle still falls.

> BIA
> What?

> ANANSI
> Her Divinity must be more specific
> than that…

> QUEEN ASASE
> Of course, let me be more clear.
>   (sighs; solemn)
> Arjana is not to engage with Osas
> Pharaoh. Will we allow things to
> progress organically.

                    BIA
          What?! Why not?

                    ANANSI
          Does Her Divinity… have a plan in
          mind?

                    QUEEN ASASE
          Not this time, Anansi. I believe
          the era of plans is past us all.

                    BIA
          Are you going mad?
              (calms herself)
          Mother, I know you are grieving,
          but we must act now! This is about
          more than just Tano!

                    QUEEN ASASE
          How do you know what this is about,
          child? Have your mere decades shown
          you the fruits of our plight? Have
          you seen something my centuries
          have not revealed to me?

                    BIA
          Is there something we're missing?
          Please share! Tell us why our
          mother, the Queen, does not want to
          avenge her son and fulfill her
          duty!

The Queen's eyes glaze over.

                    QUEEN ASASE
          Our dynasty has existed for twelve
          millennia. Twelve thousand years of
          building a beautiful sandcastle,
          protecting it from the
          inevitability of the tide. We
          called it our noble duty. Perhaps
          it truly was a just cause, but the
          wave still comes. Is it noble or
          foolhardy to fight the wave,
          knowing it could never be stopped?

                    ANANSI
          Why are you speaking as if the
          dynasty has ended? Bia and I are
          both here to take the throne.

                    QUEEN ASASE
          The dynasty was more than just the
          royal bloodline;
              (MORE)

                    QUEEN ASASE (CONT'D)
          it was the power that ran through
          it. That power ended with me.

                    BIA
          That does not matter! I do not care
          if neither of us can use a Spectral
          Flux, that power is not what makes
          us fit for the throne, just like it
          is not what makes you a great
          Queen!

                    QUEEN ASASE
          You are right. Either you or Anansi
          would make wonderful leaders, but
          the outcome would have remained the
          same… Whether it was my children,
          or your children, or the next, the
          Ophiuchus Stone would have
          eventually been restored.
                    (beat)
          And then I am left to ponder: what
          would be the legacy or Arjana? Are
          we deferrers of the End or
          obstructionists of a new beginning?

RADIO STATIC buzzes from Bia's pocket. She pulls out her GOLD
EARPIECE.

                    BIA
          The Ophiuchus Stone has already
          brought the end once. I refuse to
          watch it come again.

She puts the earpiece on, becomes confused…

                    BIA
          Buziba?! How dare yo—

                    ASA (V.O.)
          Hi, Bia! It's Asa!

                    BIA
          ASA?!

All in the room are shocked!

                    ASA (V.O.)
          So, good news: I'm alive! I lost my
          Umoya though, Pharaoh took it when
          he brought me back…

                    BIA
          But… then how are you using the
          Umoya Radio?

INT. CAIRO - VACANT BUILDING - DAY

Tau tries to listen in through Asa's earpiece.

                    ASA
          Buziba let me borrow his and
          connected it for me. He's right—

Asa turns around to see no one else in the room but Tau.

                    ASA
          Here… Or, he was.

                                        INTERCUT:

                    BIA
          Tell that trai—… Look, I'm glad you
          are alive, but I have much to do.

                    ASA
          Wait, we know where Pharaoh is!

                    BIA
          You do?

                    ASA
          Apparently, when I was…
          unconscious, Pharaoh offered to
          revive me if Darren went with him.
          He said he wants to make "everyone
          whole".

Tau presses his ear again the earpiece.

                    TAU
          We think he's gone to the ruins of
          Atlantis.

                    ASA
          And he wants Darren's help
          rebuilding it.

                    BIA
          I see. And your husband went to
          help that man, even after he
          massacred millions?

                    ASA
          Darren is keeping an eye on Pharaoh
          until we're all ready!

                    BIA
          Ready… for what?

                    ASA
          For war.

INT. MAURITANIA - GRAY PALACE - OVAL OFFICE - EVENING

A room full of halfway incredulous agents and diplomats
listen to Darren's story.

                    DARREN
          He needed all four Shards to
          rebuild that Stone, but now that he
          has it, he can do almost anything
          he wants.

                    MOUSTAPHA
          Are there limits to what he can do?

                    DARREN
          Hardly. He's had the Stone for less
          than a day and he's already turned
          the continent upside down.

                    PRESIDENT ZEIN
          What is his goal?

                    DARREN
          As far as I can tell, he wants to
          rebuild the city of Atlantis. All
          he mentioned was making it a Pan-
          African Mecca, so I don't know if
          he has any "world conquest" plans.

                    PRESIDENT ZEIN
          I see. But what does he *want*?

                    DARREN
          I just—
               (beat; contemplates)
          I don't know. He grew up in the
          apartheid, so I'm sure he has
          feelings he needs to work through.

                    PRESIDENT ZEIN
          And what about you, Moustapha?
          Surely you have some kind of
          insight into your so-called friend.

                    MOUSTAPHA
          He was always… displeased. He had a
          tendency to see injustices that
          weren't always there, projecting
          his past onto the present.
               (MORE)

> MOUSTAPHA (CONT'D)
> He claimed to see the future, but I
> always thought something behind him
> held his gaze. I suspect he may be
> a heavy-handed leader, but I don't
> think we should fear an iron fist.
> He truly wants to better the world.

> PRESIDENT ZEIN
> He is one who looks for problems.
> He'll never stop seeing them.

Zein steps away from the desk and toward the window.

> PRESIDENT ZEIN
> Darren, correct? How do you feel
> about Mauritania?

> DARREN
> I, uhm, haven't spent any time here
> yet, so I can't say.

> PRESIDENT ZEIN
> Then come have a look.

Darren walks over, gazes out the window into the city. He
sees the palace courtyard, but beyond it, the sun sets over
the ocean, a glistening outline over an unforgiving desert.

> PRESIDENT ZEIN
> Could you never find yourself
> living here?

> DARREN
> I don't have a good answer to that.

> PRESIDENT ZEIN
> Well, there is my answer.
> Foreigners have trouble seeing
> Mauritania for its true beauty.
> They see us as nothing more than an
> impoverished extension of the
> Sahara, willing to help but
> unwilling to be present. Their
> heart is not to help us; only to
> pity us, empathizing through the
> lens of their own trauma. It is an
> insult, and I sit in this office
> daily trying to ignore it. Of
> course, there is work to do, but no
> amount of work can fix the biases
> in one's perception. Pharaoh's
> trauma has made him an outsider to
> the beauty of his own continent.

279

                    DARREN
          Look, I'm not going to pretend he
          has everyone's best interest at
          heart, but that doesn't mean he
          hates the place.

                    PRESIDENT ZEIN
          But would he lay down his life for
          the welfare of the people? Of
          course not. So he is not deserving
          of the time of diplomats who would.

Zein eyes Moustapha. It is clear they agree.

                    DARREN
          Okay, even if he's a tyrant, you
          can't really ignore him now…

                    PRESIDENT ZEIN
          So then, what about you, Darren?
          Will you lay down your life to
          protect your people?

                    DARREN
          I'm not here to be a leader. All I
          wanna do is protect the people I
          care about, even if it kills me.

Zein studies Darren for a beat; likes what he sees.

                    PRESIDENT ZEIN
          Well then, maybe I should be
          negotiating with you.

He sits down again besides Moustapha and pulls out a chair.

                    PRESIDENT ZEIN
          Come, now. I would like to not take
          all night.

STATIC buzzes from under the table. All Agents in the room
check their persons; it's not theirs. Static buzzes again,
then Moustapha realizes it's him. He pulls out his walkie.

                    PRESIDENT ZEIN
          In Mauritania, it is considered
          polite to mute phones during a
          meeting, Moustapha.

                    MOUSTAPHA
          Pardon me, I didn't realize I could
          get signal here.

He clicks the walkie off.

EXT. ATLANTIS - TEMPLE - NIGHT

Pharaoh walks down a path that paves itself as he steps. It
ends at a patch of land a hundred feet from the temple.

Pharaoh waves his arm and THREE HEADSTONES form before him.
Names etch themselves into the stone, reading: "JIBRIL
PHARAOH — EVER-CLIMBING FATHER", "KHADIJA SECK — EVER-LOVING
MOTHER", and "KHADEEM SECK — EVER-LOYAL BROTHER".

He kneels before them.

                    PHARAOH
          Our kingdom has come, Baba. I can't
          bury you here, but at least you
          will be honored.
               (eyes linger on Khadeem)
          I'm sorry… I couldn't let anyone
          stop me. I made sacrifices, but it
          will be worth it… soon.

Pharaoh's eyes find the MOON. It bathes the land with light.
His eyes rest on it. It draws him in.

For a while…

He snaps out of it, as if remembering something important. He
takes another look at the headstones.

                    PHARAOH
          You will forgive me then.

WIND carries him up and away.

INT. MAURITANIA - GRAY PALACE - OVAL OFFICE - NIGHT

Darren scribbles notes into his SKETCHBOOK. He seems pleased
with his progress.

                    DARREN
          I think that'll work… and you're
          fine with this?

                    PRESIDENT ZEIN
          If it will stave off the beast for
          a while…

                    DARREN
          Cool. And Moustapha?

                    MOUSTAPHA
          My cabinet won't be pleased, but
          they will have to manage for now.

> DARREN
> All right.
> (chuckles)
> This might actually work. Consider
> violence averted.

Darren is still, frozen by a chill.

> MOUSTAPHA
> What is the matter?

Darren gets up, looks out the window. From above Pharaoh descends, looks expectantly at the Gray Palace.

> DARREN
> He's here.

> MOUSTAPHA
> Osas has always been audacious. It
> doesn't surprise me he would come
> in person.

> DARREN
> I doubt it. This is probably
> another hologram.

Zein rises from his chair.

> PRESIDENT ZEIN
> Shall we go?

The three start for the door, but another static PULSE distracts them.

> PRESIDENT ZEIN
> Goodness, Moustapha! If Mauritania
> is doomed by your rudeness during
> negotiations I'll have you locked
> up!

> MAURITANIAN AGENT 1
> My apologies, Mr. President. That
> was mine.

> MOUSTAPHA
> (pulls out his walkie)
> Technology, eh?

> DARREN
> (notices both walkies)
> Wait, can those both be set to the
> same frequency?

EXT. MAURITANIA - GRAY PALACE - NIGHT

Pharaoh's feet graces the ground as he makes contact. He is solely focused on the three men that walk toward him.

Darren, Zein, and Moustapha approach Pharaoh in the courtyard, careful not to get too close. Darren scratches behind his ear, disguising his adjustment of an EARPIECE. Zein and Moustapha have one too.

                    PHARAOH
          You all look tired. I take it this
          West African Summit went well?

                    MOUSTAPHA
          I believe you will be satisfied
          with our decision.

                    PRESIDENT ZEIN
               (quietly)
          If such a thing is possible.

                    PHARAOH
          I'm not so difficult to please.
          Now, what did you decide?

Darren reaches for his sketchbook.

                    MOUSTAPHA
          First, I need to know something.
               (beat)
          Darren told us about the Ophiuchus
          Stone, about the truth of Atlantis
          and the magic that you use. He also
          mentioned that Mama Khadija was
          involved as well.

                    PHARAOH
          Yes, she kept secrets from us both.

                    MOUSTAPHA
          I noticed as Darren spoke, he was
          careful to omit certain information
          about Khadija and Khadeem. However,
          earlier today he slipped. Whenever
          he mentioned those two, he spoke in
          past-tense.
               (Darren winces)
          Osas, what happened to them?

                    PHARAOH
          Khadija was involved in a conflict
          with the Waalisha earlier today.
          She did not make it.

>   MOUSTAPHA
>   I see. And Khadeem?

Pharaoh hesitates. Subtly shrinks to hide from shame.

>   PHARAOH
>   Khadeem fought me when he realizes
>   what my goals were. He didn't
>   survive the encounter.

>   MOUSTAPHA
>   Didn't survive? Did you… kill him?
>   (Pharaoh is silent;
>   Moustapha is betrayed)
>   I see. Darren, you may proceed.

Darren opens his notes slowly so Pharaoh's shame marinates.

Meanwhile, Mauritanian Agents glare out the window, listening via their walkies that are tuned to hear the conversation.

>   DARREN
>   These are the terms Mauritania
>   agreed to: First, the Mauritanian
>   government has chosen to
>   acknowledge Atlantis as a province
>   of the country.

>   PHARAOH
>   Only a province? Surely, you could
>   do better than that, Zein.

>   DARREN
>   That was *my* suggestion. If Atlantis
>   became a full country right off the
>   bat, we wouldn't have time or
>   resources to organize important
>   basic services. This gives Atlantis
>   independence while giving you time
>   to create a larger plan. This
>   change is effective immediately.

>   PHARAOH
>   That is a thoughtful suggestion.

>   DARREN
>   Also, the land that is considered
>   Atlantis will be all land within
>   100 square kilometers of the Eye of
>   the Sahara, where the city capital
>   resides.

>   PHARAOH
>   Hmm. It is a start.

DARREN
And now: Second, Senegal has agreed
to invest $1 billion into the
development of Atlantis'
infrastructure. That will consist
of railroads and roadways
connecting the province to
Nouakchott and drawing new
neighborhoods within the city. The
resulting accessibility to the rest
of West Africa should create a
tourist economy that'll bring all
kinds of people to the city. This
policy goes into effect next week…
That's all we came up with for now.
Does that work for you?

Pharaoh smiles, almost laughs, incredulous.

PHARAOH
Yes, yes, that is fantastic!

DARREN
Really? Great.

Darren sighs in relief as he pockets his sketchbook.

PHARAOH
This really is wonderful news!
Zein, thank you for accommodating
us under these circumstances. I'm
glad we could work out this deal
despite it all.

PRESIDENT ZEIN
"Despite", indeed.

PHARAOH
This is the future I told you
about, Moustapha. Senegal is
investing into the future of the
continent by literally paving a way
for the lost to return home. We are
building a bridge.

Moustapha emerges from a hushed gloom.

MOUSTAPHA
Is this really the future you spoke
about?

PHARAOH
Yes, we are closer than ever! It is
only a matter of time before—

                    MOUSTAPHA
Did you know then that this future
would be born from blood?
        (Pharaoh is stunned)
Millions are dead. Millions. Were
these deaths always a part of the
plan or just unfortunate
casualties?

                    PHARAOH
I determined… that the birth of a
new nation was worth the risk of
violence. I knew it couldn't be
avoided.

                    MOUSTAPHA
Was Khadeem's life worth the risk?
How could he see this future if you
killed him?

Darren and Zein view Moustapha from the side of their eye.
Darren is nervous, while Moustapha slips his fingers over the
MICROPHONE hidden in his lapel. He taps it inconspicuously.

                    PHARAOH
Khadeem stood against my cause. I
couldn't allow him to—

                    MOUSTAPHA
What is the point of building this
city if your family isn't even
around to see it? What of all the
Muzungu? I can't imagine they all
stood against your cause as well.

                    PHARAOH
Of course they did. Just by
existing they did!

                    MOUSTAPHA
Ah, so maybe there is more to your
words than you let on.

                    DARREN
Moustapha, simmer—

                    PRESIDENT ZEIN
You'll have to excuse your friend,
Osas Pharaoh. It turns out he is a
leader of exceptional scruples.
Negotiating with a tyrant is hard
to do with a calm heart.

                    DARREN
          Zein, you too! C'mon, don't make
          this turn sideways.

                    PRESIDENT ZEIN
          It is quite funny, actually. Even
          someone like Darren, who knows you
          are a man rotting from the inside,
          advocates for your dirty utopia if
          it means preventing bloodshed.
               (laughs)
          Truthfully, how can a man
          surrounded by such noble people be
          so contemptible?

                    PHARAOH
          Am I so contemptible? I sent Darren
          and Moustapha here to engage in
          diplomacy! It was even successful,
          but you are the ones letting pride
          ruin it all. Go ahead, Darren, tell
          them how foolish they're being!

Darren faces Pharaoh again, bites his lip.

                    DARREN
          Yeah, they are being foolish. But
          at least they're telling the truth.

                    PHARAOH
          Et tu? At least I know where we
          stand. Well, here is the new deal:
          Due to your brazen disrespect and
          clear animosity toward the mission
          of Atlantis, the previous terms are
          no longer satisfactory.

                    MOUSTAPHA
          We are finished negotiating.

                    PHARAOH
          As am I. Consider this a dictation.
          All land east of Nouakchott will
          secede from Mauritania. It is now
          Atlantis.

                    PRESIDENT ZEIN
          And there is the confirmation I
          needed! You truly are stupid.

                    PHARAOH
          You will agree to these terms and
          give me the land, or I will take
          it. Which is it?

                    PRESIDENT ZEIN
          You will need to pry the deed from
          my corpse.

                    PHARAOH
          Say less.

A FIREBALL swells in Pharaoh's palm. He hurls it at Zein, but
it is blocked by a STEEL DOME that emerges from the ground.

                    DARREN
          Pharaoh, that's enough! You got
          what you came for, so let's get out
          of here.

                    PHARAOH
          I came for respect. I am about to
          earn that now.

He charges another fireball, but a BULLET whizzes by his
head. He ascends to find the shooter.

A small platoon of MAURITANIAN SOLDIERS storm in, guns at-the-
ready. VEHICLES roll in from the opposite side of the Gray
Palace. Several hundred surround Zein, Darren, and Moustapha.

                    MOUSTAPHA
          My respect is beyond your reach.

Moustapha stands beside Zein, pats Darren on the shoulder.

                    DARREN
            (sighs)
          So much for diplomacy.

Darren peels away part of the dome to form a BROADSWORD.

                    PHARAOH
          I could take all your souls… just
          like I did with the Muzungu. It
          would be over in a blink. Painless.
          But I'm not going to do that…

Pharaoh raises his arms and the earth responds. TONS of dirt
rises from below the Soldiers' feet and meet FIRE and WIND in
the sky.

The dirt separates, molds into a hundred PUPPETS shaped like
Pharaoh himself. FLAME TETHERS connect his hands with their
bodies and they animate to life.

                    PRESIDENT ZEIN
          What in hell has he done?!

>   DARREN
>   (spooked)
>   That's Acacia's… Ifrit Shadow!

The hundred Ifrit Shadows prepare to strike.

>   PHARAOH
>   I will make this agonizing.

>   FADE OUT.

<u>END OF ACT TWO</u>

<u>ACT THREE</u>

                                        FADE IN:

INT. MAURITANIA - GRAY PALACE - OVAL OFFICE - NIGHT

Mauritanian Agent 1 watches from the window. He directs the
team of agents as they establish a new communications hub.
Agent 1 speaks into his EARPIECE.

                    MAURITANIAN AGENT 1
          The Armed Forces Reserves have
          arrived, Mr. President. Air Force
          is mobilizing as we speak.

                    PRESIDENT ZEIN (V.O.)
          Just in time. Hopefully we won't
          need them.

                    MAURITANIAN AGENT 1
          American, you are the most
          knowledgeable here. What can the
          enemy do so I can relay that to the
          military?

EXT. MAURITANIA - GRAY PALACE - CONTINUOUS

The Ifrit Shadows float, menacing the military below.

                    DARREN
          It might be quicker to list the
          things he can't do…

Pharaoh whips a wave through the flame threads, and the
puppets respond, lunging toward the military.

BULLETS fly, ripping through some puppets, getting caught in
others, but the puppets still come. They punch with flaming
fists, igniting the fatigues of some Soldiers. Others fight
through the flame, persist in shooting.

Puppets disintegrate from the bullets, but their falling ash
rises to the sky, reforms into more Ifrit Shadows. They
return to the battlefield.

Darren slashes through multiple puppets, but they reform into
a larger one. It ascends, then dive-bombs a group of
Soldiers. The EXPLOSION is lethal.

More puppets follow suit; they rain upon the military. Darren
raises more shields, but he cannot save many.

Soldiers spray bullets toward the sky, ripping through many diving puppets. Their ash quickly convalesces again.

> DARREN
> These are only puppets! Aim at
> Pharaoh!

Soldiers obey, firing at Pharaoh. The puppets all retreat, forming a barrier to catch the bullets.

Soldiers launch RPGs. The grenades hit the puppets from all sides. The explosions flash through the sky. Smoke screens their progress. Pharaoh falls from the resulting SMOKE CLOUD, lands on his feet below.

He barely has time to regroup before Darren bursts from the smoke and SWINGS for his neck. Darren misses. He is repelled by a GUST from Pharaoh. A voice crackles in his earpiece.

> MOUSTAPHA (V.O.)
> Did you succeed?

> DARREN
> What do you think?

BLACK LIGHTING discharges from Pharaoh's body. Darren erects steel LIGHTNING RODS just in time to absorb the strikes.

The lighting illuminates the smoke cloud enough for RPG gunners to take aim. They launch another wave of grenades.

But Pharaoh waves, suspends them all in WIND. Another push of his hand sends them back to where they came from. They almost hit before—

A LARGE STEEL WALL emerges, protects the Soldiers from harm.

Pharaoh looks at Darren, charges, swoops him into the air by his collar. He ZAPS Darren with electricity before tossing him back toward the ground. Darren tumbles next to Moustapha.

Pharaoh descends. As his feet touch the ground, the earth beneath him turns into CLAY. The clay spreads until it covers the entire palace courtyard.

CLAY BEASTS then emerge from the ground. They charge and begin to savage the Mauritanian Forces.

Moustapha helps Darren up. He is worse for wear but standing.

> MOUSTAPHA
> Stand. We are not finished yet.

291

                         DARREN
               Still don't think this'll work. I
               don't know why he bothers dodging.

                         MOUSTAPHA (V.O.)
               Just keep trying.

Darren tries to grab his sword, but it is lodged in the clay.
He tries to craft another sword from the ground, but the clay
does not move.

                         DARREN
               No, crap! Just like with Buziba…

                         PRESIDENT ZEIN
               Hurry and arm yourself!

                         DARREN
               He cut me off! I can't make a
               weapon if I can't get to the
               ground.

A CLAY HYENA beast charges at Zein. It almost bites before
Darren tackles it. He wrestles with the beast.

But the Soldiers do not fare as well. They are eviscerated by
the beasts.

                         PHARAOH
               Your pride has done this to you.
               Your pride dooms your people!

A MISSILE drops from above. Pharaoh blocks with a FORCEFIELD
before he notices the culprit. THREE FIGHTER JETS soar
overhead. Pharaoh's anger surges as he flies after them.

The clay hyena lets up slightly, enough for Darren to kick it
away. It slides into the STEEL DOME Zein shelters behind, and
Darren notices it is still steel. He pulls the dome down, and
its metal ravels around the hyena. It is bound.

Darren looks around. Suddenly, all the clay beasts are less
competent. The Soldiers gain the advantage and subdue them.
They turn their sights on Pharaoh who pursues the jets.

                         MOUSTAPHA
               Despite our trouble, I dare to say
               you oversold his powers.

                         DARREN
               Something's off…

Fire streaks from the tails of TWO falling fighter jets in
the distance.

The THIRD's engine ROARS as it plummets into the Gray Palace.
The Palace explodes, sends a shockwave that knocks over all
in the courtyard.

Pharaoh's attention returns to the ground, and the beasts
increase their intensity.

Darren looks around. The battlefield decays into a hellscape.
It's hard to see, to be in the midst of… He looks for
Pharaoh. He descends, veiled by smoke from organic flame.

>   DARREN
>   That's it…

Darren pulls a slab of steel that binds the hyena. He crafts
it into a BLADED BOOMERANG.

>   DARREN
>   Pharaoh, that's enough!

He hurls it at Pharaoh, who notices it too late… It makes
contact…

The Clay Beasts stop moving, fall over. The Soldiers finally
have respite.

The boomerang returns to the ground, lodges into the ground.
All who see it notice something along its blade: BLOOD.

>   PRESIDENT ZEIN
>   You were correct, Moustapha!

>   MOUSTAPHA
>   Osas was never one for long-
>   distance negotiations.

>   DARREN
>   He's actually here… and without the
>   Stone. We actually have a chance!

Pharaoh removes his hand from his shoulder and sees blood. He
is shocked, spooked—enraged.

>   PHARAOH
>   How could you… spurn the hand that
>   offers you peace? I must not have
>   been clear. Let me fix that.

Pharaoh lifts his hand above his head. In response, FIRE,
AIR, WATER, and EARTH meet, swirl in unison above him.

>   DARREN
>   Now what?

INT. CAIRO - VACANT BUILDING - NIGHT

Asa and Tau huddle together, gazing into a SMARTPHONE screen.
They are on a video call with King Kopano.

                    KING KOPANO
          So that's what is happening. I
          never imagined the Ophiuchus Stone
          could be so deadly. I suppose the
          legends aren't exaggerated.
               (beat)
          It's very risky.

                    ASA
          I know… Do you think you can do it?

                    TAU
          We know His Majesty is already
          being stretched skinny, but
          anything you can spare helps.

                    KING KOPANO
               (clears throat)
          I will speak to Geraldine and see
          what we can do. My responsibility
          is to Lesotho, but this may not be
          a matter we can afford to ignore. I
          will provide an update soon.

The call ends.

                    ASA
          Yes—off to a great start!

                    TAU
          Lesotho is not nothing, but we'll
          still need more.

                    ASA
          We better get busy, then!

Asa starts for the door but is startled by Anansi's
Apparition.

                    ANANSI
          Asa Davenport, Tau Lane—a moment.

Tau bows as if apologizing for a rudeness.

                    ASA
          Oh, hi, Anansi.

                    ANANSI
          It is about your husband.

                    ASA
Is something wrong?!

                    ANANSI
          (shakes head)
We neglected to offer a word of
extreme caution. When you speak to
him, make sure he knows to avoid
confrontation with Osas Pharaoh at
all costs.

                    TAU
He's stubborn, but he's not stupid.

                    ASA
Well, yeah. I doubt Darren would
try to fight Pharaoh on his own
unless he felt provoked. Why—

                    ANANSI
Those who make contact with the
Ophiuchus Stone gain access to the
power previously limited to the
Royal Family of Arjana. You
witnessed a glimpse of this during
your training in Arjana.

                    ASA
I did—Oh, the Queen's gravity
power?

                    ANANSI
Yes. Even if Pharaoh is separated
from the influence of the Stone, he
can access this power at will.

EXT. MAURITANIA - GRAY PALACE - NIGHT

A miniature STORM CLOUD funnels around Pharaoh as all four
elements gather in his hand. Darren gazes on in confusion.
This isn't a normal Soul Flux…

                    ANANSI (V.O.)
In discerning hands, it is a weapon
powerful enough to rout small
legions: A Spectral Flux.

The cloud coalesces, condenses into a dark blaze.

                    MOUSTAPHA
          (to Darren)
Perhaps you should be stopping
this.

Darren grabs the boomerang, shifts it into a STEEL BOW and ARROW. He takes aim, fires…

The arrow halts at Pharaoh's gaze. A gesture sends it back.

The arrow impales Darren's leg; he stumbles, wails in pain. Soldiers shoot at Pharaoh, but the bullets are averted, sucked into the blaze by a magnetic force.

The elements finish combining. An **EBONY SUN** the size of a basketball floats above Pharaoh's palm. Soldiers wince at its brightness, flinch at its heat.

> PHARAOH
> A new Africa will come to exist.
> Anyone who stands against it will
> burn!

Black FIRE and LIGHTNING flares, arcs away from the Ebony Sun and strikes the ground. It spreads, swallows the soldiers.

Moustapha, Zein, and Darren take cover behind the clay hyena's bound corpse. It's hardly shelter.

The flames spread. They devastate the Armed Forces, burning them alive.

Darren can't ignore the screams. He sees the Soldiers' bodies burning, disintegrating before him. They stand no chance. Some lay down their arms and kneel, but fire denies their surrender. Their guns are drawn into the Sun, destroyed.

> DARREN
> Pharaoh, STOP—they surrender!

Pharaoh's eyes meet Darren's. He turns away and continues…

Darren pounds the earth again, but the clay still prevents him from Fluxing. He is hopeless—useless.

> DARREN
> STOP IT!!!

Pharaoh ignores.

> DARREN
> Zein, give him what he wants!

Zein is frozen, stupefied in horror. The helplessness eats at his pride. He hears nothing until…

> DARREN
> ZEIN!

Zein responds, looks at Darren. He knows what to do.

He stands from behind the hyena, arms waving.

> PRESIDENT ZEIN
> I will do it! Stop!

The black flames subside. Pharaoh finds Zein below.

> PRESIDENT ZEIN
> I will give you the land… Please,
> no more carnage…

A grin creeps onto Pharaoh as the fire retreats into the Sun. Within a moment, the Ebony Sun vanishes as if it never existed.

> PHARAOH
> Was that so difficult?

He descends, floating within arms distance of the Zein.

> PHARAOH
> You see, I much prefer to receive
> the deed from living hands.

> MOUSTAPHA
> Osas… Look what you have done…

Pharaoh's eyes flit, struggling to look away from Moustapha.

> PHARAOH
> Their suffering ended quickly. Not
> all are so lucky.
> (to Zein)
> I'll allow you a week to draw the
> new map and deliver the document.

> DARREN
> (to the bodies)
> I'm sorry… I'm sorry…

> PHARAOH
> We shall be off.

Wind lifts Darren; he joins Pharaoh as they ascend. But Darren reaches into his pocket, pulls SOMETHING out, inconspicuously drops it.

It falls to the ground beside piles of crisped corpses. The two fly off, leaving a SONICBOOM in their wake.

Moustapha glances at Zein, who seethes in unfathomable rage.

> MOUSTAPHA
> You did what was wise. I would have
> also given him the deed if it saved
> lives.

> PRESIDENT ZEIN
> He will get no deed from me! The
> only thing he has earned is a war!

MEDICAL TEAMS begin to move in. They don't know where to
begin, so they start with who's closest. They are soon
overwhelmed while survivors are inconsolable.

They work in the silence of death, the breaths and weeping
that accompanies cinders… but one more sound breaks through.

A VOICE crackles through a speaker—a woman's voice. It pleads
for an answer.

Moustapha hears the voice, searches for the source. A PHONE'S
LIGHT gleams through ashes… He picks up the phone. There's
someone on the other end.

> ASA (V.O.)
> Can you hear? Don't hang up—we'll
> try a new spot!

> MOUSTAPHA
> Hello?

> ASA (V.O.)
> Darren!

> MOUSTAPHA
> He left his phone behind. I'm
> guessing it was not an accident.
> You must be his wife.

> ASA (V.O.)
> Left it? Where is he now?!

> MOUSTAPHA
> He was taken by Osas, I presume
> back to the area he called
> Atlantis.

> ASA (V.O.)
> (gathers thoughts)
> Who am I speaking to?

> MOUSTAPHA
> I'm Moustapha, President of
> Senegal.

>   ASA (V.O.)
>   President?
>   (beat; background voices)
>   Where are you now, Moustapha?

>   MOUSTAPHA
>   I am currently at the Presidential
>   Palace of Mauritania. Darren was
>   just here. There was a conflict—

>   ANANSI (O.S.)
>   Tell me what happened.

Moustapha jerks around to see Anansi's Apparition behind him.

>   ANANSI
>   Do not leave out any details.

INT. ATLANTIS - TEMPLE - NIGHT

Pharaoh and Darren float into the temple. The wind releases them as they touch the temple floor.

Pharaoh checks his wound—it's already healed. Darren struggles to remove the arrow. He pulls it out from either side and presses on the entry and exit wound.

>   PHARAOH
>   I could heal you, but letting you
>   deal with the pain will be your
>   punishment.

>   DARREN
>   How could you do that? Like, how
>   are you even capable?

>   PHARAOH
>   Sacrifices must be made in order to
>   achieve ones goals. Sometimes,
>   humanity is one of those
>   sacrifices.

>   DARREN
>   You know all those "Muzungu" you
>   hate so much? Maybe you're just
>   like them. Maybe you're worse.

Pharaoh hesitates, attempts to walk away.

>   DARREN
>   Why are you even keeping me around?
>   You could've killed me anytime you
>   wanted. You could kill me now…

299

                    PHARAOH
          I need to know if this is possible.
               (pauses; contemplates)
          You came here to find an identity
          that was lost to your family. I
          lost mine as well… Before the
          Homelands; before my family's
          murder. My people's culture,
          freedom, pride was taken from
          us—stolen. Atlantis is a once-in-a-
          millennia opportunity to restore
          what was taken. It can work, but I
          don't know if it will. That is why
          I need a case study. How can I hope
          to restore the culture of millions
          of people if I cannot do it for a
          single man who came to Africa for
          that very purpose? If Atlantis
          cannot give you what you seek, then
          I have wasted my life pursuing a
          fantasy. That will not be the case.
          Until I determine that this
          Atlantean experiment is no longer
          worth building, I will keep you
          alive.

                    DARREN
          But you're not building. You
          already started a war. You killed
          millions of people… and it's only
          been one day.

                    PHARAOH
          No revolution has ever been
          successful without spilling blood.
          How can you build a new bridge
          unless you burn the rotting one?

                    DARREN
          You and the Waalisha are just the
          same. You're perfectly fine burning
          everything to the ground as long as
          you get to be king of the ashes!

                    PHARAOH
          And what comes from ashes but
          fertilized soil?

Pharaoh walks away, leaves Darren to tend to his wound. He
stares out into the Atlantean landscape.

                    PHARAOH
          There's plenty of land to till.

EXT. CAIRO - DOWNTOWN STREETS - NIGHT

LIGHTNING BOLTS arc from the Great Pyramid, streaking across
the night sky. It is the primary sign of activity in an
otherwise ghost city.

A BLUR kicks up sand in its wake. We follow the blur to see
Tau carrying Asa piggy-back. They search the town. Asa points
to something.

                    ASA
       There!

Tau course-corrects hops over to:

EXT. CAIRO - DOWNTOWN ROOF - NIGHT

Buziba stands alone on the roof, solemnly overlooks the
necropolis. Waalisha corpses remain from a lack of people to
collect them. He is the sole life in sight…

Until Asa and Tau arrive. They hop onto the roof behind
Buziba, who ignores their presence. Asa goes to meet him.

                    TAU
            (to Asa)
       Be… careful.

Beneath Tau's Basotho blanket, he clutches his new arm. Asa
nods acknowledgement.

                    ASA
            (to Buziba)
       Hey! Are you *trying* to get struck
       by lightning?

Buziba hesitates, confused at the concern.

                  BUZIBA
       I… What do you want?

                    ASA
       Come with us. We've got a plan and
       we need your help.

Buziba coughs out an incredulous laugh.

                    ASA
       I'm serious! We're in contact with
       Senegal's president, thanks to
       Darren. Anansi is talking to him
       now. Between Senegal, Lesotho, and
       Arjana, we have a fighting chance!

                    BUZIBA
          Did Prince Anansi send you to
          collect me?

                    ASA
          No… It was my idea.
               (beat)
          Well, come on.

                    BUZIBA
          This is not the first massacre I
          have seen. Far from it. I could not
          stop those. And this one—my hands
          are filthy. What do I offer?

                    ASA
          Umm… you're strong?

                    BUZIBA
          I thought so once. There's no value
          in my strength. Nor the rest of me.

Those words make Asa's blood run cold.

                    TAU
          There's our answer. Let's get
          going, Asa.

Asa swats Buziba's back.

                    ASA
          NEVER SAY THAT!

She hesitates when Buziba falls to his knees, eyes flooding.
His breaths are heavy from the pain that labors them.

                    BUZIBA
          You and your husband sacrificed
          your own safety for each other's…
          My whole life I hoped it was the
          outsiders and Muzungu who were the
          wretched, unloving ones. Determined
          to prove that, I have harmed many,
          but two Americans disproved that.
          Alas, the common denominator of all
          the unkindness I have seen is me.

He lifts his head, gazes at the lightning.

                    BUZIBA
          So let Divinity claim me. For what
          value does one so undeserving of
          love offer in the face of the evil
          he caused?

                    ASA
          None of that matters! You hear me?!

Buziba is still until Asa spins him around to meet her eyes.

                    ASA
          It doesn't matter what anyone
          thinks about you—not me, not
          Arjana, not the world! No one else
          determines your value. Only you do!

                    BUZIBA
               (glances at Tau)
          I spilled so much blood, maimed
          those undeserving, left a blight on
          the world in service to a negligent
          kingdom, and led countless more to
          die in this conflict. What have I
          done to benefit this world?

                    ASA
          That's for you to decide.

Asa offers her hand, but she resembles GLENDA in Buziba's
eyes. He withdraws his head; his heart wrenches.

Asa sighs, walks to Tau.

                    ASA
          Come find us when you do.

Tau and Asa jet away, leaving Buziba behind.

INT. ATLANTIS - TEMPLE CORRIDOR - NIGHT

Darren limps through the halls of the temple, his leg only
halfway healed. He roams, mentally notes his surroundings.

The temple walls are ornate materials, but not artistic in
design—the architecture the work of an unskilled craftsman.

A LIGHT bleeds from a room at the corridor's end. Darren
investigates, is led into…

INT. ATLANTIS - OPHIUCHUS CHAMBER - CONTINUOUS

A wide and empty room is lit by a singular source in its
center. Darren peers into it, recognizes its shape. It is the
OPHIUCHUS STONE. It floats above a shrine-like stand.

Darren rushes toward it, stops right next to it. He scans for traps… Pharaoh is nowhere to be seen. He is unsure, but he steels himself. He cautiously reaches for the Stone…

Then he freezes.

A CHILL paralyzes him. The room around him fades into a dark white noise. He is terrorized by a force he can only feel. A DEVIL's eyes burn into his back. It stands behind him.

Darren withdraws, jerks around to see who's behind him. The room is normal again, and no devil is in sight. Only Pharaoh.

Pharaoh leans against the wall, casually observes Darren. He snickers.

> PHARAOH
> For a moment, I thought you would
> do it. You made the right choice.

> DARREN
> You really think it's smart to be
> testing me?

> PHARAOH
> Wasn't a test. Just a warning.

Pharaoh waves and the shrine sinks into the floor, takes the Stone with it. He starts for the door.

> DARREN
> That black fireball… whose Soul
> Flux was that? It was different
> than your lightning. Let me
> guess—it was a guardian who tried
> to defend a shard from you before
> you killed them for it.

> PHARAOH
> Hmph, I do not know exactly. It
> came as naturally as my Ebony Bolt,
> but it's certainly more powerful.
> No doubt another perk of my contact
> with the Ophiuchus Stone.
> (checks Darren's leg)
> You seem to be healing fine. By the
> morning you should be—

> DARREN
> How long do you think you can keep
> this up?
> (beat; solemnly)
> I didn't think the Stone would just
> be lying around here.
> (MORE)

                    DARREN (CONT'D)
It's just another weapon. At least,
in your hands it is. Even if I do
help you and all this works out,
how long until other nations come
for it?

Pharaoh absorbs Darren's words.

                    PHARAOH
When I obtained the Stone, I was…
imparted… *burdened* with a certain
wisdom. This is a coveted power.
I've seen many die trying to
prevent the world from misusing it
again. I will do the same. However,
it's also a formidable power. The
Arjanans tried to protect the Stone
without using it. I will not repeat
that mistake. So, let them come.

                    DARREN
If you say so.

                    PHARAOH
I do say so. Moreover, I'm not
worried about anyone else obtaining
the Stone.

MEMORY FLASH: Pharaoh ignores Anansi's warning in the Eastern
Temple; Pharaoh is pulled into the Stone at the Giza Plateau.

                    PHARAOH
         (beat; haunted)
It requires… a certain condition be
met to wield it; one very few meet.
Otherwise, anyone who contacts it
will not survive the encounter.

                    DARREN
A condition, huh? Wanna fill me in?

                    PHARAOH
         (chuckles)
No. Also, you are wrong about
something. It is not just a weapon
to me. The whole point of finding
it was to use its power to create,
and look what I've done so far!
I've turned this part of the Sahara
into an oasis, but there is still
much work to do.
         (exits the chamber)
Get some rest, Darren. Our work
continues tomorrow.

INT. MAURITANIA — FIRST AID TENT — NIGHT

Moustapha peeks outside the tent and sees the courtyard—a battlefield drowned in blood. Cleanup and mourning has begun.

He closes the tent and turns to Anansi.

> MOUSTAPHA
> I am ready.

> ANANSI
> Have a seat. Close your eyes.

Moustapha sits. As his eyes close we pull in, seeing nothing but his face…

INT. CAIRO — VACANT BUILDING — CONTINUOUS

Moustapha's eyes open—he is in Cairo. Asa and Tau give him a nod, expecting him. Anansi's Apparition welcomes him. Moustapha looks around, amazed he has been transported.

Then the front door opens. Buziba steps through. Anansi and Tau greet him with death stares. Asa waves him over.

> ASA
> That's everyone.

He takes his place at a table. Asa, Buziba, Moustapha's Apparition, Anansi's Apparition, Tau, and King Kopano via video chat are all in attendance.

> ASA (CONT'D)
> All right, let's get started!

FADE TO BLACK.

<u>END OF SHOW</u>

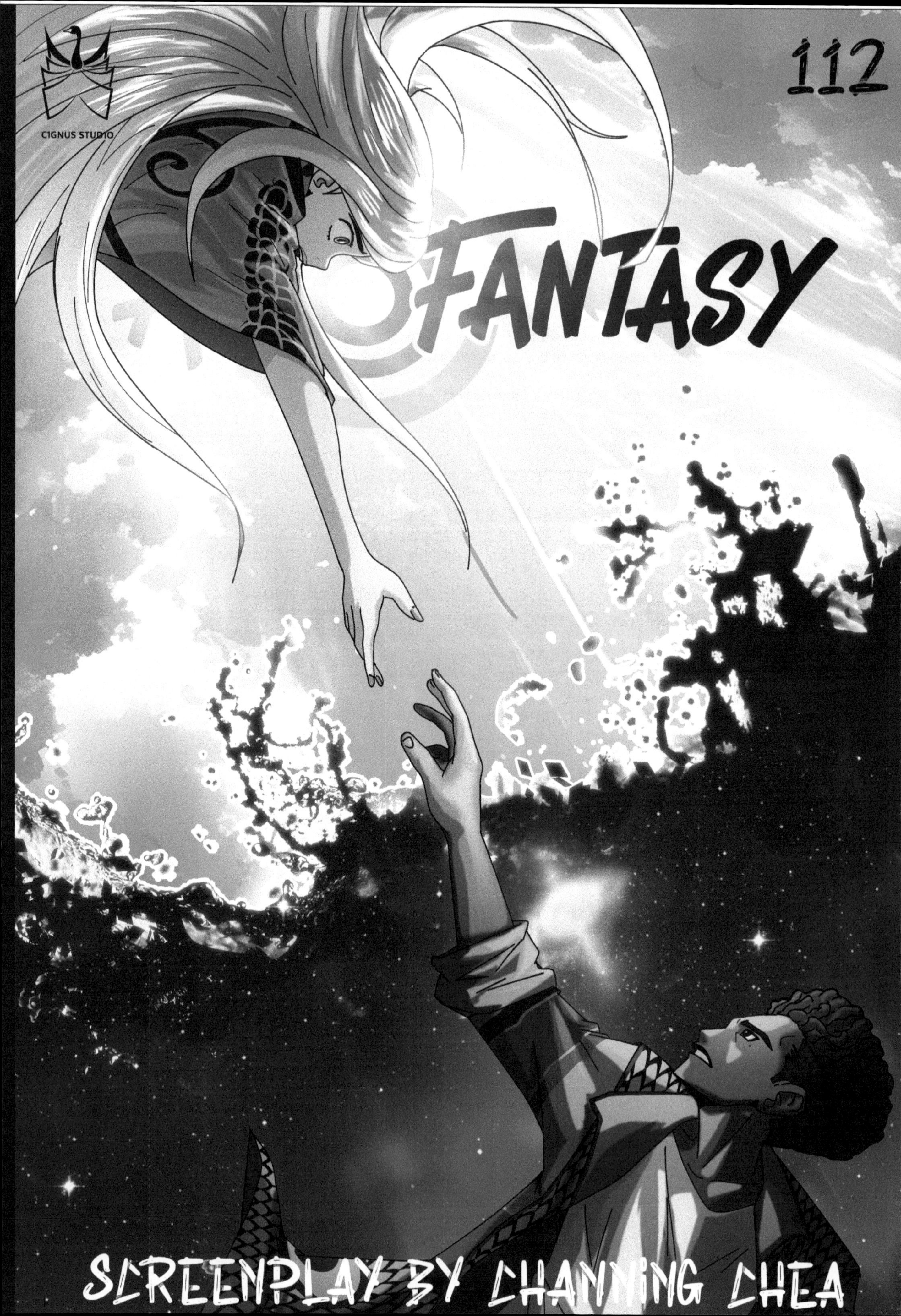
CIGNUS STUDIO
112
FANTASY
SCREENPLAY BY CHANNING CHEA

AFROFANTASY

112 – "The Anchored Soul"

Written by

Channing Chea

AFROFANTASY

"THE ANCHORED SOUL"

<u>TEASER</u>

FADE IN:

INT. KING'S LAUNDROMAT - BACK ROOM - TWILIGHT, FLASHBACK

YOUNG PHARAOH, 5, clutches a BROOM, feigns work in the back
of the laundromat. He is distracted, disturbed by the
conversation being had just around the corner…

JIBRIL argues with CLEO, late 20s female. Their words bounce
off the walls.

                    CLEO
          None of this is worth it, Jibril!

                    JIBRIL
          How could you say that? You'd give
          up on what is rightfully yours
          because the road is rough? What
          about everyone who fought for us to
          get to this point?!

                    CLEO
          I didn't sign up for this battle!
          I'm sorry your father was willing
          to risk your life for his fight.
          I'm sure that's why you don't see
          how reckless this is.

                    JIBRIL
          He sacrificed—that got us here!

                    CLEO
          But you're willing to risk *my*
          life—our *son's*?
               (beat)
          I know… the fight is noble; I don't
          doubt that. Your father was brave…

                    JIBRIL
          He… yes, he—

                    CLEO
          But look what he gave up! He was
          never able to see you buy this
          business. He never met Osas…

                    JIBRIL
          His civil disobedience paved a way
          for us to thrive. Blood was the
          cost.

                    CLEO
          I know. I'm begging you to please
          not risk the same…

Jibril's silence is heavy; revealing.

                    CLEO
          Fine… I won't hold you back. Osas!

Young Pharaoh timidly slides from behind the corner.

                    CLEO
          Say goodbye to your father.

                    JIBRIL
          He stays.

                    CLEO
          No, he does not!

                    JIBRIL
          This is his choice!

                    CLEO
          He is *FIVE*!

                    JIBRIL
          He is *African*! He chooses his path.
             (looks at the boy)
          Osas, listen. Your mother is going
          to move away, but you don't have to
          go if you don't want.

                    CLEO
          You do not have to choose, my love.
          Come with—

A bell JINGLES… WHITE OFFICER walks through the door. He eyes
the adults, curious of the raucous.

                    WHITE OFFICER
          It is about time to head to the
          Homeland, is it not?

                    CLEO
          Yes, sir! We were just—

>   JIBRIL
>   I have special permission to remain
>   after hours to finish work for a
>   client. My son will assist me.

Cleo eyeballs Jibril, astounded.

>   WHITE OFFICER
>   And the lady?

Cleo shakes her head, starts for the door.

>   CLEO
>   (to Jibril)
>   We are not done.
>   (to the boy)
>   I love you, Osas. I will be back.

Cleo leaves the building, followed by the officer after he
gives Jibril a final once-over.

>   WHITE OFFICER
>   Be brief with your work.

He leaves.

Jibril comforts Young Pharaoh, who is shaken.

>   YOUNG PHARAOH
>   Baba, when is Mama coming back? Why
>   did she leave?

>   JIBRIL
>   Your mother loves you, but… She
>   doesn't understand how important
>   what we do here is.

>   YOUNG PHARAOH
>   She… how come?

Jibril embraces his son.

END FLASHBACK.

INT. ATLANTIS - TEMPLE - MORNING

PHARAOH's eyes crack open, waking from the memory. He gazes
out a window to view the Atlantean landscape he created.

>   JIBRIL (V.O.)
>   There will always be people who do
>   not understand. But we can help
>   them understand.

He stares farther into the distance to see DARREN. He drags a CONTRAPTION behind him that rakes two PARALLEL LINES into the sand. The lines trail for over 100 meters.

                    JIBRIL (V.O.)
          They will see through our success.

                                        FADE OUT.

                    END OF TEASER

<u>ACT ONE</u>

FADE IN:

EXT. CAIRO - DEVASTATED STREETS - NIGHT

CHYRON: "The Night Before"

LIGHTNING arcs across the sky, illuminating the city below
with flashes. Wild FIRES brighten the areas the lightning
neglects, revealing road after road littered with soulless
bodies. Native EGYPTIANS and Caucasian TOURISTS alike lie
motionless throughout the city.

MALICK looks around, haunted by the corpse population. He
turns to leave when—

He trips over a corpse—this one bloodied, riddled by bullets.
The body is a soldier; one that never lived long enough to
have his soul stripped. It was stolen by another conflict.

Malick looks across the street. Fellow WAALISHA share a
similar fate as the soldier.

He grits his teeth before rushing out of the city.

INT. CAIRO - VACANT BUILDING - NIGHT

ASA, MOUSTAPHA's Apparition, ANANSI's Apparition, TAU,
BUZIBA, and KING KOPANO via SMARTPHONE video chat stand
around a table in the abandoned building.

LIGHTNING illuminates the room in FLASHES. It keeps all
present awake. A CLOCK ticks away in the room's corner. It
reads "03:13".

                         ASA
               All right, Anansi, when was the
               last time something like this
               happened, and how was it handled?

                         ANANSI
               For this, there is no historical
               precedent. All of Arjana's
               provisions were meant to prevent
               this from happening. The last time
               the Ophiuchus Stone was used, it
               was not retrieved until after the
               calamity it caused.

                    TAU
Then we'll have to grab it before
that happens!

                    BUZIBA
That will not be easy. Pharaoh has
grown accustomed to using its power
in the short time he's held the
Shards. It won't be like fighting
the Waalisha.

                    KING KOPANO
Even if Acacia's death was the
moment Pharaoh first contacted one
of the Shards, he has accomplished
wondrous feats in a short time. How
has he become so adroit so quickly?

                    ASA
Respectfully, guys, it doesn't
matter. We just need to make sure
we throw everything we have at him!
Your Majesty, are you still
confident you can get 1,000
soldiers in Mauritania soon?

                    KING KOPANO
Yes, but it is all I can spare. The
other half must remain in Lesotho.

                    TAU
With His Majesty's permission, I'll
gladly lead the charge!

                    ASA
    (scribbles notes)
Great! Okay, Anansi, and Arjana?

                    ANANSI
The remaining Arjanan soldiers will
fight alongside the Spectral Guard.
That number approximates 500.

                    ASA
Nice! Will you lead that, Buziba?

                    ANANSI
He will not.

                    BUZIBA
I will… go where I am valuable.

                    ASA
          Then you're in the right place.
          Okay, Moustapha, what about
          Senegal?

Moustapha snaps from a silent transfixion on the table.

                    MOUSTAPHA
          Yes… If you are certain the
          Waalisha are no longer a threat, I
          will give all I can to the cause,
          and I am sure President Zein will
          do the same.

                    ASA
          So that's…?

                    MOUSTAPHA
          15,000 from Senegal. I do not know
          Mauritania's number.

Asa jots the numbers again.

                    ASA
          So that makes… let's say 16,500
          plus whatever Mauritania
          contributes! That's gotta be enough
          when it comes to numbers, right?

                    ANANSI
          It is a start.

                    TAU
          Better than nothing.

Moustapha remains fixated on the table.

                    ASA
          Moustapha, you've been quiet.

                    MOUSTAPHA
          Forgive me, my thoughts have been
          elsewhere.

                    KING KOPANO
          You are needed here. All have a
          voice, so please, use yours.

                    MOUSTAPHA
          Mine has caused enough trouble.

                    ASA
          What happened earlier wasn't your
          fault, you know.

                    MOUSTAPHA
          As a politician, you don't get to
          pick which of your words are
          consequential. They all are. I
          spoke rashly, pridefully, letting
          my anger guide me. Darren did an
          exceptional job getting me and Zein
          to come to a compromise that could
          have saved lives, and I squandered
          it because I learned of my friend's
          passing. Osas slaughtered many
          because I contested him…

                    KING KOPANO
          He killed those people because he
          was a murderer. That is all there
          is to say.

King Kopano speaks through static before Asa's phone dies.

                    MOUSTAPHA
          I wish that were true…

                    ANANSI
          In any case, it seems Darren
          Davenport attempted his best at
          mediating the situation. Despite
          his efforts, violence ensued. There
          is no negotiation with Osas
          Pharaoh. Are you committed to
          stopping him even if he dies?

Moustapha's eyes dart left. KHADIJA's body lies covered with
a blanket. It's the reassurance he needs.

                    MOUSTAPHA
          Yes, I am.

                    ASA
          All right, does everyone know what
          they're doing?
                    (collective nods)
          Then, let's break! We'll be in
          touch.

All present rise from the table.

Moustapha observes Khadija. He kneels beside her.

                    ANANSI
                    (to Moustapha)
          I will end the connection now.

                    MOUSTAPHA
          A moment, please.
              (to Asa)
          Mrs. Davenport, are you certain
          about all of this?

                    ASA
          Why wouldn't I be?

                    MOUSTAPHA
          Darren did an admirable job trying
          to prevent conflict and fighting to
          defend those slaughtered. I'm
          convinced he truly wants to avoid
          violence at all costs. I am sure he
          wouldn't want to put a loved one at
          risk.

                    ASA
          I'm already at risk, that's why
          he's doing this.
              (smiles)
          Darren is risking everything to
          give us a chance to fight back. I
          know he doesn't want to fight, but
          he will. So I'll fight with him.

                    MOUSTAPHA
          I see. And your inability to use
          this "magic" won't be a hindrance?
          What will you do?

                    ASA
          The only thing I could ever do: The
          best I can. Khadija taught me a
          little something about that.

Moustapha grins subtly. He rises, nods at Anansi. The
Apparitions fade in a blink.

EXT. ATLANTIS - TEMPLE CEMETERY - DAY

An exhausted Darren searches for Pharaoh, finds him in the
courtyard.

Pharaoh stares off beyond the gravestones.

                    PHARAOH
          There is so much they won't see.
          Khadija, Khadeem, My father… my
          mother.
                    (MORE)

> PHARAOH (CONT'D)
> They won't get to see the things
> I'll do… or how the world has
> become. Something about that, more
> than their loss, feels unfair.

Pharaoh's vulnerability tempers Darren's grudge.

> DARREN
> And if they were here, what do you
> think they'd say?

The answer sits on Pharaoh's tongue. He doesn't speak it. But a faint WHISTLE catches his ear. Darren hears it too. They look around but find no one.

The whistle strengthens, sounds like a plummeting falcon. The realization hits them both.

They look at the sky and see the smoking tail of a falling MISSILE. It SCREAMS as it descends, only seconds away.

Pharaoh shouts and the WINDS roar. Darren retreats beneath a DOME SHIELD he fluxes. He waits for impact until…

Nothing… The winds recede.

Darren peeks from behind his dome and sees the missile levitating, Pharaoh suspends it in place above the ground.

Darren searches for breath; Pharaoh's eyes pierce with anger.

> PHARAOH
> A gift from your friends?

> DARREN
> Are you serious? I'm standing right
> next to you!

Pharaoh examines the weapon as he tempers his rage.

> PHARAOH
> I am going to see Zein.

> DARREN
> You think he sent that?

> PHARAOH
> We will see. Either way, he owes me
> a deed. Keep working. We will
> continue when I return.

Pharaoh ascends, departs west… takes the missile. Darren stays in the cemetery. He turns toward the headstones again.

                    DARREN
          What *would* you all say? Something
          to calm him down, I hope.

                    ANANSI (O.S.)
          Darren Davenport.

Darren's head snaps to see Anansi behind him.

                    DARREN
          Who are you? How long've—
               (notices wardrobe)
          You're Arjanan?

                    ANANSI
          I am Anansi, Prince of Arjana, and
          Advisor to the Queen.

                    DARREN
          Oh… it's nice to—

                    ANANSI
          We do not have much time. Update me
          on the situation, and assume I am
          up to speed on the events in
          Nouakchott.

                    DARREN
          Well, we almost got blown sky high
          a second ago. Was that you?

                    ANANSI
          I am aware, but no. No one from our
          company.

                    DARREN
          All right, then…
               (points to the temple)
          Pharaoh's keeping the Ophiuchus
          Stone in that building, but I can't
          get to it because it's locked away.
          Maybe you can give it a shot…

                    ANANSI
          My Apparitions are intangible. They
          cannot interact with physical mass.

                    DARREN
          Apparitions… that's right. It's
          your Soul Flux he's been using.

                    ANANSI
          What others have you seen him use?

                    DARREN
Well, he likes to stick with fire
and lightning, but I saw him make
gold like Amani, use Acacia's Ifrit
Shadow, and create monsters out of
clay.
        (Anansi scowls)
But at the end, he used something
I'd never seen before. It was
unreal…

                    ANANSI
A Spectral Flux, a combination of
all Base Fluxes granted to wielders
of the Stone; the greatest weapon
he has behind the Stone itself.

                    DARREN
So if we can grab the Stone, maybe—

                    ANANSI
Do NOT touch it, do you understand?
Souls that are not anchored to this
world are absorbed by the Stone if
they make contact. It is a mystery
how Pharaoh survived. If the time
comes, be certain to contain it
using your Flux only.

                    DARREN
Okay, got it…

                    ANANSI
Good. I will be off, then.

                    DARREN
Wait! Tell me what's going on!

                    ANANSI
Your ploy to leave your phone
behind was effective. Asa is now in
contact with President Moustapha,
King Kopano, and Arjana. She has
even formed an alliance with
Buziba. She is… quite impressive.

                    DARREN
Yeah, she is.

                    ANANSI
One of my Apparitions will follow
each party to remain in constant
contact.
        (MORE)

                         ANANSI (CONT'D)
              I can only be in eight places at
              once, so I must be efficient.

                         DARREN
              Eight, huh? Right. Well, I'll keep
              you posted.

Anansi nods and his Apparition begins to fade, but his head
remains just long enough to speak.

                         ANANSI
              Darren Davenport, you and Asa have…
              inspired this new allied force. Do
              not dash their hope by dying.

The Apparition fades.

                         DARREN
              That's the plan, but no promises.

EXT. GIZA PLATEAU - NECROPOLIS - DAY

MALICK hides behind a shack, pokes his head from around a
corner. From not far away, he sees Asa, Buziba, Tau holding
Khadija's cane, and wrapped body. He observes them.

The ground SPLITS, forms a shallow chasm wide enough for a
person. Asa, Buziba, and Tau stand above it. WIND carries
Khadija's body, lowers it into the ground.

                         ASA
              We'll be back for you—promise…

Buziba gestures and the ground closes above the body.

A moment of reverence passes, interrupted by footsteps in
sand. Buziba notices.

                         BUZIBA
              What do you want?

Malick halts, and the others take notice.

                         MALICK
              I don't want trouble. I just…

                         ASA
              You—your name was… Malick, right?
              Why're you still here?

                    MALICK
        I don't know what's going on, but…
        all this… it's the Waalisha's
        fault, isn't it?

                    BUZIBA
        It is hardly so simple.

                    TAU
        "Yes" wouldn't be wrong.

                    MALICK
        I thought so. I want to help.

Tau chokes out a laugh, but before he speaks—

                    ASA
        That would be great!

                    TAU
        Wha—WHY? Him?

                    ASA
        We need all the help we can get.

                    TAU
        But from the Waalisha?

                    ASA
        Come on, we were just about to head
        out anyway!

Malick is filled with relief. He approaches the group. Tau
scoffs under his breath. Buziba is less hostile.

                    MALICK
        So, where are we going?

                    ASA
        Ever heard of the city of Atlantis?

INT. MAURITANIA - GRAY PALACE RUINS - OVAL OFFICE - DAY

PRESIDENT ZEIN sits in his office, surrounded by MAURITANIAN
SOLDIERS, and CLERICAL AIDS. Communication in the room is
chaotic as the office is in tatters.

CLERICAL AID A hangs up the phone. She's nervous.

                    CLERICAL AID A
        Mr. President, word from the
        General's office.
            (Zein perks up)
            (MORE)

                    CLERICAL AID A (CONT'D)
          He says after assessment of the
          casualties, available personnel has
          dropped approximately 22% below the
          expected numbers.

                    PRESIDENT ZEIN
          How?! There could not have been
          that many casualties…

                    CLERICAL AID A
          It is not just the casualties. In
          addition, soldiers have demanded
          higher pay for their service…
          noting that the Waalisha gold flood
          has inflated prices…

Zein is stern, focused. But that focus is broken as the
Soldiers make a raucous. They point their guns at the window.

Pharaoh floats outside and glances into the building.

                    PRESIDENT ZEIN
          Put your guns away, you idiots!

The Soldiers obey, and Zein opens the window.

                    PHARAOH
          Is this one of your toys?

The missile drops into view of the office and all within are
afraid. Except Zein, who eyes the device.

                    PRESIDENT ZEIN
          No. I have no interest in bombing
          my own land.

Pharaoh studies Zein before speaking.

                    PHARAOH
          Very well.

The missiles drops, shakes the ground, induces more panic,
but it doesn't explode.

                    PHARAOH
          May I come in?

He floats through the window, feet not touching the floor.

                    PHARAOH
          I am here for my deed.

Zein snaps. An AID hands him a thick yellow ENVELOPE.

>   PRESIDENT ZEIN
>   Here you are: The deed to the
>   Province of Atlantis.
>
>   PHARAOH
>   That was not the agreement.
>
>   PRESIDENT ZEIN
>   If you knew me, you would know I
>   would die first.

The two lock eyes. There is an understanding. Pharaoh nods, takes the deed, and floats through the window.

>   PHARAOH
>   I am no stranger to earning my
>   rewards. May our next encounter
>   herald your last breath.

Pharaoh soars away, leaves the missile behind.

Zein is quiet, solemn. He turns to his Aid.

>   PRESIDENT ZEIN
>   Tell the General to give the
>   soldiers what they want.

The Aid nods and makes the call.

>   PRESIDENT ZEIN
>   A small price for freedom…

EXT. MAURITANIA - GRAY PALACE - DAY

Anansi's Apparition watches Pharaoh fly away.

He glimpses at the discarded missile before disappearing.

EXT. ARJANA - CENTRAL MALL - DAY

HUNDREDS of ARJANAN SOLDIERS flood the mall. They polish their weapons, brandish their armor, prepare for combat.

JAMBI, ZAILA, CYMBA, and TYMPANI do the same just outside the Queen's Palace. BIA checks in with them before entering the palace.

INT. ARJANA - QUEEN'S THRONE - CONTINUOUS

Bia enters the throne room, where QUEEN ASASE sits besides the real Anansi. Bia approaches them both.

The burden that weighs on Asase's shoulders is heavy today, but she manages to lift her head.

                    QUEEN ASASE
          The time has come.

EXT. ATLANTIS - A THOUSAND FEET UP - DAY

Pharaoh stares over Atlantis, scans the distance beyond.

He creates FIVE APPARITIONS that circle him. With a wave, they fly away and into the distance. Satisfied, he descends.

INT. ATLANTIS - TEMPLE - DAY

Darren reviews a hand drawn diagram in his SKETCHBOOK as Pharaoh approaches.

                    PHARAOH
          Have you completed the railroad
          outline?

                    DARREN
          Yeah, the first part. I traced the
          outline for a few miles out. If you
          follow that path to Nouakchott, we—

Pharaoh raises his arms and the Ophiuchus Stone's LIGHT shines from inside the Temple, envelopes him. He outstretches his hand and the earth responds.

The land around the lines in the sand transforms, molds itself into an eight-lane ASPHALT ROAD. The road stretches into the distance, into the desert—an endless black path.

                    DARREN
          Oh, well, the highway was gonna be
          phase two… but the more
          infrastructure the better, I guess.

The Stone's light subsides. Pharaoh turns and finds his throne.

                    PHARAOH
          We would not want to keep visitors
          away—be they favorable or hostile—
          would we?

                    DARREN
          Which kind are you expecting?

PHARAOH
It does not matter. Let them come.

FADE OUT.

<u>END OF ACT ONE</u>

ACT TWO

FADE IN:

EXT. CAIRO - DEVASTATED STREETS - DAY

Malick leads the group through the streets. Asa and Tau veer their eyes from the carnage; Buziba is numb to it.

> MALICK
> It's just up ahead.

They arrive at a Waalisha BUS, damaged from stray gunfire. The group observes it. Tau hesitates to approach, clutching his new arm.

> ASA
> Are you sure this'll get us there?

> MALICK
> We fueled it before entering the city. It should get us close.

> ASA
> Better than nothing, I guess.

They pry open the door and enter the bus, except for Tau.

> TAU
> I can't do it.

> ASA
> What's wrong?

Tau struggles to speak. Buziba notices him clutching his arm.

> BUZIBA
> Perhaps the extra weight has gone to your head.

> TAU
> Maybe. For the first time in years I know what it feels like to be balanced. For the first time since I was little, I am whole…
>   (beat)
> So why should I work with the one who broke me to begin with?

Tau's eyes meet Buziba's, and Asa draws the connection.

                    BUZIBA
          I am sure you've done more
          difficult things.

                    TAU
          What would you know of the
          difficulty I've been through?

                    ASA
          Tau, this is a lot on everyone, but
          we can't focus on that now. We
          have—

                    TAU
          No? Maybe it's easier to ignore the
          pain if it hasn't disabled you for
          half of your life. Why else would
          you be willing to work with the
          Waalisha and a murderer? You've
          only just met them, after all. Of
          course you trust them!

Malick and Buziba retreat, unwilling to defend themselves.

                    ASA
          Did you forget you tried to kill me
          too?! Look around you! The guy who
          stole all of these lives is still
          out there. That's why I'm working
          with them. These dead people's pain
          is a lot worse then ours, got it?
               (beat)
          What is it? Suddenly your problem
          is fixed so you stop fighting for
          everyone else's?

                    TAU
          Tsk… That's not fair!

                    BUZIBA
               (introspective)
          No, nothing is. Perhaps all we can
          do is try to make things more fair.

Tau is angry but responsive. He finally approaches the bus,
silent as he boards. As he sits, the group notices Anansi
standing inside.

                    ANANSI
          You will meet with Senegal's army
          before going to Atlantis.

                    ASA
          Okay, where are they?

Anansi's eyes drift upward, as if waiting for a response.

EXT. SENEGAL - WESTERN SAHARA DESERT - DAY

DOZENS of TANKS and HUNDREDS of JEEPS filled with armed
SENEGALESE SOLDIERS hold formation.

> ANANSI (V.O.)
> You will meet them south of the
> Richat Structure and travel the
> remaining way with them.

Moustapha salutes the caravan of vehicles as they are sent on
their way. As they drive off, Anansi and Moustapha exchange a
glance. Anansi's Apparition disappears in the dust.

EXT. ARJANA - CENTRAL MALL - DAY

HUNDREDS of ARJANAN SOLDIERS line up in the Central Mall. In
the front of their ranks stand BIA, the SPECTRAL GUARD, and
the real Anansi.

Bia begins her march and the Soldiers follow her. Anansi
stays behind.

EXT. LESOTHO - ROYAL PALACE - DAY

ONE THOUSAND BASOTHO SOLDIERS drive off, saluting King Kopano
as they depart. GERALDINE triple-checks their numbers.

Anansi joins them in watching their departure.

> ANANSI (V.O.)
> The Basotho and Arjanan forces will
> join as soon as they can. It all
> rests on us now…

INT. ATLANTIS - TEMPLE - DAY

Darren and Pharaoh stand around a table. On it is a hand-
drawn DIAGRAM of the Atlantis landscape. Darren marks and
points to the inner ring of water on the map. Pharaoh is
engrossed.

EXT. ATLANTIS - INNER HARBOR - CONTINUOUS

Pharaoh stands at the edge of the inner harbor and peers
across it. Darren finishes carving an OUTLINE into the sand.

He pulls sand from the ground and fluxes it into an elaborate MODEL BRIDGE. Pharaoh observes, lifts his arms.

His body glows under the influence of the Ophiuchus Stone, and the earth bends to his will.

MOUNDS of ROCK rise, shift, bend into a life-size replica of Darren's model. The mile-long BRIDGE extends across the water. Each of the concentric land rings is now connected.

INT. ATLANTIS - TEMPLE - CONTINUOUS

Darren draws a circle around the Rings of Land on the map, one that resembles train tracks…

EXT. ATLANTIS - SECOND HARBOR - CONTINUOUS

Darren finishes another set of diagrams in the sand, and Pharaoh traces those diagrams with freshly created RAILROADS.

The train tracks circle the entire land mass, and they repeat this for every ring of land.

EXT. ATLANTIS - NORTHERN MOUNTAINS - CONTINUOUS

Darren points over the landscape. Pharaoh adjusts the flow of the RIVERS; they form a more uniform structure that irrigates the land in a new way.

Pharaoh grins, pleased at the transforming landscape. Darren stares into the distance—no armies in sight.

A night passes.

EXT. ATLANTIS - EASTERN PLAINS - DAY

Darren produces a model WIND TURBINE. Pharaoh studies it, carefully reproduces it by the dozen. A WIND FARM is born.

EXT. ATLANTIS - SOUTH RIVER - CONTINUOUS

Darren and Pharaoh watch as the shores form a BEACH. Multiple DOCKS of wooden planks domino themselves along a mile's worth of river. They await boats to occupy them.

Another night passes…

INT. ATLANTIS - TEMPLE - DAY

Darren stares out of a temple window. He watches the sky
intently, clutching diagrams in his hands.

              PHARAOH
    Expecting more missiles?

              DARREN
    I don't know what to expect.

              PHARAOH
    In a few short days, we've been
    able to achieve something that
    would take developed countries
    years to complete. Take ownership
    of this victory.

              DARREN
    I can't own the victory without
    owning the blood, too.

              PHARAOH
    That is my burden.

              DARREN
    And you're just okay with that?
        (beat)
    Are you aware… like, have you even
    processed what you've done?

              PHARAOH
    Do you think it's possible for me
    to achieve a plan this elaborate
    without having premeditated every
    aspect of it? I know what I've
    done. I will live with it for the
    rest of my life. But I'll also live
    knowing I created a Mecca for our
    people that will never be topped.

Darren steps closer to Pharaoh, peers earnestly at him.

              DARREN
    You actually thought people would
    be okay with this, didn't you?

Pharaoh pauses, for the first time seems caught off guard.

              PHARAOH
    I thought… they would understand.
    It was not only me who was
    displaced—orphaned.
        (MORE)

                    PHARAOH (CONT'D)
The fire in me burned so intensely,
I knew others must have felt that
same heat. How could they not? I
thought I could use that heat to
forge something new—a path to a
better land. I could create that
land, and welcome them home, offer
them a place to feel found.
          (looks at Darren)
Do you not feel found?

                    DARREN
I don't think being in an
unfamiliar place makes me "lost".
And being in a location made for me
doesn't make me "found", especially
if that place is empty.

                    PHARAOH
Then why did you come here,
Darren?! You left your home
searching to be found, did you not?
Have you found yourself? Perhaps
your Muzungu wife, who's incapable
of understanding your plight, is
keeping you from what you want.

                    DARREN
Maybe she won't ever understand the
feeling that brought me here. But
she loves me.
          (cracks a smile)
Maybe, that's all I need.

                    PHARAOH
Well, for those who have lost the
people who love them, may they find
Atlantis.

Pharaoh stares through Darren—past him. Beyond the rings of
water, something kicks up sand from the West.

Darren turns to look, squints to see what could only be a
caravan of vehicles.

                    PHARAOH
They have come.

Pharaoh walks to the temple window, prepares to depart.

                    DARREN
We don't have to do this!
          (Pharaoh hesitates)
               (MORE)

                         DARREN (CONT'D)
          Bring all those people back you
          killed… Just… turn back.

                         PHARAOH
          Turning back is for the lost.

Pharaoh soars away, toward the approaching caravan.

EXT. ATLANTIS - SOUTHWESTERN PLAINS - DAY

The WAALISHA BUS stops when it reaches a PAVED ROAD. Its
doors open, and Asa and company exit, watch as the Senegalese
Military role in.

The leading tank stops, and a Jeep strolls from behind it.
GENERAL SALL, 40s, steps out and approaches the group.

                         GENERAL SALL
          Are you Asa Davenport?

                         ASA
          Yes! You must sent by Moustapha—

                         GENERAL SALL
          Call off your forces!

                         ASA
          Wha—this is our whole group!

                         GENERAL SALL
          Then whose forces are those?

He points North. A DUST CLOUD trails an almost invisible line
of vehicles in the distance. Asa squints to see.

                         ASA
          That isn't—

                         ANANSI
          The Mauritanians. They were
          supposed to meet us here before
          engaging!

General Sall rushes to the Jeep, picks up a RADIO.

                         GENERAL SALL
             (into radio)
          Attention: this is General Sall of
          Senegal. Do you copy?
             (silence)
          Mauritanian Army, this is General
          Sall. Respond!

I/E. ATLANTIS - WESTERN PLAINS - ARMORED SUV - CONTINUOUS

President Zein sits in an armored SUV in military attire. His radio screeches as Sall's words pierce the air.

>   GENERAL SALL (V.O.)
>   You are not to engage with the
>   enemy until allied forces arrive!
>   Repeat: do not—

Zein clicks off the radio.

>   PRESIDENT ZEIN
>   This battle is not Senegal's. We
>   will not wait for their permission
>   to defend ourselves.

>   MAURITANIAN SOLDIER A
>   Mr. President, he is here!

Zein peers through the windshield. Pharaoh hovers above the ground, low enough to be seen, high enough to be ethereal.

EXT. ATLANTIS - WESTERN PLAINS - DAY

Zein steps out of the SUV, and hundreds of Mauritanian Soldiers find their position and aim at Pharaoh.

>   PHARAOH
>   I do appreciate a good parade, but
>   how many men does it really take to
>   deliver a single document?

>   PRESIDENT ZEIN
>   There will be no deed from me. We
>   will defend Mauritania from
>   terrorists like you with every last
>   breath we have.

>   PHARAOH
>   Are you certain about this?

>   PRESIDENT ZEIN
>   I have never been more. TAKE AIM!

HUNDREDS of MAURITANIAN SOLDIERS take aim; TANKS do the same.

>   PHARAOH
>   It… doesn't have to end this way.

>   PRESIDENT ZEIN
>   It could never have ended
>   differently. FIRE!

The Soldiers obey. Bullets WHISTLE, CRACK through the air as they whiz toward Pharaoh, but he doesn't budge.

The bullets halt, swarm Pharaoh as WIND seizes them in place.

> PHARAOH
> Perhaps… you are right.

The bullets dart in reverse, return to their sender. They ricochet and obliterate dozens of Soldiers in one swoop.

> PHARAOH
> Perhaps there was no other way.

> PRESIDENT ZEIN
> Keep going!!!

Tanks fire. Projectiles approach Pharaoh with the same results. They seize before him, some bumping into the next and triggering an explosion that catches dozens more soldiers with shrapnel.

The smoke from the explosion clears, reveals Pharaoh is unharmed, but his mind his elsewhere.

He descends. Walks toward Zein, an entranced zombie.

MEMORY FLASH: CLEO pleads with JIBRIL to no avail.

> PHARAOH
> Some will never understand.

Mauritanian Soldiers shoot. Those without ammo charge with BLADES. Each meets his end.

Pharaoh's FIRE engulfs the melee attackers. His EBONY BOLT webs and arcs across waves of shooters. All the while, he closes in on Zein.

> PHARAOH
> But we can help them to…

FROM THE SOUTH

Asa's company and the Senegalese Soldiers ride to the action, but they are still too far. They see the devastation.

Asa sees Tau—Khadija's CANE is attacked to his belt. She grabs it. Tau is confused…

> ASA
> I need you to sprint me over there!

> TAU
> But you don't have—

> ASA
> Just do it!

Tau grabs Asa's wrist and WIND blasts them into the fray.

INT. ATLANTIS - TEMPLE - CONTINUOUS

Darren hears the gunshots and explosions in the distance, but he also hears something behind him…

The OPHIUCHUS STONE rises from its chamber. It ascends…

Darren leaps for it, fluxes a STEEL RECEPTACLE. He nabs the Stone, ensnaring it in the receptacle… but it fights back.

The Stone still ascends, taking Darren with it. It rips away from the receptacle and takes off toward Pharaoh.

> DARREN
> No!

Darren looks around; there's nothing for him here.

> DARREN
> CRAFTSMAN!

The floor rips up to form something LARGE…

EXT. ATLANTIS - WESTERN PLAINS - CONTINUOUS

The Ophiuchus Stone descends, hovers above Pharaoh, glows…

The WATERS from the harbor rise, stretches into the battlefield. It swallows the majority of Mauritania's forces, drags them into the harbor… But not Zein.

Pharaoh zooms over, snatches Zein's neck.

> PHARAOH
> Sacrifices are made to pave a new
> way…

Zein claws for freedom, but light fades from his eyes.

He dies in Pharaoh's grip. Pharaoh drops him unceremoniously.

He turns to the remaining Mauritanians. They are spooked, but not finished. They take aim. Pharaoh raises his arm on preparation of another strike, when—

Tau and Asa appear before Pharaoh. He notices them. He is
surprised, peeved. He turns his hand toward Asa.

But Asa holds up Khadija's cane.

Pharaoh freezes like a child caught in a lie.

> PHARAOH
> How do you…

> ASA
> I was there that day—when you
> showed up at Khadija's house. She
> told me everything about you—about
> herself. She fought so hard to
> escape her family's legacy. All she
> wanted to do was undo the harm she
> felt they did. She died fighting
> tyranny and sacrificed everything
> to make things right. And here you
> are making the same mistake all
> over again.

> PHARAOH
> Yet another curse of the Muzungu.
> She blamed herself for sins that
> weren't her own. Her shame was
> misplaced.

> ASA
> But the cause she fought for was
> good, wasn't it?

> PHARAOH
> Of course, I fight for the same
> cause!

> ASA
> But you're hurting so many people!
> You're doing exactly what she spent
> her entire life fighting. She knew
> that you would… and she loved you
> anyway.

Pharaoh's eyes flit, searching for solace, but they only see…

MEMORY FLASH: Khadijah smiles at a Young Pharaoh.

> PHARAOH
> She didn't understand…

MEMORY FLASH: She sobs as an adult Pharaoh leaves the home.

                    PHARAOH
          None of you understand!

SPARKS arc from Pharaoh's body. He charges an attack. A COAL
PILLAR erupts from below, almost pommels Pharaoh, but he
catches it. Enraged, he smashes it, sending debris all over.

Then come more bullets, this time from the Senegalese
Soldiers. They fire but receive the same result. The bullets
return to them, lodged in their chests and heads. Buziba and
Malick avoid being hit. They join Asa and Tau.

A GUST of wind blows them all back, clustering them with the
two militaries. Asa hands the cane back to Tau.

Pharaoh summons a CLAY BEAST. A massive earthen SERPENT
emerges from the ground. It menaces the opposing armies.

                    PHARAOH
          So I will make you.

Then comes the whistle of another descending missile. Pharaoh
scans the sky. He finds the source, but it's no missile.

It's Darren. He bombards the Serpent's head with his fist.
The beast crumbles apart.

He lands, steel AIRPLANE WINGS strapped to his back.

                    DARREN
          Wasn't sure if that would work…

INT. ATLANTIS - TEMPLE - CONTINUOUS

A giant, METAL, HUMAN CATAPULT recoils in the temple.

                    DARREN (V.O.)
          …but I got here just in time.

EXT. ATLANTIS - WESTERN PLAINS - CONTINUOUS

The airplane wings reshape into a BROADSWORD. He grabs it.

                    DARREN
          That's enough, Pharaoh! Just stop.

                    ASA
          Darren!

                    DARREN
               (shyly)
          Hey, babe… Good to see you awake.

                    PHARAOH
            (incredulous; maniacal)
     Do you plan to stop me? You with
     your metal toothpick?
            (he ascends)
     And your broken shepherd… and your
     traitorous Rwandan… and your
     toothless armies?

Pharaoh raises his hand above him. All elements converge in
his palm. His Spectral Flux charges.

                    PHARAOH
     I have changed my mind about you,
     Darren.

The EBONY SUN forms in his palm, its darkened heat distorts
the sunlight.

                    PHARAOH
     You are not worth saving.

The black FLAMES discharge, leap toward Darren, but they
drop, flatten against the ground.

The Ebony Sun contorts before it vanishes. Then Pharaoh drops
to the ground, bound by a highly localized field of GRAVITY.
Pharaoh struggles to move, looks around.

JAMBI, ZAILA, CYMBA, and TYMPANI surround him, kneeling in a
meditative state.

                    JAMBI
     Spectral Flux: active!

                    ZAILA
     Now, Princess!

Bia arrives, leaps into action. She throws water upward,
toward the Ophiuchus Stone. The water grabs it, pulls it
inward. Bia almost grabs it before—

Pharaoh punches the ground, sends black lightning rippling
through the earth. It erupts beneath and knocks the Spectral
Guard back. The gravity field falls.

The Stone returns to Pharaoh. He soars into the air. Notices…

The Arjanan army has arrived. They notice the flying tyrant
and circle him from below.

                    ASA
     Bia! Just in time!

339

>   BIA
>   It's good to see you, Asa, but you
>   should not be here!
>   (notices Buziba)
>   Both of you should not.

>   TAU
>   Agreed on both, Princess!

Anansi's Apparition appears between them all.

>   ANANSI
>   Not now—be on guard!

Pharaoh sees the Arjanans, gets even angrier. He prepares
another attack—

But he's blown out the sky by an EXPLOSIVE. He crashes into
the waters.

Darren tracks the projectile's source. They find the LESOTHO
ARMY arriving, their TANKS and ARMAMENTS at the ready.

>   TAU
>   His Highness came through!

The THOUSANDS of total Soldiers from each faction spread into
a formation that appears predetermined. They surround
Pharaoh's crash point.

LIGHTING strikes the crash point, and Pharaoh emerges,
glowing in the glory of Ophiuchus. He is beyond words.

The Stone merges, attaches to his belt. He is a walking deity
once more.

>   DARREN
>   This is it! He's taken so much from
>   all of us. We won't let him dictate
>   Africa's fate!

All present scream in expectant victory. Pharaoh smiles
maddeningly.

We see from his eyes. The world charges toward him. Soldiers
from multiple corners of Africa take up their weapons.
Pharaohs steels himself. Accepts the challenge.

The Lesotho Soldiers leads the charge.

Pharaoh's body flickers as he dashes forward. His fingers
impale the first unprepared soldier. Pharaoh dashes to the
next, leaves behind GLOWING holes in his victim, charged with
electric energy.

He repeats, dashes between dozens of Soldiers in a flash, perforates their bodies with his fingers.

He withdraws, snaps his fingers, and the glowing holes in the Soldiers EXPLODE with lightning. An entire section falls.

Pharaoh continues moving from the Lesothoans to the Arjanans, his movement nearly untraceable.

> PHARAOH
> You ungrateful victims… trapped in infinite servitude. You spurn the finger that directs you, step on the feet that lead you.

But his fingers cannot pierce Jambi. Jambi summons ARMOR—intricate and blazing—that absorb Pharaoh's repeated, but unsuccessful attempts. This is his Soul Flux: **ARSENAL**.

> PHARAOH
> …resist the hand that frees you…

Jambi grabs Pharaoh's arms.

> JAMBI
> Do it!

Zaila leads SCORES of Arjanans as they throw a DELUGE of WATER at Pharaoh. He's ripped from Jamba's arms, washed back.

Pharaoh resists the force enough to stand, then the water spins around him. He stands at the eye of a giant WHIRLPOOL.

> PHARAOH
> …bite the hand that attempts to feed you.

He looks up, notices Cymba soaring above him. CLOUDS of LIGHT swirl, build in his palms, focus into a single point.

Cymba fires his Soul Flux: **PIERCE TYPHOON**. A TORNADO-shaped DRILL descends onto Pharaoh.

Pharaoh raises his hand, catches the point of the drill. The dispersing energy blows away the whirlpool. Cymba keeps pressing…

> PHARAOH
> You don't deserve this new world.

Soldiers from all armies fire their ROCKET projectiles. Again Pharaoh halts them in place.

                         PHARAOH
              And you clearly do not learn—

                         DARREN
              Now!

Darren, Buziba, Malick and Tau raise a WALL all around
Pharaoh with their respective fluxes. It seals him within.
The only opening is the top.

Tympani launches herself high, takes Cymba's place. She uses
her Soul Flux: **SCORCHLOOP**, to toss FLAMING HOOPS into the
enclosed space. The hoops hit the rockets, trigger cascading
explosions all within the rocky enclosure.

She escapes the path of a TOWER OF FIRE that erupts like a
volcano as Pharaoh is scorched within.

                         MALICK
              Did we get him?

But the flames recede, implode as if being absorbed within
the wall. Then a BLADE of fire slices the wall open from
within, blasting away the barrier. Pharaoh emerges from
behind it, holding a BLAZING SABER that looks 20 meters long.

He swings it into his enemies. The fire burns the scores of
soldiers nearby, then slices the ones who survive. Pharaoh
swings again horizontally. Darren and crew are in its path—

But Tau creates a SKY-BLOCK that boosts the crew up and out
of its path. They narrowly escape the swipe.

Bia throws her ACID WHEEL at Pharaoh. He drops the saber to
catch the wheel. He examines it—smiles.

He raises his arms and the waters from the river respond,
turn to ACID. He throws an Acid Tsunami at the enemy.

Darren reacts, summons a METAL PLATFORM to elevate the area,
but he can only save himself and company. FLYING ARJANANS
lift as many up as they can.

HUNDREDS of fighters from all factions are caught in the
Acid. They melt way.

But Pharaoh is bombarded from above by an AURORA BOREALIS
beam from above. It stuns him, and the acid ceases flowing.
He looks up and sees an ARJANAN WOMAN.

In a blink, he flies to her, grabs her, launches her into the
earth with FISSURING force. The earth quakes and the acid
recedes into the cracks.

But the quakes cause Malick to fall from Darren's platform. Buziba notices Malick too late. He falls into the acid-filled fissure.

Buziba then looks at the battlefield. The carnage is too familiar. It fills him with rage.

Another AURORA BOREALIS shoots down from the sky, circles Pharaoh until it becomes a BLAZING AURA of auroras. He descends again; his feet touching the ground. His aura's intensity staves off bullets and projectiles. The aurora's presence interferes with the machineries' functions.

> PHARAOH
> You don't deserve to see the
> kingdom I create!

Then, multiple MASSIVE slabs of COAL bombard Pharaoh. It's just enough to faze him. He searches for the offender.

Buziba charges in. The earth blackens beneath him, propels him faster then ever before. He reaches for Pharaoh's face—

> PHARAOH
> Again, you joined the wrong team.

But Pharaoh knocks his hand away, grabs Buziba's face instead. Buziba cannot break away…

Pharaoh's hand turns black, prepares to use Buziba's own Flux. The skin where his fingers meet Buziba's face sears.

> PHARAOH
> Now, join the losers who preceded
> you.

Tau heralds the GUST that propels him forward, Khadija's cane in hand—in use. In a blink, Pharaoh's arm suddenly separates from his body! Buziba is free. The matter from Tau's SKY-BLOCK flows through Khadija's cane, resembles a saber.

Darren touches the ground, fluxes a giant METAL ARM that grabs Buziba and Tau, throws them out of harms way and toward himself and Asa. They crash next to them.

Pharaoh regenerates a new arm just before weaponizing his auroral aura. The aura explodes, discharges into LASERS of explosive light. The lasers spray the battlefield.

Soldiers find shelter. Those who can't are blown away.

Arjanans flux defenses, but many cannot in time. They are killed on impact.

343

Darren fluxes a metal DOME around him and his comrades, but the dome doesn't close in time…

A laser bores Darren's side torso, eviscerates Buziba's. The resulting explosion maims them both, injures Asa and Tau.

Darren holds his wounded torso. With an agonized shout, conjures one more DOME to protect the injured group. They shelter behind it.

Pharaoh begins a new spree of killing. He parses the battlefield with the efficiency of death itself. The screams of the fallen pierce the air.

Tau, Buziba, Asa, and Darren take stock of their injuries. Tau and Asa are fine, Darren is badly hurt, but Buziba…

He lies on his back, covers his wound, tries to stop the bleeding, but it's no use. He looks at the others. Tau tries to steel himself. Asa and Darren huddle close, knowing this might be the end… There is a contentment in their faces, one that exists when two individuals are a unit.

The solemn moment washes over Buziba. His pain eases a bit in the silence his own revelation brings him.

                    BUZIBA
          I have harmed… all of you.

                    TAU
          What?

                    BUZIBA
          Tau, you were right to defend them.
          What these two are… is
          real—authentic.

Buziba checks the blood on his hand. He becomes convicted.

                    BUZIBA
               (beat)
          Nothing I do can make up for what I
          have done to you, but if you would
          be gracious enough to grant me your
          trust this once, I can give you a
          gift to win this battle.

                    TAU
          You had something this whole time
          and didn't tell us? What changed?

                    BUZIBA
          Now, you won't have me to hold you
          back. Before I die, I will Soul
          Transfer.

                    ASA
          Buziba, stop with—

                    BUZIBA
          Asa is your name, yes? For once in
          my life, let me be valuable.

                    DARREN
          Sounds like you have a plan.

                    BUZIBA
          It will require each of us to risk
          what is dear to us.

Tau, Asa, and Darren nod.

Buziba smiles, reaches for Asa's face. Darren hesitates, but
Asa calms him. She allows Buziba to make contact.

                    BUZIBA
          Thank you. Now, listen carefully…

ELSEWHERE

Pharaoh continues his rampage, savagely ripping through the
opposition. But he stops when he hears…

                    DARREN
          PHARAOH!

Pharaoh searches for the voice, sees Darren.

                    BUZIBA (V.O.)
          That tyrant has a soft spot for
          Darren, so he will be a distraction
          while…

Tau zooms in, grabs the Ophiuchus Stone on Pharaoh's belt,
tries to pry it away with Khadija's Cane.

                    BUZIBA (V.O.)
          Tau will move for the Stone.

Pharaoh notices, tries to knock Tau away, but Tau's
FORCEFIELD blocks for just long enough.

Asa steps onto the battlefield. She makes a claw shape with
her hand just like Buziba would…

                    BUZIBA (V.O.)
           Then, Asa, take what's left of my
           soul, and do the one thing I have
           ever known to do. *Destroy!*

Asa *slams* the ground, and BURNING COAL erupts from the ground beneath Pharaoh! It burns away Khadija's Cane, blasts away Tau's new arm, and *destroys* Pharaoh's belt.

The Ophiuchus Stone flings through the air.

                    BUZIBA (V.O.)
           Then Darren, you will do what you
           do best…

Darren eyes the Stone, fluxes a COIL SPRING platform beneath him, lines up his path… launches himself!

                    BUZIBA (V.O.)
           Overcome!

He and Pharaoh reach for the Stone, but Darren touches it first! He grabs it, tumbles from the inertia of the launch.

The divine glow from Pharaoh fades. He is human again.

But the light appears elsewhere… on the Stone. It glows uncontrollably, rumbles in Darren's hands.

It creates a VORTEX that pulls in its surroundings, but all that surrounds it now is Darren. Darren's body distorts, spaghettifies as he's sucked into the Stone.

                  PHARAOH
           Now, we'll see if the lost can find
           his way back!

Darren screams as he disappears into the Stone. He enters…

I/E. PURGATORY - UNKNOWN

Darren wakes to a realm of darkness. CLOUDS dance like ghosts above and below him, and there is no floor to reveal which way is down. His body is in shadow, only his outline being visible. He thinks he is alone. He is not.

SEVEN GIANTS appear around him. They are dressed in foreign splendor, but their eyes burn like stars from Hell. They are:

ODIN, WAKAN TANKA, KASOGONAGA, IZANAGI and IZANAMI, and directly before him stands POSEIDON.

Poseidon reaches for Darren. His hand morphs into a shadowy ooze as he grabs him.

Then the space below opens to reveal an abyss where WHIMPERING VOICES can be heard. Darren is pulled toward them.

Darren is powerless to resist, but he tries anyway.

He grasps for the nothingness around, failing to find leverage. He sinks even lower, until…

                    ASA (O.S.)
          Darren!

He hears the voice… the one that empowers him.

                    ASA
          Darren, pull through! Come back to
          me!!!

Darren sees her. An image of Asa in the distance reaches out. Is it really her? Doesn't matter. Darren reaches back. He reaches with all his might. Asa does the same.

They close the gap, inching ever closer. Her hand is within reach! He goes to grab it when—

EXT. ATLANTIS - WESTERN PLAINS - DAY

Darren's fingers sink into the dirt, anchors him as he pulls hisself back into this world and out of the Stone. The ELEMENTS rip around him as dimensions briefly connect.

All brace to avoid being blown away. All except Pharaoh, who stands dumbfounded.

Darren emerges from the Stone, seemingly merges with its light. With a final scream like THUNDER, the elements subside, and all present can see the outcome.

Darren's body glows with the same divine light of the Ophiuchus Stone he holds in his hand. He is in control. He stands with the stillness of a deity.

Soldiers from every faction are in awe. Pharaoh is in disbelief.

                    PHARAOH
          A *fluke*… It's a fluke!

Pharaoh hurls an EBONY BOLT at Darren, but it halts, suspended in the air without Darren turning his head. The lightning bolt evaporates into fire.

Pharaoh tries again. He charges with more lightning in his hand. Darren finally turns, snaps.

A STEEL TOWER bursts from the ground. It strikes Pharaoh from below, launches him a mile high and away. After several seconds, we see him crash through the Atlantis Temple roof.

Darren lifts the Stone above him, allows it to float upward. The tower transforms into a giant VAULT, and the Stone enters it. The vault seals itself.

Then the divine glow fades from Darren. He is fully healed.

He turns toward Asa and smiles. They have won.

Asa sprints to Darren, and the surviving company find now a good time to celebrate.

Asa tries to talk but is unintelligible through her tears.

> DARREN
> I know, I know. I love you, too.

> TAU
> (walks over; winces)
> You… you did it.

> DARREN
> *We* did! Oh, you're hurt!

Tau grasps his arm, freshly severed from Asa's blast. Darren reaches for it. It is instantly smoothed into a healed nub.

> DARREN
> Oh, wait, you probably want the
> full arm back. Hold on.

> TAU
> (pulls away)
> No. This… maybe this is fine.

Darren nods. He remembers someone; walks over to the dome.

Behind it, Buziba lies breathless and still. His hair completely whitened.

EXT. ATLANTIS - WESTERN PLAINS - FLASHBACK

Buziba's hand releases Asa's face, dims from its ethereal glow. His body begins to pale, and his hair whitens. His face resembles what may even be peace.

>   BUZIBA
>   This power has been hoarded by so
>   few, feared by so many. Take it
>   back from that man who wishes
>   himself a King, and do what no one
>   else has done with it before:

He pulls something from his pocket—it's the Crest of Atlantis
necklace. His weakening hands give it to Darren.

>   BUZIBA
>   Create a world for all peoples.

Buziba takes his last breath.

END FLASHBACK.

EXT. ATLANTIS - WESTERN PLAINS - DAY

Darren and Asa contemplate Buziba's last words.

>   ASA
>   He really was valuable. I hope he
>   knew that.

Bia and Anansi approach the group.

>   BIA
>   Darren, you touched the Stone!

>   ANANSI
>   And remain of sound mind and body!

>   DARREN
>   Meh, debatable.

He scans the area, notices celebrations ending to care for
the injured.

He raises his arm, and light from the Stone floods the area.
Instantly, all injuries are healed.

>   DARREN
>   I hope that worked. Can you make
>   sure I didn't miss anyone, Tau.
>   (Tau nods; zooms off)
>   Princess Bia, you can watch the
>   Stone while I'm gone, right?

>   BIA
>   Where are you going?

                    DARREN
          The war's not over yet.

                    ASA
          Maybe you should take the Stone
          with you!

                    DARREN
          I'm hoping he listens to reason.

WIND lifts Darren up. He floats upward.

                    ASA
          You better come back to me…

                    DARREN
          You know I will.

Darren flies off toward the Temple.

                              FADE OUT.

                    END OF ACT TWO

ACT THREE

FADE IN:

INT. ATLANTIS - TEMPLE - DAY

Pharaoh peels himself from the floor. On his knees, his eyes drift to the temple's high ceiling.

His mind draws NOOSES on the ceiling. They hang like the ones that ended his father, like the ones that haunt the Execution Exhibit in Johannesburg.

He blinks and they disappear, now replaced by Darren as he descends through the Pharaoh's entry hole. He lands.

>   PHARAOH
>   Have you come to martyr me?
>   (scoffs)
>   Just as well. I would prefer it
>   that way.

>   DARREN
>   I'm not here to fight, just to take
>   you in. So, please, just come
>   quietly.

>   PHARAOH
>   You think I've come this far to let
>   myself get dragged away, thrown
>   into prison to rot forever?

>   DARREN
>   Well, maybe you deserve it.

>   PHARAOH
>   What about the ones who did not
>   deserve it?! What about those who
>   bled and died and rotted so the
>   rest of us could take back what is
>   ours?! Are they okay to stay where
>   they are?

>   DARREN
>   I can't change any of that,
>   Pharaoh. Neither can you.

>   PHARAOH
>   You are at peace with this, then—
>   allowing this broken history to
>   remain in disrepair?

                    DARREN
          I don't like that any more than
          you.

                    PHARAOH
          And yet, you meddle. All you have
          done since coming here has been
          interrupting others' quest for
          justice! And for the Muzungu?

Darren takes a beat to process.

                    PHARAOH
          These people have done nothing for
          you; only taken… from you… from
          your grandmother. Ravaged your
          ancestral lands. Stole your
          identity. And the Waalisha—radical
          as they were—stopping them did not
          bring you any closer to your goal.
          So why? Why risk so much and fight
          so hard for people who show no
          concern for you?!

                    DARREN
          Don't know…

A wholesome smile brightens Darren's face.

                    DARREN
          I guess it's just who I am.

This answer doesn't satisfy Pharaoh.

                    PHARAOH
          Then who you are ends here.

A solemn beat passes. Both faces are filled with dread, but
that dread quickly turns into resolve.

EXT. ATLANTIS - WESTERN PLAINS - DAY

The Spectral Guard finds a post around the Ophiuchus Stone's
makeshift vault.

Asa gazes nervously into the distant Temple. She looks down,
tries to Flux the water. It doesn't budge.

She looks right and sees the BRIDGE Darren and Pharaoh
created. It's still in tact. She runs to it.

                    BIA
          Where are *you* going?

                              ASA
                    To help my husband!

Bia motions to stop her but promptly gives up.

INT. ATLANTIS - TEMPLE - DAY

Wind blows a lone LEAF into the temple. The leaf surfs the
breeze until it touches the floor. It signals their start.

                          PHARAOH
                    IGNITE!

FLAMES burst from Pharaoh's body, rush Darren like a WAVE.

                          DARREN
                    CRAFTSMAN!

A STONE WALL erupts from the floor, blocks the fire. The
flames push, distort the wall, but it holds.

Then Pharaoh appears behind Darren, goes for a strike, but
Darren notices. He dodges, and Pharaoh punches the wall
instead. His fist is caught in the stone. The stone tries to
absorb him…

But Pharaoh shouts, discharges EBONY BOLTS form his body,
frees himself. He floats up, fires black lightning at Darren.

Darren stomps, kicks up multiple of Amani's MIDAS SPEARS from
the floor. The golden spires absorb the lighting.

Darren grabs a spear, reshapes it into a CROSSBOW, fires
multiple bolts at Pharaoh.

Pharaoh evades them all, but attacks with something familiar:
Muni's VANGUARD SHEAR. He flings several at Darren. They
miss, but explode as they hit the ground. Darren flies back…

Pharaoh lifts multiple BOULDERS from the ground. They
transform into giant CLAY BEASTS. They growl, prepare to
strike. But Darren summons a dozen IFRIT SHADOWS. He flings
them at the Beasts.

The Beasts and Ifrit Shadows attack each other, blow debris
all around… just enough to cloak a SABER LIMB as hit grabs
Darren.

It swings him around the room, slams him into the floor. His
Ifrit Shadows vanish, and the Clay Beasts attack. They try to
maul Darren, but he raises a forcefield in time to defend.

The Beasts persist. They almost break through. But Darren summons a CLOUD of SAND. It floods the temple, seizes the Beasts, suspends them in the air.

Then Darren points, fires from his finger a flurry of VAPOR BULLETS. They annihilate the beasts, blasts a *larger* hole through the temple's ceiling.

Pharaoh doesn't stop. He tackles Darren.

EXT. ATLANTIS - TEMPLE ROOF - CONTINUOUS

The roof collapses, transforming the temple into a tiny colosseum. It's convenient for Asa, who arrives at the rooftop. She observes the action.

From above, she watches the two demigods exchange blows, conjuring weapons from nothing, fighting for something greater than themselves. They don't notice Asa.

                    ASA
          Don't worry, hun, I'm here for you.

She prepares to flux, takes aim at Pharaoh…

But Pharaoh steps back, showers the area with EBONY BOLTS.

One hardly misses Asa. She trips, falls over, sighs.

                    ASA
          Okay, maybe I'm a bit out of my
          league, here. At least I'm here if
          he needs me.

She crosses her legs, watches as a spectator instead. She fails to hold back a proud smile.

                    ASA
          You get him, hun!

I/E. ATLANTIS - COLLAPSED TEMPLE - CONTINUOUS

Pharaoh bombards the area with a barrage of STEAMBURST bombs. Darren evades, propels himself forward with WIND, and lands his fist against Pharaoh's jaw. The impact sends him flying.

He hits a wall, recovers in time to catch the SWORD that Darren *almost* impales him with. A jolt of ELECTRICITY repels Darren, gives Pharaoh enough space to launch an Ebony Bolt.

Darren defends with a STEEL SHIELD, but it reddens with heat
as Pharaoh presses in. He doesn't let up. The force pushes
Darren into the opposite wall—almost through the wall.

It's almost overwhelming… but Darren pushes through, summons
a MIDAS GOLEM. The Golem towers over the crumbled temple as
it forms. It raises its fist and slams it into Pharaoh,
pinning him.

The lightning stops, but only for a moment; until another
blast of lighting signals Pharaoh's escape. He flies up,
soars high into the sky.

Darren stands atop the Golem's head. It elevates him.

EXT. ATLANTIS - HIGH ABOVE THE TEMPLE - CONTINUOUS

Frustration, desperation bleeds from Pharaoh's eyes.

                    PHARAOH
          You choose to die with the
          colonizers you fight so hard to
          defend! Go ahead!

He raises his hand and all the elements merge again to form
the EBONY SUN. The dense and blackened fireball sucks in
every cloud in the region. His sun blacks out the true one.

                    PHARAOH
          *You will die LOST and ALONE just
          like your grandmother!*

Darren sees the Ebony Sun. He knows what it is. He knows what
to do.

He cuffs his hands, and all elements merge between them to
form something new, unique… *Spectral*.

A lustrous and ethereal cloud of energy gathers in his hands.
It seems to infinitely shift between states of matter. This
is Darren's Spectral Flux: **OMNIMATTER**. The amorphous
phenomenon takes the shape of a massive SWORD.

Darren looks down, notices Asa for the first time. He smiles,
reaches out to her as if inviting her to take his hand. She
smiles and reaches back.

                    DARREN
          That cycle ends here, 'cause
          someone's already found me.

He returns his hand to the Omnimatter Sword, and its color
changes ever so slightly.

                    DARREN
          I will never be alone!

Pharaoh drops, descends like a falling star. Darren leaps to meet him, ascends like a rising sun. The two Spectral Fluxes collide.

The desert skies twist, churn in response to the colliding powers. An impromptu HURRICANE quakes the entire region. The eye of the storm are Pharaoh and Darren.

The two Fluxes struggle to dominate one another. They are nearly even. Nearly.

But the Omnimatter gains leverage, digs deep into the Sun.

Pharaoh looks at Darren, but he sees something he cannot process. The Omnimatter Sword is gripped by more than just Darren's hands—Asa's. Those hands help swing the blade as it…

SLICES THROUGH the Ebony Sun, SMASHES against Pharaoh. The impact sends Pharaoh hurdling into the temple like a meteor.

The hurricane ROARS its loudest before the tempest finally subsides. Darren falls, loses control in the wind… exhaustion taking its toll… He drops the Omnimatter Blade, and it lands…

I/E. ATLANTIS - DEVASTATED TEMPLE - CONTINUOUS

Right next to a weak but standing fire…

A COAL WALL falls down, reveals Asa sheltering behind it. She notices the fire and the blade, and the two titans they belong to…

Pharaoh attempts to climb to his feet. His strength fails him. He finally collapses, and the fire extinguishes itself…

The battle ends.

Darren drops to his knees, simultaneously touching the ground and fluxing STEEL SHACKLES onto Pharaoh.

Asa rushes to Darren, helps him up.

They walk over to Pharaoh, who's senses betray him. He chokes as he process his defeat. The only word he can manage is…

                    PHARAOH
          Why?

He blacks out. Darren and Asa embrace.

                         DARREN
                Let's go.

EXT. ATLANTIS - WESTERN PLAINS - DAY

Tau waves, hails Darren and Asa as they approach. Darren
carries Asa as he flies. The wind carries Pharaoh in tow.

Tau hugs the couple. Asa hugs them both back.

                         TAU
                You Americans are stuffed with
                surprises, I swear!

                         ASA
                Yes he is, isn't he?

                         DARREN
                Ouch—not so tight!

The Spectral Guard rushes over. They promptly seize Pharaoh.

Darren notices Bia and Anansi. They are flabbergasted. He
walks over to them.

                         BIA
                Darren Davenport, Asa… you've taken
                down a wielder of the Ophiuchus
                Stone, liberated multiple nations…

                         DARREN
                I don't know about all that—

She hugs them both.

                         BIA
                …avenged my brother… Thank you.

She lets go. They turn to Anansi.

                         ASA
                So, um, now what?

                         ANANSI
                There will be plenty of rebuilding
                to do, but for now, you've earned a
                rest.

                         DARREN
                Sounds like a plan!

Darren leans against the Ophiuchus Stone vault when he
realizes…

357

                              DARREN
                   Oh, yeah! There's something I
                   should probably do this first.

Darren lifts his arms, closes his eyes.

The Ophiuchus Stone responds. It WAILS with the sounds of
millions of simultaneous breaths as it expels millions of
hoarded SOULS. The souls swarm the skies and fly away.

EXT. MASERU, LESOTHO - SETSOTO STADIUM - DAY

Souls dive into the bodies of bedridden corpses. The faces of
fallen Caucasians blush as they come to life.

The waking bodies startle the doctors, but King Kopano only
laughs. He beams with pride.

EXT. CAIRO - DOWNTOWN - DAY

LIGHTNING arcs across the sky as souls rain upon the nation.
Arab locals and Caucasian Tourists alike wake from their
indefinite slumber with stiff necks and dirty clothes. They
see to each other's needs.

EXT. ATLANTIS - WESTERN PLAINS - DAY

Finally, a soul shoots into Asa, knocks her over, but a
nearby PUDDLE catches her. She manipulates the puddle,
realizes it was her. She struggles to fight off tears.

The remaining souls flood the sky in milky neons as they find
their way home.

INT. DAVENPORT BEDROOM - MORNING

CHYRON: "Two Months Later"

Darren and Asa lie in bed. Asa sleeps with a smile, while
Darren's tired eyes stare at the ALARM CLOCK. It reads 07:59.

08:00 comes, sounds the alarm. Darren reaches to turn off the
alarm, but Asa beats him to it.

                              ASA
                   Today's the day!!

She mounts him, shakes him awake.

                         ASA
          It's your big day—I'm so
          excited—are you excited?—I am!!!
               (Darren groans)
          Didn't sleep? First day of school
          vibes, huh?

                         DARREN
          Something like that.

Asa slides off and heads to the window, opens it.

Sunlight pours into the room. From outside we see a
developing Atlantis with modest construction all over. Darren
shields his eyes.

                         DARREN
          I'm still not sure this is a good
          idea.

                         ASA
          Everyone else is, so it's a good
          thing it's not totally up to you.

Darren manages a smile, finally sits up. Asa heads for the
closet.

                         ASA
          Hurry and get dressed. King Kopano
          is waiting.

EXT. ATLANTIS - RENOVATED TEMPLE - MORNING

Darren and Asa exit the Temple. There's no one around on the
center island, but the construction in the distance kicks up
DUST.

                         DARREN
          Ready?

Darren takes Asa's hand as wind lifts them off the ground.

                         ASA
          Not too high, please!

                         DARREN
          I've gotcha. Come on.

EXT. ATLANTIS - CITY FLYOVER - MORNING

The two fly off, across the rings of water, where small,
FERRY BOATS tour.

Over the inner and outer harbors, where marketplaces set up their TENTS. And into the mainland, where CAMPSITE PLAZAS trace the streams with RVs and vehicles.

INHABITANTS exit their RVs, African and Caucasian alike. They notice Darren and Asa flying overhead. Some offer a friendly wave while others gaze in wonder.

The couple heads North. They scale the mountains until they reach the top.

EXT. ATLANTIS - NORTHERN MOUNTAIN GRAVES - MORNING

As they arrive, they are greeted by Bia, Anansi, Moustapha, Geraldine, Tau, and King Kopano. They stand in front of HUNDREDS of GRAVESTONES. However, four are in the front.

The couple lands.

>   TAU
>   Nice of you to finally join us,
>   *Your Divinity*.

>   DARREN
>   Oh, stop. It's not even official.

>   KING KOPANO
>   It will be soon enough. It is a
>   position well-deserved.

>   MOUSTAPHA
>   And one well-earned.

Asa goes to Bia and Anansi, tries to hug them, but she slips right through Bia.

>   ANANSI
>   We cannot stay long. Apparitions
>   will suffice.

>   BIA
>   But it is nice to see you, too.

Asa notices the four closest graves. Their names are etched in English and Arjanan RUNES. They are "Khadija Seck", "Khadeem Seck", "Buziba of Rwanda", and "Kwesi Kogi".

>   ASA
>   But what about…

>   BIA
>   Tano was laid to rest in Arjana. It
>   is what he would've preferred.

                    MOUSTAPHA
          And Zein was buried in Nouakchott.
          I am sure his ceremony was grand.

                    GERALDINE
          Shall we get started?

The group gathers before the graves. King Kopano steps
forward. He takes a moment to collect his breath. The others
do the same, bow their heads.

                    KING KOPANO
          These hundreds of gravestones,
          represent the hundreds of men and
          women, soldiers and citizens,
          leaders and followers, who
          sacrificed themselves in order to
          undo one of the greatest tragedies
          this world has ever seen. With
          their sacrifices, we did just that,
          but the cost was great. We lost
          what cannot be measured by erected
          stones or statisticians, for we
          lost fathers, mothers, friends, and
          mentors.

Kopano steps closer to the stones, touches Khadija's. Tau
eyes Buziba's… he cannot escape a scowl.

                    KING KOPANO
          Today we honor them all, not only
          because they fought to correct a
          past injustice, but because these
          individuals are the first to have
          died for the sake of a new future
          that begins here. May their bodies
          nourish the soil that will incubate
          seeds of hope. And may this hope
          root itself firmly in the soil of
          this mountain, so that its shade
          shelters the land it watches over.

All clasp their hands and bow, pay their respects. The
ceremony ends.

Moustapha kneels by Khadija and Khadeem's graves.

                    MOUSTAPHA
          There was so much I never knew
          about you two… but I'm glad I knew
          your love.

                    BIA
Speaking of which, this Kwesi Kogi…
I hadn't heard of him. Who was he?

                    ASA
A very good friend we met in
Nairobi. He was loyal to the end.

                    DARREN
He sure didn't have to be, but he
was.

                    BIA
I see. How did he meet his end?

                    ASA
Well, it was…

                    TAU
Buziba, wasn't it?

                    DARREN
Yeah, when he was working with the
Waalisha. Kwesi stood up to him.

                    TAU
Ha, Buziba never liked when people
did that, did he?

                    GERALDINE
Tau, that's enough!

                    TAU
Is it? Of course it is, because
what's one more victim to add to
his count.

                    GERALDINE
What's gotten in—

King Kopano stops her.

                    KING KOPANO
Tau, speak your peace—respectfully.

Tau steps in front of Buziba's grave, grips his arm stump.

                    TAU
All I ever heard was good things
about Khadija and Khadeem. Same
with this Kwesi guy. But Buziba?
All I've ever known of him was the
pain he brought with him and the
Curse that followed him.

> KING KOPANO
> Yes, but that was his duty.

> TAU
> He was supposed to snuff outsiders,
> but he terrorized my father… me.
> (beat)
> He acted like he was the judge and
> executioner… then he turns around
> and betrays Arjana itself. Then he
> changes his mind before he dies and
> I'm supposed to forget about it?
> Why should I act like that never
> happened? I'm the one with the
> reminder that won't go away!

> KING KOPANO
> Buziba… did make many mistakes. He
> carried a darkness that followed
> him like a shadow. He wrestled with
> that shadow for years. He was in
> pain. Unfortunately, that pain
> spilled over and drenched whoever
> was closest.

> TAU
> Like me! My family was closest. Now
> I'm the hurt one… His pain is gone,
> and I'm supposed to be happy for
> him?

> KING KOPANO
> Sometimes it takes several wrong
> turns before you find the right
> direction.

Kopano places a gentle hand on Tau's shoulder, who struggles
to hold back tears of frustration, confusion.

> KING KOPANO
> Tau, I pray you find the grace to
> offer to those who cannot navigate
> life as well as you.

Tau has no words. He only kneels.

King Kopano turns to the others, smiles.

> KING KOPANO
> Let's depart. We wouldn't want to
> miss the coronation.

Anansi and Bia vanish, Darren and Asa fly away, but Kopano
and Geraldine remain with Tau for a while longer.

INT. ATLANTIS - TEMPLE FOYER - DAY

Darren steps into the foyer. He and all present are dressed immaculately. As he's seen, the small crowd erupts into cheers. The loudest of which being his family.

Darren's FATHER, MOTHER, and brother DAVID rush over to him. They hug, dap, give him love. They also greet Asa.

Al the while, Moustapha's voice can be heard, blaring over speakers outside.

Darren takes his position on a RED CARPET, he presents his arm for Asa to take. She does. He whispers to her…

> DARREN
> Stay close.

The carpet leads to two LARGE DOORS that open automatically as they approach. They walk through to enter.

EXT. ATLANTIS - CENTRAL PARK - CONTINUOUS

THOUSANDS of people sit in the park, Africans, Caucasians, Arabs alike, listening as Moustapha speaks on a DAIS. NEWS CAMERAS roll, turn as Darren and Asa exit the Temple.

> MOUSTAPHA
> (to the crowd)
> And as our ancestors paved the way
> for us, we now pass the torch to a
> new generation of leader. Please
> welcome the shepherd of this
> nation: King Darren Davenport!

The crowd cheers as Darren takes Moustapha's place on the dais. He shakes Darren's hand and says:

> MOUSTAPHA
> Show them who you are.

He leaves Darren and stands beside Asa.

Darren looks at these people—his people.

> DARREN
> When I came to Africa, I was… lost.
> I didn't know who I was, and I
> thought I would find myself in
> pages recorded in some history
> book. I wanted to learn myself
> through events I wasn't even there
> to see.
> (MORE)

                    DARREN (CONT'D)
But I can't control the past; none
of us can. And when an ideologue
resurrected this land with the
promise of restoring what I never
had, I almost believed he could.
But I realized that the land I
stand in doesn't make me who I am.
Neither does knowing the name of
the boat that stole my ancestors
were on. It's the decisions I make
every day, the life I choose to
lead…
            (turns to Asa)
…and the people I choose to live
that life with.

He extends his hand, and the crowd no longer knows who Darren
is truly talking to.

                    DARREN
Maybe this land can be a home for
all people, no matter where you
come from or how you got there. But
if you'd trust me, we can make this
a home for everyone… together.

But Asa knows. She takes his hand.

                    DARREN
May everyone who comes to Atlantis
feel as found as I do right now!

An APPLAUSE roars. They take pictures and shout, and the King
and Queen share a moment together before the world.

EXT. ATLANTIS - CENTRAL PARK - EVENING

Darren and David sit on the dais, overlook the Atlantean
landscape as CREWS clean up the park.

                    DAVID
So they elected *you*?

                    DARREN
Moustapha suggested it, then King
Kopano, the Arjanans, and
Mauritania's VP all thought it made
sense. Someone had to watch over
the Stone, and I'm kinda the only
one qualified. Besides, I had to
one-up you somehow!

                         DAVID
              Not bad, little brother.
                   (beat)
              When you left, I didn't actually
              think you'd be able to do it.

                         DARREN
              This was in the realm of
              possibility for you?

                         DAVID
              Not this—finding your history! I
              know Gumma would've been crazy
              proud. Hell, you even found an
              ancient city history didn't even
              know existed! That's overachieving.

                         DARREN
              Actually, I never found my *history*.
              All that was just a byproduct.

                         DAVID
              Then what do you call all this?

                         DARREN
              Finding myself.

Zaila timidly walks over to them.

                         ZAILA
              Excuse me, Your Divinity, but the
              prisoner requested an audience with
              you and the Queen.

                         DAVID
              "Your Divinity"? I'll give you two
              days before that goes to your head!

                         DARREN
              I don't really need his opinion
              right now.

                         ZAILA
              He said it was urgent… "about the
              Stone…"

Darren relents, gets up.

                         DARREN
              Stick around, I gotta talk to you
              about something.

He goes with Zaila.

INT. ATLANTIS - DIAMOND DUNGEON - EVENING

Pharaoh sits in a CRYSTALLINE prison cell, meditating as he waits. He perks up to hear two pairs of footsteps descending nearby stairs. Darren steps in front of the cell.

> DARREN
> I guess this stuff really can hold you. A good call by Anansi.

> PHARAOH
> Perhaps I just haven't tried to escape yet.

> DARREN
> Have you?

> PHARAOH
> I've been preoccupied.

> DARREN
> With what, being trapped?

> PHARAOH
> No, ugh, I… asked for you both to be here.

> DARREN
> You're asking for a lot.

> PHARAOH
> It's… important.
>   (sighs)
> I already know she's here…

Asa steps from around the corner.

> ASA
> Okay, now what do you want?

> PHARAOH
> First… I haven't been able to figure it out. Why did I lose that struggle?

> DARREN
> Wha—'cause I was better! What kinda question—

> PHARAOH
> The Spectral Fluxes!
>   (beat)
>   (MORE)

                    PHARAOH (CONT'D)
          You and I both know they should
          have had equal power… Just like
          when I used it earlier, they should
          have cancelled out one another. But
          yours prevailed… How? Your lone
          power against mine, it should have—

Darren scoffs, shakes his head.

                    DARREN
          I don't know how many times I need
          to tell you this. I wasn't alone.

Pharaoh glimpses the couple. They are a unit. He finally gets
it.

                    PHARAOH
          Well, then, it's good you are both
          here to hear this. It's actually
          more of a message for the Muzungu—

                    ASA
          Asa!

                    DARREN
          Queen Asa.

                    PHARAOH
          But you'll want to hear this, too.

                    ASA
          Well, spit it out.

                    PHARAOH
               (beat)
          After making sure Zein didn't send
          that missile, I hypothesized it
          could have come from overseas. So I
          used the Ophiuchus Stone's power to
          produce multiple Apparitions and
          sent them to Europe. I wanted to
          warn them not to interfere with our
          nation's affairs.

                    DARREN
          Way to make more enemies. How'd
          that go?

                    PHARAOH
          They never made it. As soon as they
          stepped on the next continent, they
          could no longer hold their form. It
          took me a while to realize why.

                    DARREN
          Was it the distance?

                    PHARAOH
          No. It wasn't that the Stone didn't
          have enough power to maintain them…
          It didn't have the *jurisdiction*.

Asa takes a moment to piece the facts together, while Darren
fights off shock. He and Asa slowly start for the exit.

                    PHARAOH
          Darren, I assume you saw the same
          thing in the Stone that I did, so
          you know…

Asa figures it out. Her jaw drops.

                    PHARAOH
          This world will soon get a lot
          bigger.

EXT. ATLANTIS - TEMPLE THRONE ROOM - EVENING

Darren and Asa enter the throne room. Asa immediately begins
pacing, while Darren feels a new weight on his shoulders.

                    ASA
          There're more? Oh my god, there are
          more! Of course there's more. Where
          even are they?

                    DARREN
          I had a feeling, but I didn't wanna
          say. Had no way to confirm.

                    ASA
          And what gave you that feeling, the
          Stone?
               (beat)
          What did you see in there? You
          never told me…

                    DARREN
          Still trying to make sense of it…
          I'll tell ya one day soon. Promise.

Asa is only partially satisfied. She takes a beat, thinks.
Then she perks up.

                    ASA
          Ya know, it might be helpful if
          someone was out there demystifying
          Umoya for people. And along the
          way, maybe it wouldn't hurt if the
          Queen of Atlantis made some friends
          overseas.

                    DARREN
          It's risky.

                    ASA
          Meh, we've done risky before.

Darren takes Asa's hand.

                    DARREN
          If you do this, you can't—

                    ASA
          Won't tell a soul… Flux.
               (giggles)

The two hug in agreement.

                    ASA
          I should probably go pack.

She leaves the room just as David enters. He observes the
throne.

                    DAVID
          Now, this is an office! I wouldn't
          mind a workplace like this.

                    DARREN
          Speaking of which… looks like I'm
          gonna need some help with
          diplomacy… and administration… and
          other city-running endeavors.

                    DAVID
          I'll reach out to some colleagues.
          I'm sure they'd love to be
          involved. Also I'm always here to
          give you pointers.

                    DARREN
          I was thinking you'd be a more
          permanent presence.

                    DAVID
          What? I'm the Mayor back home! I
          can't just—

                    DARREN
          How does "Advisor to the King"
          sound?

                    DAVID
               (laughs; relents)
          It sounds… fantastic. We have a lot
          of work to do.

     Darren walks over and sits on the throne. He gets
     comfortable, but not too comfortable. He grins.

                    DARREN
          Then, let's get started.

                                   FADE TO BLACK.

                    <u>END OF SHOW</u>

Character Guide

Darren Davenport | Male, late twenties, African American

A talented civil engineer, Darren is a craftsman at heart. There's more to him than designing bridges, but if only he knew what that was. Lacking knowledge about his ancestry leaves him feeling like an imposter in his own skin.

The thing Darren fears most is dying as his grandmother did: without a connection to her heritage. If avoiding that end means hunting for an ancient treasure or fighting off a terrorist faction, so be it. Then again, maybe he's looking to find his identity in the wrong places.

Asa Davenport | Female, mid-twenties, Caucasian American

As a loving and supportive wife, Asa has much to offer her husband Darren. So why didn't his grandmother see it that way? She may not understand her husband's plight, but is that really as bad as everyone makes it out to be?

Not if Asa has anything to say about it. She has the spunk and the determination to prove them all wrong. Perhaps the only approval she needs is her own. But how many people need to question you before you start to question yourself?

Osas Pharaoh | Male, mid-thirties, South African

As a political activist, it's easy to be fooled by Pharaoh's proclamations of peace and unity. But in truth, his definition of peace has a particular meaning: restoring Africa to its full glory by eliminating the people who have colonized it.

His suave and cordial demeanor is a mask that holds at bay the anger brewing within. A victim of Apartheid, Pharaoh has experienced many atrocities and witnessed even more. He has dreamed of reparations for years, but revenge may be just as fruitful.

Buziba, Agent of Arjana | Male, mid-forties, Rwandan

Even though 'Buziba' is not the only name he's ever known, it's the only one he claims as his own. A young Tutsi orphaned during the Rwandan Genocide, he was taken in by American expatriates. But when all expats were evacuated during the zenith of the genocide, he was separated from his caretakers—left behind and abandoned.

Tau Lane | Male, mid-twenties, Basotho

Tau is the young the Southern Guardian of Arjana, stationed in the Kingdom of Lesotho, the main user of Umoya in the region. He is the person who initially instructed Darren and Asa in Umoya Fluxing.

His father was an Umoya user who passed down what he knew to his son, but he was killed by an Arjana agent who discovered that his father attempted to teach Umoya to outsiders.

King Kopano | Male, fifties, Basotho

The reigning King of the Kingdom of Lesotho has seen many tragedies. He wishes for Lesotho to not befall another one during his dynasty, but alas, their democracy is young.

After Tau's father's untimely death, Kopano stepped in to fill the role. He is a kind leader who understands the laws and why they are in place. However, wisdom allows him to discern when some laws should be bent.

Acacia, Southern Guardian | Female, early thirties, Arjanan

A fierce warrior, Acacia is the first Temple Guardian Darren and Asa meet on their journey. While she despises trespassers, as her duty demands, she enjoys the process of expelling them perhaps a little too much.

Her Soul Flux, the Ifrit Shadow, is the first Soul Flux the Davenports witness, and she protects the Wind Shard from outsiders who seek it.

Khadija Seck, Western Guardian | Female, sixties, Senegalese

With her gregarious personality, the Senegalese would have no idea Khadija was hiding a massive secret. That being that she is the Guardian of the Western Temple.

One of the wealthiest women in West Africa, Khadija resides in Dakar and frequently spends time at the House of Slaves, being a gracious host to whatever American tourists she stumbles across. This time, she bumps into the Davenports.

While the wealth is nice, it comes with baggage that she is still learning to unpack.

Kwesi Kogi | Male, mid-twenties, Kenyan

Several months prior to the start of the series, Kwesi broke up with his girlfriend of two years. She had recently discovered that he was of the Kikuyu tribe of Kenya, who traditionally had practices she wasn't a fan of.

And with that, she determined the two were not compatible. Ever since, Kwesi has been hellbent on restoring their relationship, and he feels the best way to do that is by disproving the claims about the Kikuyu... as they relate to him, anyway. But how?

Amani Suleyman | Female, late twenties, Sudanese

Amani is the leader of the Waalisha Khufu, though she is anything but "self-proclaimed". She is respected as the head of this new familial society and is fiercely protective over it.

But the ones she holds dearest are her own siblings, Muni and Joseph. Not much is known about their background, but the goal of the Waalisha is no secret: Eliminate all governments and let the people rule themselves.

Muni Suleyman | Male, early thirties, Sudanese

Muni prides himself on being the vanguard muscle of the Waalisha. He carries a shotel wherever he goes; a symbol of power. Of which, he has plenty, being the second-in-command of the Waalisha.

Not much scares him in this world, except for his younger sister Amani. The authority her presence commands is intimidating. She is a natural born leader... shouldn't he be as well?

Asase, Queen of Arjana | Female, centuries old, Arjanan

Queen Asase is the reigning monarch of Arjana and the matriarch of the Arjanan Royal Family. She has ruled over the Remnant Kingdom for centuries, and those centuries have given her the wisdom to be shaken by very little in this world.

But that wisdom can be a burden. After millennia of Arjana's existence, is secrecy a policy worth upholding in the face of the these new threats? If not, where does that leave her legacy?

Bia, Princess of Arjana | Female, thirties, Arjanan

The youngest of Queen Asase's children, Bia is the only princess of Arjana. While she has plenty of fun teasing her brothers when she thinks they are taking themselves too seriously, she can also be focused and fierce.

Those attributes make her the perfect leader for the Queen's Spectral Guard. She serves as both their captain and the Queen's personal bodyguard.

Anansi, Prince of Arjana | Male, forties, Arjanan

Anansi is the second prince of Arjana. He is always the most level-headed and analytical of the royal siblings. His Soul Flux, **Apparition**, makes him a fantastic multitasker and allows him to be a highly effective reconnaissance officer.

This combination of skills earns him a place at the Queen's side as her top advisor.

Tano, Prince of Arjana | Male, fifties, Arjanan

The eldest of the royal siblings, Tano's duty has always been to Arjana. He has the strongest personality among the Royal Family, which may lead him to butt heads with his siblings or earn the occasional joke from Bia.

He fiercely defends his home, and that's why he was put in charge of the Arjanan military. If someone manages to stumble across Arjana's borders, he will be the first and last thing they see.

Flux Glossary

(light spoilers ahead)

Soul Fluxes

In Order of Appearance (from episode 1)

Burning Coal | Earth, Fire, Earth

Buziba can transform nearby earth into scorching hot pillars or platforms of coal. If he makes contact with a person, he can even use the natural earth within that person's body to create coal within them.

Glass Wall | Earth, Air, Water

King Kopano creates glass barriers from nearby earth. This Flux is not well-suited to combat, so he generally does not rely on it for self defense.

Sky-Block | Wind, Earth, Fire

Tau creates tangible platforms by solidifying molecules in the air. He can use these platforms as forcefields for defense or as footing to increase his mobility while airborne. He prefers the latter.

Ifrit Shadow | Fire, Earth, Air

Acacia can create multiple puppets made from fire and ash. These Shadows take the same shape as Acacia, and she controls them via flaming threads that connect to her fingers. She can also speak through the puppets remotely and use them as armor.

Ebony Bolt | Fire, Fire, Fire

Pharaoh produces black lightning bolts. They behave like normal electricity, but they can be directed at specified targets or focused into a singular point at will.

Beamform | Wind, Fire, Earth

Erratic saber-like energy extends from Khadija's cane. She can shape this energy into various weapons and tools according to her needs.

Harmattan | Earth, Wind, Water

Khadeem summons a localized sandstorm. He can manipulate the sand to confine targets to a specific area or conceal his presence.

Craftsman | Earth, Water, Earth

Darren creates steel from nearby earth and crafts it into any tool or object he knows how to build. He can also manipulate nearby steel if it is within eyeshot.

Soul Fluxes

(Continued)

Vanguard Shear | Wind, Earth, Fire

Muni creates a concussive wind shear that can slice through solid objects. He often chooses to launch it from his sword.

Midas Spear | Earth, Water, Air

Amani can create javelin-like weapons of various sizes made from solid gold. She can launch, propel, and manipulate their trajectory with bursts of air.

Mobilizer | Earth, Water, Air

Marula can transport herself or others through the ground at high speed. She cannot travel through synthetic materials or substances that could harm her.

Steamburst | Air, Water, Fire

Sage creates a compressed bomb of steam that he can fire at a target. He can create and launch multiple at once.

Phantasm | Fire, Air, Air

Udanga can create large-scale illusions that mask sections of a landscape.

Gleam Dart | Fire, Earth, Air

Tano creates a laser-based arrow that he snipes opponents with. He has full control over its movements.

Blaze Kylie | Fire, Earth, Air

Buchu conjures a flaming boomerang that he can control mid-flight.

Apparition | Air, Fire, Air

Anansi can create lifelike illusions of himself that serve as an extension of his consciousness. They cannot physically interact with the environment, but he can create a total of eight and exchange information between them.

Saber Limb | Fire, Water, Earth

Jarrah can create an extendable limb of pure plasmic energy which she can use to manipulate objects in her environment.

Soul Fluxes

(Continued)

Claymated Beasts | Earth, Air, Water

Malva spawns multiple beasts from clay that he forms from the earth. He can fully control their movements like puppets.

Faithful Flare | Fire, Earth, Air

Kwesi conjures a flaming boomerang that he can control mid-flight. This is indeed the same as Buchu's Soul Flux.

Acid Wheel | Water, Fire, Earth

Bia transmutes water into a potent acid. She can wield this acid in the form of a spinning wheel that she can use to either eviscerate or dissolve a target.

Vapor Bullet | Water, Air, Fire

Asa compresses hydrogen at a point near her body, usually a finger tip, and fires it like a projectile. She can charge the bullet to different sizes as desired.

Arsenal | Earth, Fire, Water

Jambi creates lightweight, aluminum armor from the earth that he can strengthen to an amazing degree.

Pierce Typhoon | Air, Fire, Water

Cymba gathers a funnel cloud into a highly compressed and spinning typhoon. When released, it resembles a beam that drills into its target.

Scorchloop | Fire, Water, Earth

Tympani creates fire and forms it into flaming hoops. This allows the fire to maintain a solid form, and the hoops can be thrown as projectiles without the flames dissipating over short distances.

Spectral Fluxes

In Order of Appearance

Burden

Queen Asase can amplify the pull of gravity in a localized zone. Everything that exists within the area of effect can experience time dilation if the gravitational pull is strong enough. When the Spectral Guard works in concert to harmonize the full capacity of their Primary Fluxes, they can duplicate this effect.

Ebony Sun

Pharaoh creates a small, black plasma ball that duplicates many properties of a star. This includes its electromagnetic properties, intense heat, and propensity for solar flares.

Omnimatter

Darrens creates a dense mass of energy that shifts between all forms of matter simultaneously and constantly. He can craft this mass into any shape he desires, and if necessary, he can choose which form of matter this Flux will land on when he cancels it.

Umoya

Overview and Mechanics

Overview

Umoya is a lost mystic art that was hidden away from the world during the dawn of African colonization. It was hidden to avoid it being stolen by colonizers, and as such became known as Africa's Final Treasure.

Though it is an ability all humans have, a catalyst is required to awaken the power within a person. Once awakened, it can be used freely, but requires a lot of training to master the art.

A catalyst may be either direct exposure to another's Umoya energy or contact with one of the mystic relics (or any Umoya-infused artifact).

Mechanics of Umoya

Fluxing

Fluxing is the act of manipulating the elements by flowing one's own Umoya energy into it. It is categorized into four different types and two separate tiers.

Types:

1. Terraflux–
   Any Base or Soul Fluxes formed from Earth.

2. Hydroflux–
   Any Base or Soul Fluxes formed from Water.

3. Aeroflux–
   Any Base or Soul Fluxes formed from Air.

4. Pyroflux–
   Any Base or Soul Fluxes formed from Fire.

Activation

In order to activate one's ability, they must choose a method of activation. This programs the individual's body and Umoya to react when called upon. Advanced Umoya users can generally Flux without doing this, but it's still a best practice.

Activation methods can range from gestures, poses, or verbal calls.

Earth

Primary effects of Earth Fluxes allow the user to control the earth around them. Secondary and tertiary effects allow the user's ability to manifest in an overtly tangible way.

Earth-based Fluxes:

- Metal
- Mineral
- Gems/crystals
- Soil
- Asphalt/concrete
- Lava
- Healing flesh with dust/dirt
- Ash
- Wood
- Magnetism
- Seashell

Water

Primary effects of Water Fluxes allow the user to control nearby water. Secondary and tertiary effects allow the user to manipulate their primary element with increased and liquid-like fluidity. It also adds the necessary moisture or water content to produce a desired Soul Flux result.

Water-based Fluxes:

- All Liquids
- Ice
- Acid
- Vapor
- Hydrogen

Fire

Primary effects if Fire Fluxes allow the user to control nearby flames or produce their own. Secondary and tertiary effects allow the user to add heat to produce the desired Soul Flux, or to power up the primary element with some type of energy. Often, it will be used to initiate an energetic instability into an element.

Fire-based Fluxes:

- Electricity/lightning
- Light
- lasers
- Heat
- Auroras
- Neon light/gas
- Plasma
- Microwaves

Air

Primary effects of Air Fluxes allow the user to control or produce wind. Secondary and tertiary effects of Air allow users to add air or wind to produce the desired Soul Flux, to increase mobility of the primarily manipulated element, possibly allowing the user to control the ability remotely).

Air-based Fluxes:

- Steam
- Flight/hypermobility
- Consciousness transferring
- Shockwaves/concussion blasts
- Combustible gasses
- Forcefields

Tiers

Higher levels of Fluxing can be achieved depending on a user's experience with Umoya. While acquired skill is always a factor, the user's personal life journey is just as important. There is no set rule on how long it should take to achieve higher levels of Fluxing, but all humans have the ability to use a Base and Soul Flux.

Base Flux: This is the primary level of Fluxing that consists of manipulating one of the four basic elements. All Umoya users can Base Flux the element they were born into with the most potency. Their secondary and tertiary elements can also be controlled, but to a much lesser degree.

An individual who was born with a primary Base Flux of water can control water with 100% potency. But if this same individual has a secondary Flux of air and a tertiary of fire, he/she can control air to only 50% potency and fire to 25%.

Soul Flux: This is an advanced Fluxing technique that incorporates the user's primary, secondary, and tertiary elements into a single manifestation. Each Soul Flux and method of using it is unique to each individual. Any instance of a Soul Flux is many times more potent than any instance of a Base Flux.

Unity Flux: This is an instance of two individuals attempting to Flux the same element in one accord. A Unity can be a combination of Base or Soul Fluxes, though the latter is much more rare. This is extremely difficult to do and are generally only attempted by highly-trained users.

Spectral Flux: This is the highest level of Fluxing, which only becomes available to a person who has made contact with the Ophiuchus Stone. When this happens, the user combines all four elements to produce dark matter. Once this power is accessed, the user develops his or her own unique implementation of the power, often aligned with their Base Flux. The power of a Spectral Flux is astronomical in comparison to a Soul. A single user can destroy a small mountain. It is speculated that the Spectral Flux of King Atlas that was powered by an Ophiuchus Stone was what caused the Younger Dryas event, and thus the destruction of Atlantis.

Element Manipulation

When Activating a Base Flux, any Umoya user is capable of manipulating their natural element if that material is nearby. Water, Earth, and Air users can only use as much of their element as is available to them in the environment. Fire, however, can be produced out of the ether.

Multiple Umoya users that share a Base Flux may simultaneously hold control over the same element (Unity Flux). This becomes useful for increasing the effectiveness of an instance of a Flux, but this requires training and the users to be on the same page. These users may always compete for control over the same element, and the result will be the stronger Umoya user assuming control of the element, though he/she will experience resistance while fighting the weaker user.

Soul Fluxes are unique to each Umoya user and thus cannot be controlled by another user. Even if a Soul Flux can be reproduced by another user, he/she is still incapable of assuming control of an object another Soul Fluxer created.

Unity Fluxes between users who have a great relationship is possible, and it results in their Base Flux combining into something new. (An earth user and a water user can create a Mud Flux). This is difficult but not completely uncommon.

Soul Flux combinations are rarely seen. They require extreme precision and spiritual unity between users to accomplish.

Zodiac Signs and Fluxes

The zodiac sign of the Umoya user can significantly influence the manifestation of their Soul Flux. The primary, secondary, and tertiary Base Fluxes of the user are determined by their Sun, Moon, and Rising signs respectively.

Each sign is responsible for a different effect manifesting within the user's Flux. While the effects of the Sun sign will likely be most prominent in the Flux, the Moon and Rising signs will also contribute in varying capacities. Not knowing one's zodiac signs does not necessarily mean they cannot manifest their Soul Flux, but the information can be helpful.

Below is a list of zodiac signs and their usual effect contributions.

Capricorn — Earth

Capricorns will normally create some type of construct with their Umoya element. This could range from handheld objects to larger platforms, structures, or shelters.

Aquarius — Air

Aquarius users will use their Umoya to vastly increase their mobility. Advanced Aquarians have the ability to fly, and they are more proficient at increasing their speed and moving other remote objects.

Pisces — Water

Pisces users tend to change the acidity of the water they manipulate. Consequentially, Soul Fluxes from Pisceans may result in the control/manifestation of different types of synthetic materials.

Aries — Fire

Aries manifestations may often involve self-strengthening, either by strengthening a construct, separate object, or by powering up one's own body.

Taurus — Earth

Taurus Soul Fluxes may manifest as armor or other methods of fortification. When connected to the Earth, they can traverse through or on the surface of the ground. This affords them increased mobility.

Gemini — Air

Geminis may have the ability to extend their consciousness into the element they control. Examples include the ability to create clones or creatures that can be manipulated remotely or listen in on conversations from a distance with a Base Flux.

Cancer — Water

Cancer Umoya users will manipulate their environment, bending the element around them as an extension of their own bodies with greater ease.

Leo — Fire

Leo manifestations may involve discharging energy from the user's body. Light manipulation may also fall under this sign.

Virgo — Earth

Virgo Umoya users tend to produce precious metals or stones. They have no affinity for a particular application to their Umoya, but their Base Flux allows for the purification of earthly elements.

Libra — Air

Libras will generally have an increased physicality to their air-based Fluxes. This may create effects like forcefields, but an earth sign may be required to add true tactility to the Flux.

Scorpio — Water

Umoya manifestations of Scorpios will often be very direct, involve little complexity, and will usually be designed to pierce or overwhelm defenses (e.g. a rush of water; a piercing bullet).

Sagittarius — Fire

Sagittarius users can emit energy over a distance. They may specialize in long-range style combat, usually creating some type of projectile.

9 798218 491253